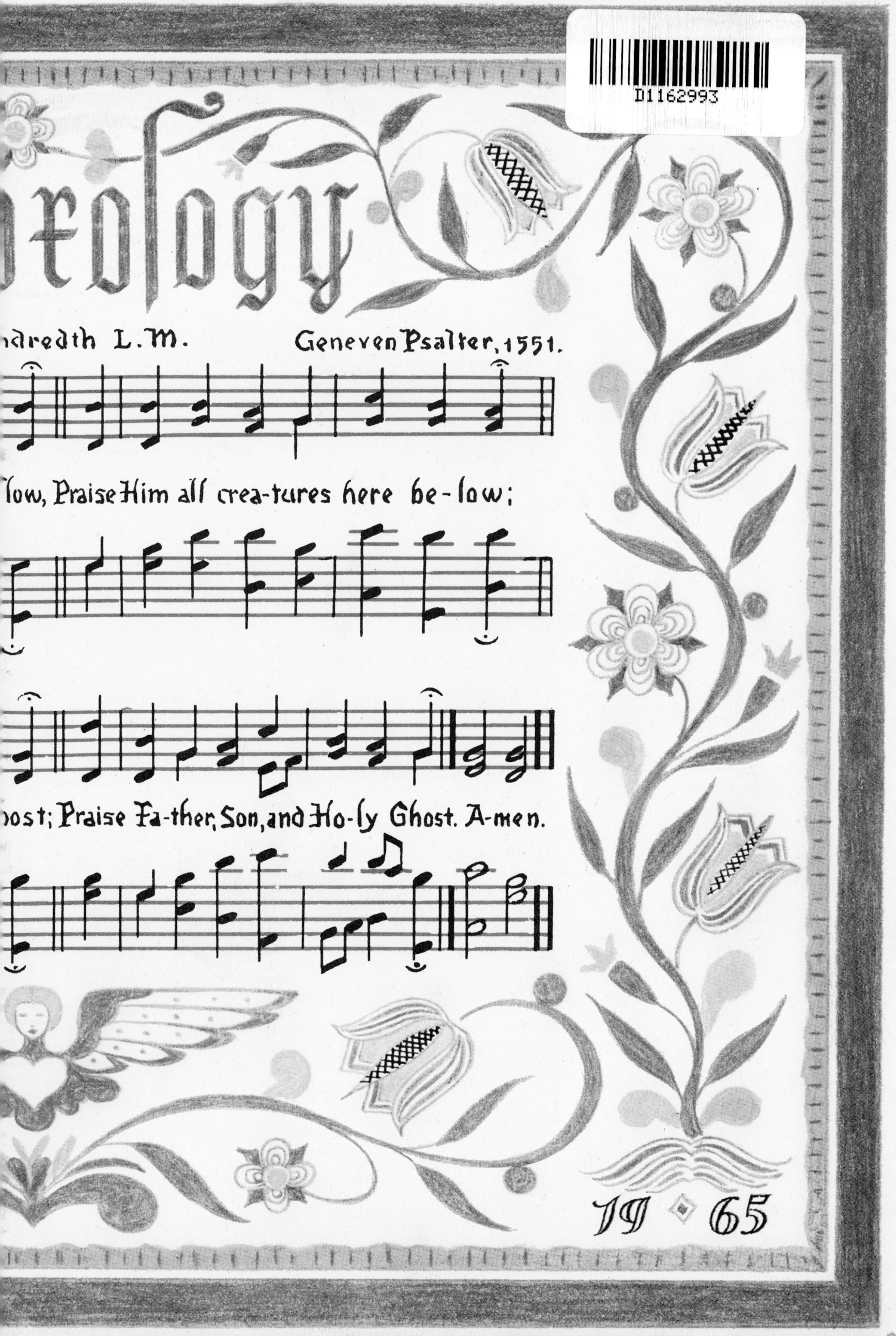

...ology
...ndredth L.M.
Geneven Psalter, 1551.
...low, Praise Him all crea-tures here be-low;
...host; Praise Fa-ther, Son, and Ho-ly Ghost. A-men.
19 65

BEST LOVED
SONGS AND HYMNS

BEST LOVED SONGS AND HYMNS

Popular, Patriotic and Folk Songs
Church Hymns and Gospel Songs
Spirituals and Carols

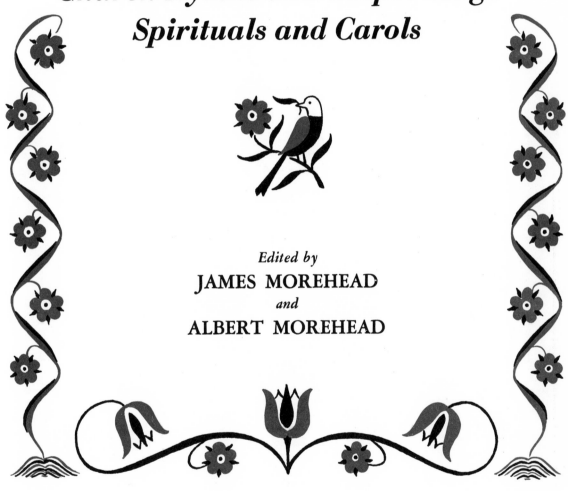

Edited by
JAMES MOREHEAD
and
ALBERT MOREHEAD

THE WORLD PUBLISHING COMPANY

Cleveland and New York

Published by THE WORLD PUBLISHING COMPANY
2231 West 110th Street, Cleveland 2, Ohio
Published simultaneously in Canada by NELSON, FOSTER & SCOTT LTD.
Library of Congress Catalog Card Number: 65-23361

FOREWORD

THESE ARE THE SONGS that most of us have known all our lives. Our mothers crooned them as they bent over our cradles, our fathers sang them robustly about the house, we sang them with our schoolmates and our first sweethearts. Among them are songs that have restored faith, inspired armies, swayed public opinion, and told the course of empire; but most of the songs have been selected because so many people, for such a long time, have found them good to sing. For that reason they will be as familiar as old friends.

All arrangements are in four-part harmony, playable on piano, organ, or accordion. Except for the hymns and sacred songs, there are diagrams for ukulele and symbols for guitar. The ukulele chords have been simplified so that a novice can master the fingering with ease. The vocal arrangements, with few exceptions, have been made adaptable to various combinations of voices, even when a full quartet is not available, and also practical for unison singing, since the melody remains in the "top note" throughout.

SOURCES OF SONGS. To trace composers, authors and translators of many songs; to untangle the maze of error, perpetuated over many years as each "new" songbook copied from its predecessors, editors must become detectives. Sometimes their best efforts end in failure and in sincere regret—for example, that the translator of *La Paloma* should himself remain unsung while his work is sung and loved throughout the English-speaking world.

In some cases, omissions from the "catalog of the public domain" are all but incredible. The editors have tried to repair these omissions.

For example, after literally months of searching the editors could find no translation of *La Marseillaise;* the "prevailing English version" is hardly even a paraphrase. In several other cases, translations were found to exist but to lack the indispensable quality of a song lyric—they are not singable. We have supplied translations for these songs.

HYMNS. Our selection embraces some classical hymns and hymns sung frequently in formal church services, but chiefly we present those more informal numbers called "Sunday School hymns," "Gospel hymns," or "sacred songs." This book is not a hymnal and its purpose —to provide words and music for singing at home and in informal groups—can better be served by songs having moderate range and high melodic quality.

In making our selections we have had the advice of clergymen and laymen of all denominations, in all sections of the United States, and in Canada. *Christian Herald* magazine very generously conducted a poll of its hundreds of thousands of readers on our behalf, and we relied heavily on the preferences they expressed; we thank the magazine's editor, Dr. Daniel A. Poling, and Dr. Clarence W. Hall, then its executive editor, now senior editor of *The Reader's Digest,* for this assistance. Several pastors polled their congregations on our behalf and to them too we give our thanks.

All our selections have been made on merit; we have not had to make a single omission on account of copyright restrictions. The copyright owners kindly granted us permission for every one that we wanted to include, and we take this opportunity to express our gratitude to them.

So that we might display both words and music as large as possible, we omitted the terminal Amen from the hymns but supplied a musical arrangement for every key; these appear on the last page of this book. The pianist, organist or choral director can turn to this page almost without pause to find the music appropriate to his selection.

BALLADS. Here we cannot say, as we did in the case of our hymnodic selections, that copyright restrictions were no problem. Publishers of popular music in the United States—the group generally called "Tin Pan Alley"—as a matter of policy and mutual agreement do not release their copyrights for republication in anthologies such as this.

Nevertheless the editors found this policy cause for regret in only two or perhaps three cases. The statutory copyright in the United States expires after fifty-six years. Usually it takes longer than that for a song to become a true "standard" and much, much longer for it to merit classification as a "folk song."

Longevity is a primary requirement for a "best-loved" song. Songs may become popular very quickly, but they can lose their popularity almost as quickly. The editors have been acutely conscious of trends. Forty years ago it would have been unthinkable to leave "The Old Oaken Bucket" out of such a book as this; today that song does not qualify. With the exception of some patriotic or inspirational songs, the most recent applicants that are best-known and -loved today date from the 1890's and early 1900's. Incidentally, we use the designation "Gay 'Nineties" for some songs that were actually written shortly after the turn of the century, because they are in the same spirit.

FOLK SONGS. There are few really great songs. The most famous melodies are basic and of great antiquity. Many of our folk songs derive from tunes that were known to the bards and troubadours; they have endured, with slight changes, for hundreds or thousands of years.

The editors of this compilation have elected in most cases to present these songs as they are actually sung. No attempt has been made to formalize such songs as *John Henry, The Old Chisholm Trail, Barb'ry Allen;* we transcribe them as we have heard them. Some songs, or versions of songs, here appear in print for the first time. For example the spiritual *Lord I'm Troublin'*, here presented as sung by a group of field hands on a South Carolina plantation. All efforts to uncover a printed version have failed, yet W. C. Handy, in his eightieth year, informed us that he remembered it from the time he was five years old.

We have not hesitated, where we think it appropriate, to present the words as they have been adapted by successive generations, rather than the historic versions that scholarly anthologies may pardonably consider obligatory. An example might be "Yankee Doodle" or some lyrics of Stephen C. Foster. Such deviations (which we will note in our prefatory comments) should be considered a matter of editorial judgment and not inadequate research.

ACKNOWLEDGMENTS. First, to J. Franklin Whitman, who designed this book and executed the beautifully decorative end pages. Louis Pennino engraved the music, and Jane Derrick McDowell and Earle Pitts prepared the copy for the printers. The late William C. Handy in folk music and Dr. Reginald McAll in hymnology were valuable personal consultants, and of course, like all who delve into American music, the editors are indebted to the works of John and Alan Lomax, Sigmund Spaeth, David Ewen, and others.

JAMES MOREHEAD
ALBERT MOREHEAD

New York 1965

CONTENTS

See also Alphabetical Index of All Titles, First Lines, Composers, Arrangers, Authors, and Translators, on page 397.

PATRIOTIC SONGS

AMERICA

Samuel Francis Smith | **Uncertain origin**

Mr. Smith, a Boston minister, wrote the American words for a service at the Park Street Church on July 4, 1831, taking the melody from a German songbook lent him by Lowell Mason and unaware that it was the tune of the British national anthem (see facing page). Until *The Star-Spangled Banner* was made official in 1931 this was a prime candidate for the national anthem of the United States and most Americans still stand up for it. Henry Carey was once credited with the tune, based on a claim made by his son after his death, but this claim has been discredited, though without stigma on Carey. Other British and continental claims have proved equally unreliable and none seems now to have hope of verification. Union of words and music in *God Save the King* has not been traced back beyond 1743, though both are very likely older.

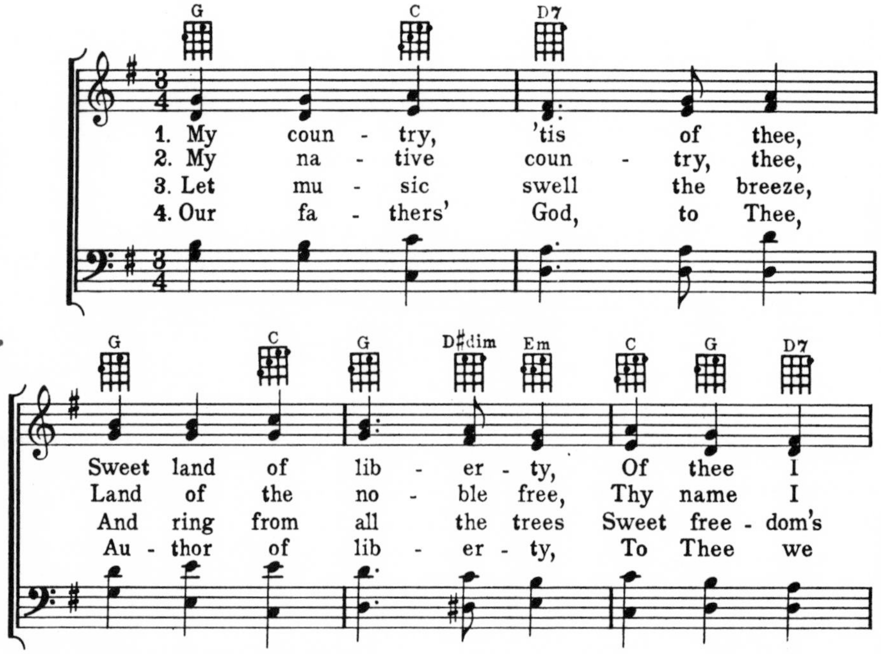
G C D7
1. My coun - try, 'tis of thee,
2. My na - tive coun - try, thee,
3. Let mu - sic swell the breeze,
4. Our fa - thers' God, to Thee,
G C G D♯dim Em C G D7
Sweet land of lib - er - ty, Of thee I
Land of the no - ble free, Thy name I
And ring from all the trees Sweet free - dom's
Au - thor of lib - er - ty, To Thee we
G
sing. Land where my fa - thers died!
love. I love thy rocks and rills,
song. Let mor - tal tongues a - wake;
sing. Long may our land be bright

D7
G
Land of the Pil - grims' pride! From ev' - ry
Thy woods and tem - pled hills; My heart with
Let all that breathe par - take; Let rocks their
With free - dom's ho - ly light; Pro - tect us
G
D7
G
C
G
D7
G
moun - tain side, Let free - dom ring!
rap - ture thrills Like that a - bove.
si - lence break, The sound pro - long.
by Thy might, Great God, our King!

God Save the Queen

THE TITLE FLUCTUATES according to the sex of the British monarch, but most often it is GOD SAVE THE KING. By authoritative proclamation in 1931, only the tune is the British national anthem, the words being unofficial. Most stanzas date from the early 18th century and are recited below in the form best reputed since the accession of Elizabeth II.

1. God save our gracious Queen,
Long live our noble Queen,
God save the Queen!
Send her victorious,
Happy and glorious,
Long to reign over us,
God save the Queen!

2. O Lord, our God, arise,
Scatter our enemies
And make them fall;
Confound their politics,
Frustrate their knavish tricks.
On Him our hopes we fix.
O save us all!

3. Of many a race and birth,
From utmost ends of earth,
God save us all.
Did strife and hatred cease,
Did hope and joy increase,
Spread universal peace.
God save us all.

4. Nor on this land alone,
But be God's mercies shown
From shore to shore.
Lord, make the nations see
That men should brothers be
And form one family
The wide world o'er.

THE STAR-SPANGLED BANNER

Francis Scott Key **John Stafford Smith**

The tune of The Star-Spangled Banner was popular in America before the words were written; it was originally called *To Anacreon in Heaven,* and was written for the Anacreontic Society of London, about 1775. Key wrote the inspired text as a prisoner on a British ship that was bombarding Fort McHenry (at Baltimore) in 1814. Just before dawn the firing stopped, and with daybreak those on the ship could see the flag still flying over the fort.

With Spirit
f
1. Oh_ say! can you see, by the dawn's ear - ly
2. On the shore, dim - ly seen thro' the mists of the
3. Oh,_ thus be it ev - er when free men shall
light, What so proud - ly we hailed at the twi-light's last
deep, Where the foe's haugh - ty host in dread si - lence re -
stand Be - tween their lov'd homes and the war's de - so -
gleam - ing? Whose broad stripes and bright stars thro' the
pos - es, What is that which the breeze, o'er the
la - tion! Blest with vic - t'ry and peace, may the
per - il - ous fight, O'er the ram-parts we watch'd, were so
tow - er - ing steep, As it fit - ful - ly blows, half con -
heav'n - res - cued land Praise the Pow'r that hath made and pre -

mf
gal - lant - ly stream - ing? And the rock - ets' red
ceals half dis - clos - es? Now it catch - es the
served us a na - tion! Then con - quer we
glare, the bombs burst - ing in air, Gave proof thro' the
gleam of the morn - ing's first beam In full glo - ry re -
must, when our cause it is just, And this be our
ff
night that our flag was still there. Oh, say, does that
flec - ted now shines on the stream; 'Tis the Star span - gled
mot - to: "In God is our trust!" And the Star span - gled
Star span - gled Ban - ner yet wave O'er the
Ban - ner, Oh, long may it wave O'er the
Ban - ner in tri - umph shall wave O'er the
fff
land of the free and the home of the brave!
land of the free and the home of the brave!
land of the free and the home of the brave!

AMERICA THE BEAUTIFUL

KATHERINE LEE BATES — SAMUEL A. WARD

ONE OF THE great patriotic songs of the United States, this was written in 1893 by Miss Bates, who was Professor of English at Wellesley College, to the hymn tune *Materna*. Shortly before writing it she had made a trip to the West, and from the summit of Pike's Peak had seen "spacious skies" above the "fruited plains."

C
G7
1. O beau - ti-ful for spa-cious skies, For
2. O beau - ti-ful for pil-grim feet Whose
3. O beau - ti-ful for he-roes prov'd In
4. O beau - ti-ful for pa-triot dream That
C
G7
C
am-ber waves of grain, For pur-ple moun-tain
stern im-pas-sion'd stress A thor-ough-fare for
lib-er-at-ing strife, Who more than self their
sees be-yond the years, Thine al-a-bas-ter
G
D7
G
G7
maj-es-ties A-bove the fruit-ed plain. A-
free-dom beat A-cross the wil-der-ness. A-
coun-try lov'd And mer-cy more than life. A-
cit-ies gleam, Un-dimmed by hu-man tears. A-

C
G7
mer - i - ca! A - mer - i - ca! God
mer - i - ca! A - mer - i - ca! God
mer - i - ca! A - mer - i - ca! May
mer - i - ca! A - mer - i - ca! God
C
C7
F
shed His grace on thee,_ And crown thy good with
mend thine ev - 'ry flaw,_ Con-firm thy soul in
God thy gold re - fine_ Till all suc-cess be
shed His grace on thee,_ And crown thy good with
C
F
G7
C
broth - er-hood From sea to shin-ing sea.
self - con-trol, Thy lib - er - ty in law.
no - ble-ness, And ev - 'ry gain di - vine.
broth - er-hood From sea to shin-ing sea.

THE BATTLE HYMN OF THE REPUBLIC

JULIA WARD HOWE — *Ascribed to* **WILLIAM STEFFE**

WHILE MRS. HOWE was visiting in Washington during the Civil War, she heard the Union soldiers singing "John Brown's Body" to the tune of a popular Sunday-school hymn. The melody remained in her mind, and during the night she wrote her magnificent lyric. The result was this classic marching song, known and sung all over the world, even where it has no patriotic significance. Its thunderous eloquence is not exceeded anywhere in the realm of patriotic poetry, and may be equalled only by the *Marseillaise.*

Bb
1. Mine— eyes have seen the glo - ry of the
2. I have seen Him in the watch-fires of a
3. He has sound - ed forth the trum - pet that shall
4. In the beau - ty of the lil - ies Christ was
com - ing of the Lord; He is
hun - dred cir - cling camps; They have
nev - er call re - treat; He is
born a - cross the sea; With a
Eb
tramp - ling out the vin - tage where the
build - ed Him an al - tar in the
sift - ing out the hearts of men be -
glo - ry in His bos - om that trans -
Bb
grapes of wrath are stored; He hath
eve - ning dews and damps; I can
fore His judg - ment seat; Oh, be
fig - ures you and me; As He

loosed the fate - ful light - ning of His
read His right - eous sen - tence by the
swift, my soul, to an - swer Him! be
died to make men ho - ly, let us
Cm7 Bb F7 Bb
ter - ri - ble swift sword. His truth is march - ing on.
dim and flar - ing lamps. His day is march - ing on.
ju - bi - lant, my feet! Our God is march - ing on.
die to make men free, While God is march - ing on.
Bb
Glo - ry! glo - ry hal - le - lu - jah!
Eb Bb
Glo - ry! glo - ry hal - le - lu - jah! Glo - ry! glo - ry hal - le -
Cm7 Bb F7 Bb
lu - jah! His truth is march - ing on.

THE ARMY GOES ROLLING ALONG

Edmund L. Gruber; H. W. Arberg — **Edmund L. Gruber**

For nearly half a century every American knew "The caissons go rolling along," written by General Gruber (when he was a lieutenant) for his beloved Field Artillery and expanded by John Philip Sousa to the formal *Field Artillery March.* When artillery faded under airpower, and coincidentally the U. S. Army wished to adopt an official song, Dr. Arberg was in charge of selection. He adapted Gruber's 1909 original and Sousa's 1918 expansion, and this is the result—still a classic.

Eb
Ebmaj7
1. First to fight for the right, and to
2. Val - ley Forge, Cus - ter's ranks, San Juan
3. Men in rags, men who froze, still that
Cm7
Eb
Bb7
build the Na - tion's might, and The Ar - my goes
Hill and Pat - ton's tanks, and The Ar - my went
Ar - my met its foes, and The Ar - my went
Eb
roll - ing a - long. Proud of
roll - ing a - long. Min - ute
roll - ing a - long. Faith in
Ebmaj7
Cm7
all we have done, Fight - ing till the bat - tle's
men from the start, Al - ways fight - ing from the
God, then we're right, And we'll fight with all our

Eb Bb7 Eb
won, And the Ar - my goes roll - ing a - long.
heart, And the Ar - my goes roll - ing a - long.
night, And the Ar - my goes roll - ing a - long.
Ab
Then it's Hi! Hi! Hey! The Ar - my's on its
Eb Bb Cm F7 Bb7
way. Count off the ca - dence loud and strong! (Two!
Eb G7 Ab
Three!) For where - e'er we go You will al - ways
Eb Bb7 Eb
know that the Ar - my goes roll - ing a - long.

ANCHORS AWEIGH

ALFRED H. MILES

CHARLES A. ZIMMERMAN

ZIMMERMAN, BANDMASTER at the U. S. Naval Academy (Annapolis), collaborated with Miles when the former was a lieutenant and the latter a midshipman. The song was first sung at the Army-Navy football game of 1906 (and Navy won). The public treats ANCHOR'S AWEIGH (the apostrophe is proper) as the theme song of the United States Navy; enlisted men in the Navy have never quite shared that view, considering it the officers' song, although they too take pride in it.

C
Am
1. Stand Na - vy down the field,
2. Get un - der way, Na - vy,
3. Blue of the sev - en seas,
C
G7
C
F
Sails set to the sky,——— We'll
Decks cleared for the fray,——— We'll
Gold of God's great sun,——— Let
C
E♭dim
G7
C
D7
nev - er change our course, So Ar - my you steer
hoist true Na - vy Blue, So Ar - my down your
these our col - ors be Till all of time be

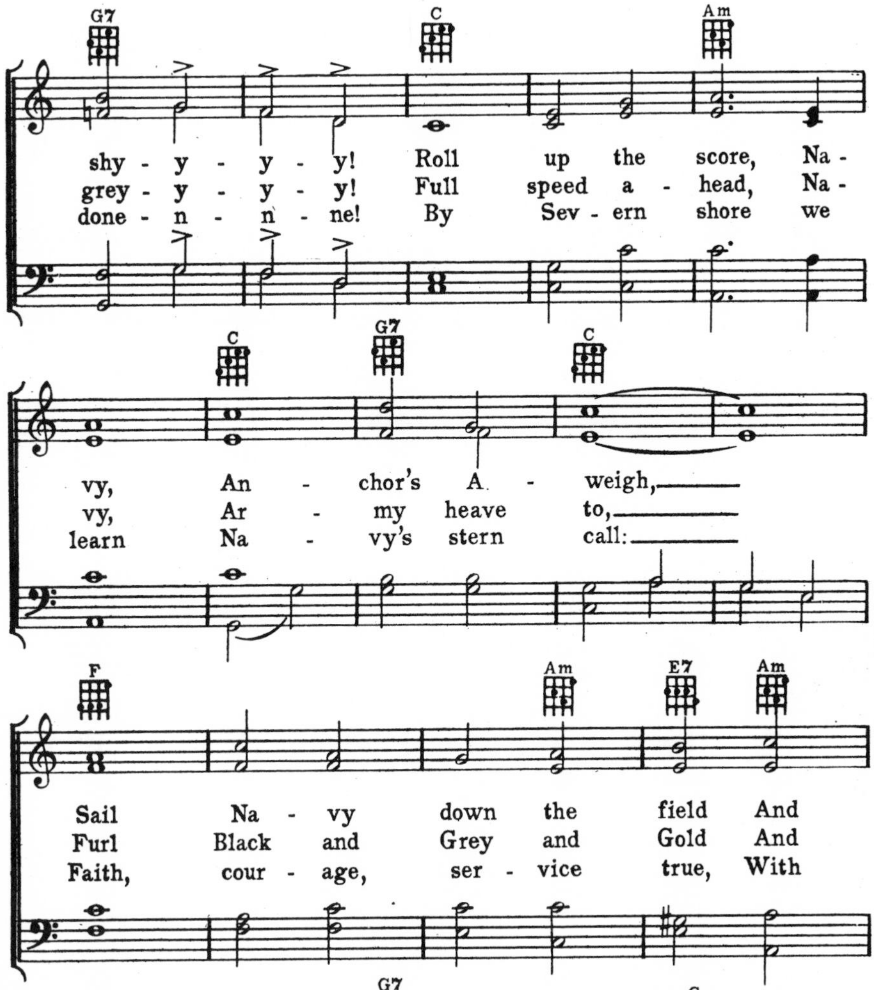
G7 C Am
shy - y - y - y! Roll up the score, Na -
grey - y - y - y! Full speed a - head, Na -
done - n - n - ne! By Sev - ern shore we
C G7 C
vy, An - chor's A - weigh,
vy, Ar - my heave to,
learn Na - vy's stern call:
F Am E7 Am
Sail Na - vy down the field And
Furl Black and Grey and Gold And
Faith, cour - age, ser - vice true, With
C G7 C
sink the Ar - my, sink the Ar - my Grey!
hoist the Na - vy, hoist the Na - vy Blue!
hon - or o - ver hon - or o - ver all.

THE NAVY HYMN

WILLIAM WHITING

JOHN BACCHUS DYKES

THIS IS the most widely used hymn addressed to the Father of seafarers Who created the waters, Whose power can soothe the storm (MATTHEW 8:23). It is always a part of the service on British ships, and is the official hymn of the United States Naval Academy.

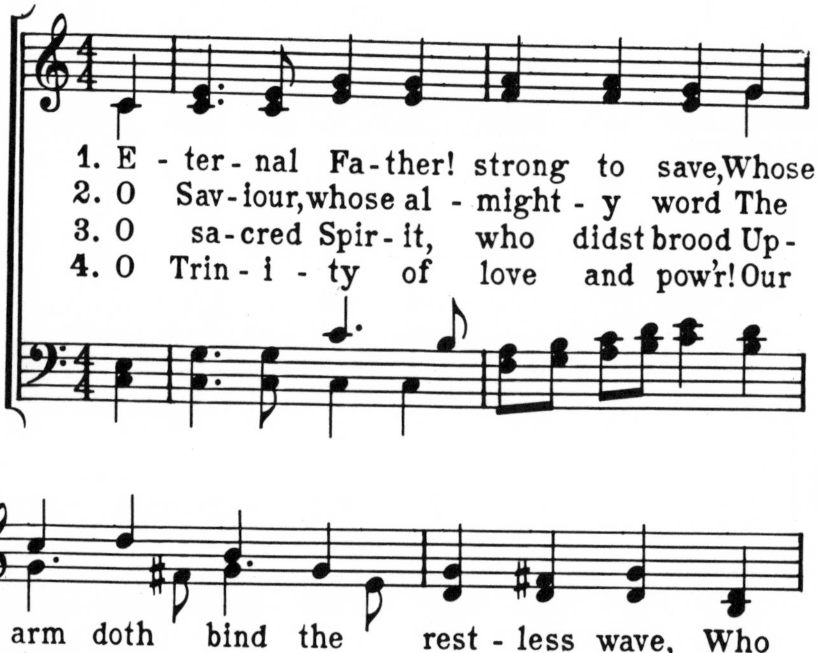
1. E - ter - nal Fa - ther! strong to save, Whose
2. O Sav - iour, whose al - might - y word The
3. O sa - cred Spir - it, who didst brood Up -
4. O Trin - i - ty of love and pow'r! Our
arm doth bind the rest - less wave, Who
winds and waves sub - mis - sive heard, Who
on the cha - os dark and rude, Who
breth - ren shield in dan - ger's hour; From
bid'st the might - y o - cean deep Its
walk - edst in the foam - ing deep, And
bad'st its an - gry tu - mult cease, And
rock and tem - pest, fire and foe, Pro -

own ap - point-ed lim - its keep; O
calm a - mid its rage didst sleep; O
gav - est light, and life, and peace; O
tect them where-so - e'er they go, Thus
hear us when we cry to Thee, For
hear us when we cry to Thee For
hear us when we cry to Thee For
ev - er let there rise to Thee Glad
those in per - il on the sea.
those in per - il on the sea!
those in per - il on the sea!
hymns of praise from land and sea!

THE MARINES' HYMN

ANONYMOUS

THE MARINES' HYMN is historically older than most other American patriotic songs, as is attested by the first two lines referring to the war against the Barbary Pirates of North Africa and the Mexican War (whence the reference to the Halls of Montezuma). All attempts to trace the origin have met with failure.

Eb
Bb7
Eb
1. From the Halls of Mon-te - zu - ma To the
2. Here's health to you and to our Corps Which
Bb7
Eb
shores of Trip - o - li We fight our
we are proud to serve; In man - y a
Bb7
Eb
Bb7
Eb
coun-try's bat - tles On the land as on the sea.
strife we've fought for life And nev-er lost our nerve.

Ab
Eb
First to fight for right and free -
If the Ar - my and the Na -
Ab
Eb
Edim
dom And to keep our hon - or clean,
vy Ev - er look on Heav - en's scenes,
Bb7
Eb
Bb7
Eb
We are proud to claim the ti -
They will find the streets are guard -
Bb7
Eb
tle Of U - nit - ed States Ma - rines.
ed By U - nit - ed States Ma - rines!

THE AIR FORCE BLUE

Scott-Textor

There is some controversy as to whether the United States Air Force has ever had an official song—the Air Force has taken no such action since it succeeded the U. S. Army Air Corps in 1947—but this is the song bought from its writers by the Air Force, for use as a recuiting song, and placed in the public domain so that it can be freely reprinted. The "blue" in the title has a double meaning, representing both the uniform and the sky.

F Bb C7
They took the 1. blue from the skies, And a
2. men with a dream On A -
F Bb C7 F
pret - ty girl's eyes, And a touch of Old
mer - i - ca's team, They're a rug - ged and
C7 F F7+ Bb
Glo - ry's hue, And gave it to the
read - y crew, And you can bet your

C7 Am Dm Gm
men Who proud - ly wear The
boots, The world looks up To U. S.
1. 2. 3. Fine
Air Force Blue! Oh they are They
G7 C Am
know where they're go - ing, They've set their course; The
B♭ D7 Gm G7 C7
D. S. 𝄋 al Fine
sky's no lim - it in the Air Force! They took the

YANKEE DOODLE

AUTHOR UNKNOWN

YANKEE DOODLE is the subtitle of the famous painting "The Spirit of '76." Sigmund Spaeth, after citing several pages of sober (and conflicting) views by historians, says: "It is a safe guess that YANKEE DOODLE was originally an instrumental tune, coming to this country from England, Scotland, or Ireland, with various texts added from time to time."

A E7
Yan - kee Doo - dle went to town
Yan - kee Doo - dle went to town, To
Fath'r and I went down to camp, A-
And there we saw a thou-sand men, As
And there was Cap-tain Wash-ing-ton Up-
A E7 A E7
Rid - ing on a po - ny,
buy a pair of trou - sers, He
long with Cap - tain Good - win, And
rich as Squire Da - vid, And
on a slap - ping stal - lion, A -
A E7 A D6 D♯dim
Stuck a feath - er in his crown, And
swore he could not see the town Be -
there we saw the men and boys As
what they wast - ed ev - 'ry day, I
giv - ing or - ders to his men; I

E7
A
called it mac - a - ro - ni.
cause of all the hous - es.
thick as hast - y pud - din'.
wish it could be sav - ed.
guess there was a mil - lion.
CHORUS
D
Yan - kee Doo - dle, keep it up,
A
D
Yan - kee Doo - dle dan - dy; Mind the mu - sic
A
E7
A
and the step, And with the girls be han - dy.

DIXIE

DANIEL DECATUR EMMETT

A MEASURE of the quality of DIXIE is that Abraham Lincoln loved to hear it, and Northern soldiers sang it, even though it represented the enemy. It was written as a "walk-around" for Dan Bryant's Minstrel Show in New York. There are many conflicting stories as to how it came to mean the land below the Mason-Dixon line (probably a pure accident); but there is no doubt that it was the great inspirational song of the Confederacy.

D
mf
1. I wish I was in the land of cot - ton,
Dix - ie land where I was born in
2. There's buck-wheat cake and_ In - dian bat - ter,
hoe it down and_ scratch your gravel, To
G
Old times there are not for - got - ten, Look a -
Ear - ly on a frost - y morn - in', Look a -
Makes you fat or a lit - tle fat - ter, Look a -
Dix - ie's land I'm bound to trav - el Look a -
D
f
way, look a - way, look a -
way, look a - way, look a -
way, look a - way, look a -
way, look a - way, look a -
look a - way, look a - way,
D
A7
1. D
2. D
way, Dix - ie land. 1. In land.
2. Then
look a - way,

REFRAIN
cresc
Then I wish I was in Dix - ie, Hoo - ray! Hoo - ray! In Dix - ie land I'll take my stand To live and die in
Dix - ie, . A - way, a - way, a - way, a - way, a -
way down South in Dix - ie. A - way, a - way, a -
way, a - way, a - way down South in Dix - ie.
cresc

O CANADA!

R. Stanley Weir (English)
Adolphe Routhier (French)

Calixa Lavallée

This great song, the product in music of one of Canada's great composers, and in its words of two of Canada's eminent jurists, was completed in its various forms at the turn of the century. Mr. Weir called it "a humble effort to do a great thing: to supply Canada with a National Song." The result, far from humble, was worthy of its purpose; but the reception ran afoul of politics. French-Canadian in inception, the anthem failed to displace the popular *The Maple Leaf Forever;* in 1965 the argument is unabated.

Eb Bb7 Cm Bb7 Eb Ab
1. O Can - a - da! Our home and na - tive
2. O Can - a - da! Where pines and ma - ples
3. O Can - a - da! Be - neath thy shin - ing
4. Rul - er su - preme, who hear - est hum - ble
Eb F7 Bb Cm Bb F7
land! True pa - triot - love in all thy sons com-
grow, Great prai - ries spread and lord - ly riv - ers
skies May stal - wart sons and gen - tle maid - ens
prayer, Hold our Do - min - ion in Thy lov - ing
Bb7 Eb
mand. With glow - ing hearts we see thee rise The
flow, How dear to us thy broad do - main, From
rise; To keep thee stead - fast through the years From
care. Help us to find, O God, in Thee A

Ab Eb Ab F7 Bb Bb7
True North strong and free; And stand on guard, O
East to West-ern sea! Thou land of hope for
East to West-ern sea, Our own be-lov-ed
last-ing, rich re-ward, As wait-ing for the
Eb Gdim Bb F7 Bb7
Can-a-da. We stand on guard for thee.
all who toil! Thou True North strong and free!
na-tive land, Our True North strong and free.
Bet-ter Day We ev-er stand on guard.
CHORUS
Eb Cm Fm Ab6 Bb7
O Can-a-da! Glor-ious and free!
Eb Eb7+ Ab Fm Eb Fm Cm Fm G
We stand on guard, We stand on guard for thee.
Eb G+ Ab Fm Eb Ab Eb Bb7 Eb
O Can-a-da! We stand on guard for thee.
rit.

THE MAPLE LEAF FOREVER

Alexander Muir

Alexander Muir was born in Scotland, but was brought to Canada at the age of three. After graduating from Queen's University he became a song writer. The Maple Leaf Forever is regarded as the national song of Canada. The words refer to the hero of Canadian history, James Wolfe, who defeated Montcalm at Quebec and so gave "New France" to the English crown. Nootka Sound is on Vancouver Island, all the way across the continent.

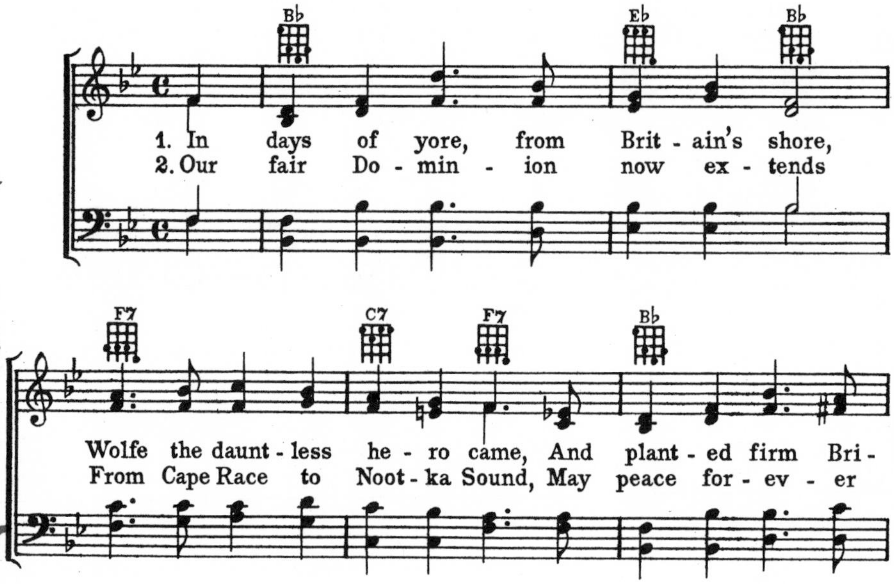
Bb Eb Bb
1. In days of yore, from Brit - ain's shore,
2. Our fair Do - min - ion now ex - tends
F7 C7 F7 Bb
Wolfe the daunt - less he - ro came, And plant - ed firm Bri -
From Cape Race to Noot - ka Sound, May peace for - ev - er
Gm C7 F C7
tan - nia's flag, On Can - a - da's fair do -
be our lot, And plen - te - ous store a -
F7 Bb Eb Bb
main; Here may it wave, our boast and pride, And
bound; And may those ties of love be ours, Which

G7 Cm F7 Bb
join in love to - geth - er, The This - tle, Sham-rock,
dis - cord can - not sev - er, And flour - ish green o'er
Eb Bb Eb6 Bb F7 Bb
Rose en - twine The Ma - ple Leaf for - ev - er.
Free - dom's home, The Ma - ple Leaf for - ev - er.
CHORUS
Bb Eb Bb
The Ma - ple Leaf, our em - blem dear, The
F7 Bb
Ma - ple Leaf for - ev - er, God save our King and
Eb Bb Eb6 Bb F7 Bb
Heav - en bless The Ma - ple Leaf for - ev - er.

RULE BRITANNIA

James Thomson　　　　Thomas Augustine Arne

Rule Britannia, the national song of Great Britain, was originally an ode sung in the masque *Alfred*, the music for which was composed by Arne in 1739. The masque was later made into an opera (1745) but the ode was retained. Handel used the melody in his *Occasional Oratorios.*

A D A E7 A
1. When Brit-ain first, at Heav'n's com-mand, A-
2. The mus-es, still with free-dom found, Shall
F♯m B7 E
rose from out the az - ure main, A-
to thy hap-py coast re-pair, Shall
F♯m E B7 E
rose from out the the az-ure main,
to thy hap - py coast re-pair;

A D Bm7 E E7
This was the char-ter, the char-ter of the land, And
Blest Isle of free-dom, with match-less beau-ty crown'd, And
A E7 A D A E7 A
guard - ian an - gels sang this strain:
man - ly hearts to guard the fair,
A D F#7 Bm E
Rule, Bri-tan-nia, Bri-tan-nia rule the waves,
A E7 A D 1.A E7 A 2.A E7 A
never, never, never
Bri-tons nev - er shall be slaves. shall be slaves.

LA MARSEILLAISE

Tr. Albert Morehead — Claude Joseph Rouget de Lisle

Rouget de Lisle, a young French officer, wrote the words and almost as surely the music at Strasbourg in 1792; the song received its name when revolutionaries from Marseilles sang it so enthusiastically later that year. Beethoven and many other composers have used the musical theme. The first stanza, unsurpassed in patriotic poetry, in English versions is usually only paraphrased; here it is translated except for the closing lines, which mean "Let [their] impure blood irrigate our fields!"

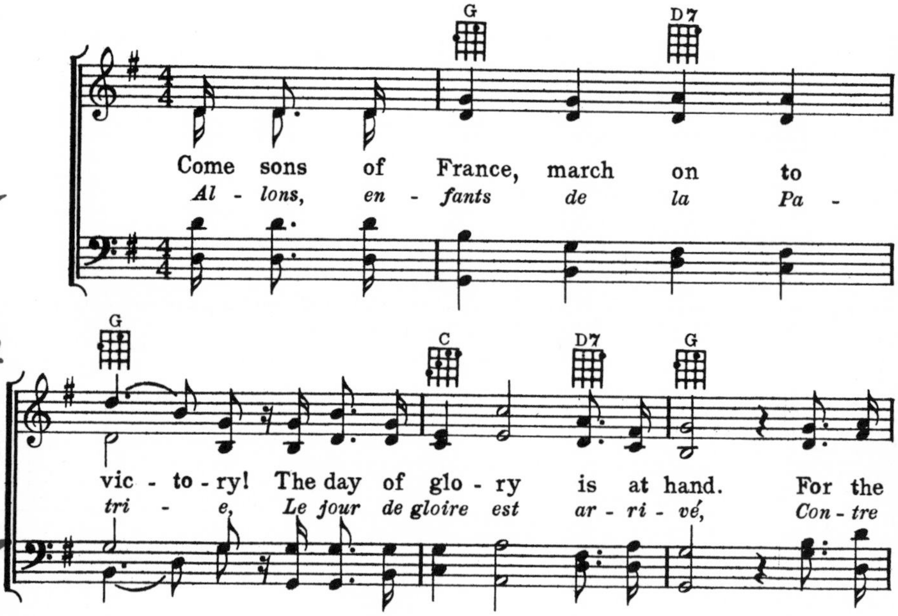
G
D7
Come sons of France, march on to
Al - lons, en - fants de la Pa -
G
C
D7
G
vic - to - ry! The day of glo - ry is at hand. For the
tri - e, Le jour de gloire est ar - ri - vé, Con - tre
D7
ty - rant march-es a - gainst us, On his flag the blood of our
nous, de la ty - ran - ni - e L'é - ten - dard san-glant est le -
G
D7
land; On his flag is the blood of our land. And do you
vé, L'é - ten - dard san-glant est le - vé. En-ten-dez-

G C Em A7
hear these vile ma - raud - ers who roar like beasts in our
vous, dan ces cam - pa - gnes, Mu - gir ces fé ro ces sol -
D7 Gm D7
farms? Who tear our loved ones from our arms, — Who at -
dats? Ils vien - nent jus - que dans nos bras, — E - gor -
Gm D7 G
tack our wives, our sons and daugh-ters? To arms, — men of
ger nos fils, nos com - pa - gnes! Aux ar - mes, Ci - toy -
D7 G D7 G D7 G7
France! Close ranks — As we ad-vance! March on, march on;
ens, For - mez — vos ba - tail - lons! Mar - chons, mar - chons,
C G C♯dim D7 G D7 G
Long live our land, And death — to foes of France! —
Qu'un sang im - pur A - breu - ve nos sil - lons! —

THE WEARING OF THE GREEN

Revised by **Dion Boucicault**

During the Irish Rebellion of 1796, members of the Volunteers were identified by their insignia, the green shamrock. When they were caught, the penalty was execution. Their leader and hero was James Napper Tandy, an Irish patriot who attempted an independence movement modeled on the American Revolution. The tune is also that of the old West Point song *Benny Havens, Oh!*

F
1. O___ Pad - dy, dear, and did you hear the
2. Saint___ Pat - rick's day no more we'll keep, his
C
Bb
news that's go - ing 'round? The sham - rock is for -
col - or can't be seen, For there's a blood - y
F
C7
F
bid by law to grow on I - rish ground;
law a - gin' the wear - in' o' the green.
Bb
F
I___ met with Nap - per Tan - dy and he

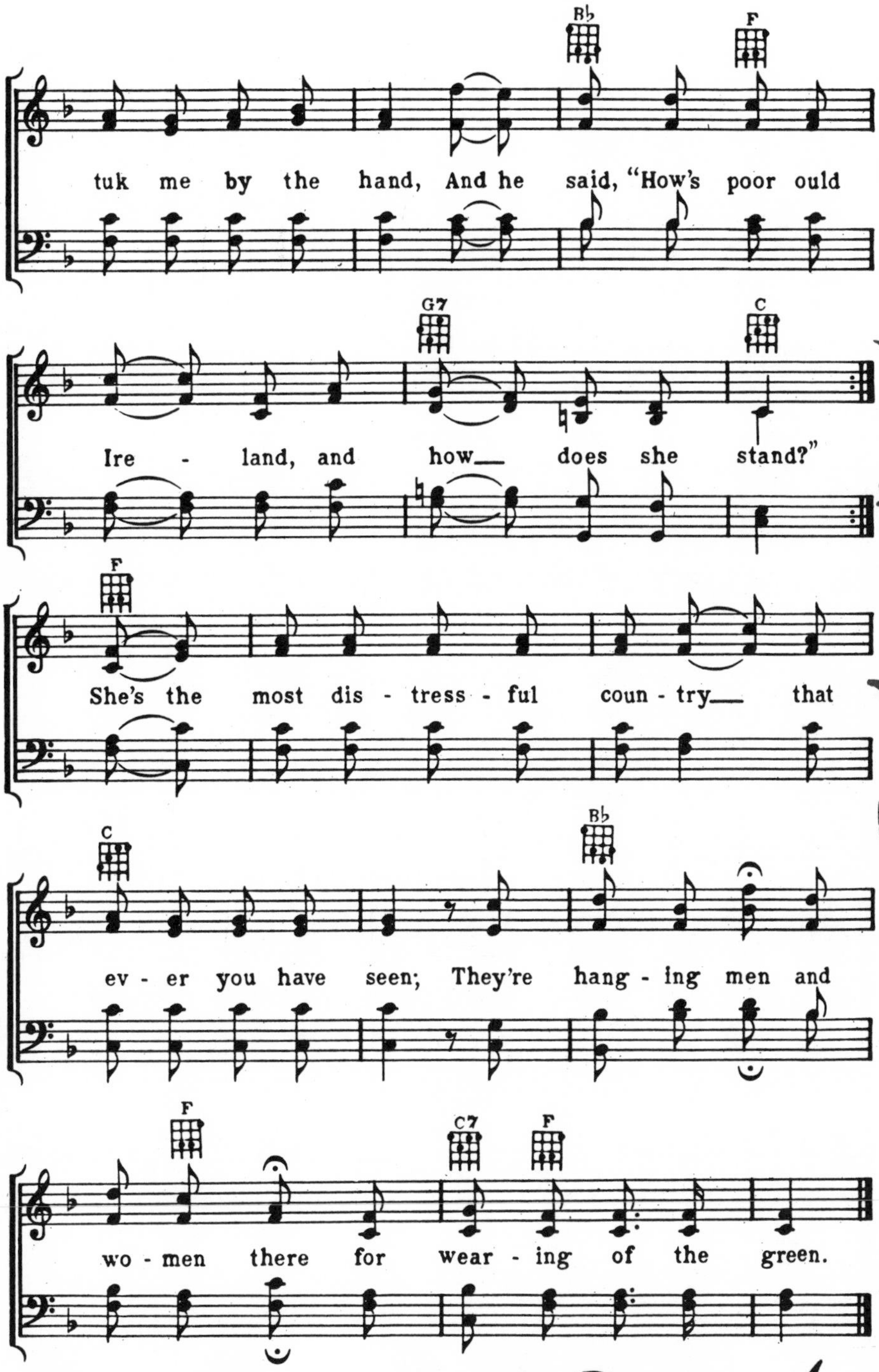

B♭ F
tuk me by the hand, And he said, "How's poor ould
G7 C
Ire - land, and how__ does she stand?"
F
She's the most dis - tress - ful coun - try__ that
C B♭
ev - er you have seen; They're hang - ing men and
F C7 F
wo - men there for wear - ing of the green.

THE PLEDGE TO THE FLAG

FRANCIS BELLAMY | JAMES MOREHEAD

THE WORDS OF THE PLEDGE are official by Act of Congress; a brief but well-researched history of them may be read in *World Almanac.* The beautifully rhythmic text of Bellamy's original has been wounded twice: by including *of the United States of America,* lest unreconstructed rebels might secretly mean the Confederate flag; and by the insertion in 1954 of the words *under God,* by legislators who presumably believed that there can be a nation that is not under God.

I pledge al-le-giance to the flag___ of the
U - nit - ed States of A - mer - i - ca And
to the Re - pub - lic for which it stands, One
na-tion, un-der God, in - di - vis - i - ble, With
lib - er - ty and jus - tice for all.___

SENTIMENTAL BALLADS

BEAUTIFUL DREAMER

Stephen C. Foster

Stephen Foster's "last song, written only a few days before his death." It was published in 1864, shortly after he died (at the age of 38). His work had deteriorated greatly during the last few years of his life, and it is not unreasonable to suppose that this song, one of his finest efforts, was an earlier composition, unearthed and perhaps revised to make an immediate sale.

D
G
Em7
Beau - ti - ful dream - er, wake un - to me,
A7
D
Star - light and dew - drops are wait - ing for thee,
G
Em7
Sounds of the rude world, heard in the day,
A7
D
Lull'd by the moon - light have all passed a - way.

A7 D
Beau - ti - ful dream - er, Queen of my song,
Bm E7 A7
List while I woo thee, with soft mel - o - dy;
D G Em7
Gone are the cares of life's bus - y throng,
A7 D F#7 Bm
Beau - ti - ful dream - er, a - wake un - to me!
G D A7 D
Beau - ti - ful dream - er, a - wake un - to me!

DRINK TO ME ONLY WITH THINE EYES

Ben Jonson *Old English Tune*

Ben Jonson's *Song, To Celia* was published in a volume of poems in 1616. It is certainly as well known, and well loved, as any song in the English language. The origin of the tune remains a mystery; it is probably from the 16th century.

Eb Bb7 Eb Bb7
1. Drink to me on-ly with thine eyes, And
2. I sent thee late a ros - y wreath, Not
Eb Ab Eb Bb7 Eb
I will pledge with mine;
so much hon - 'ring thee
Bb7 Eb Bb7
Or leave a kiss but in the cup And
As giv - ing it a hope that there It

Eb Ab Eb Bb7 Eb
I'll not look for wine.— The
could not with-ered be;— But
thirst that from the soul doth rise Doth
thou there - on didst on - ly breathe And
Ab Eb Bb7 Eb Bb7 Eb Bb7
ask a drink di - vine;— But might I of Jove's
sent'st it back to me;— Since when it grows, and
Eb Eb7 Ab Eb Ab Eb Bb7 Eb
nec - tar sup I would not change for thine.—
smells, I swear, Not of it - self but thee!—

HOW CAN I LEAVE THEE?

FRIEDRICH WILHELM KÜCKEN

THERE IS no doubt that Kücken himself wrote the beautiful German song *Ach, wie ist's möglich dann,* about 1827, but several early editions failed to credit him, including a Baltimore publication of 1851. In English translation his melody has been popular for more than one hundred years. It is sometimes known as *Thuringian Folk Song,* and often listed as anonymous. Kücken, the son of a peasant, distinguished himself in music and became tutor to German princes.

B♭
1. How can I leave thee!
2. Blue is a flow'r - et
3. Would I a bird were!
F7
B♭
How can I from thee part! Thou on - ly
Called the "For - get - me - not," Wear it up -
Soon at thy side to be, Fal - con nor
E♭
B♭
C7
F7
hast my heart, Dear one, be - lieve.
on thy heart, And think of me!
hawk would fear, Speed - ing to thee.

Bb
Thou hast this soul of mine
Flow'r - et and hope may die,
When by the fowl - er slain,
G7
Cm
F7
So close - ly bound to thine, No oth - er
Yet love with us shall stay, That can-not
I at thy feet should lie, Thou sad - ly
Bb
C7
F7
Bb
can I love, Save thee a - lone!
pass a - way, Dear one, be - lieve.
shouldst com - plain, Joy - ful I'd die.

CARELESS LOVE

ANONYMOUS

NO OTHER folk song is better known than CARELESS LOVE, and there is no doubt about the universality of its theme, with the closing resolution: "Going to cry tonight . . . and cry no more."

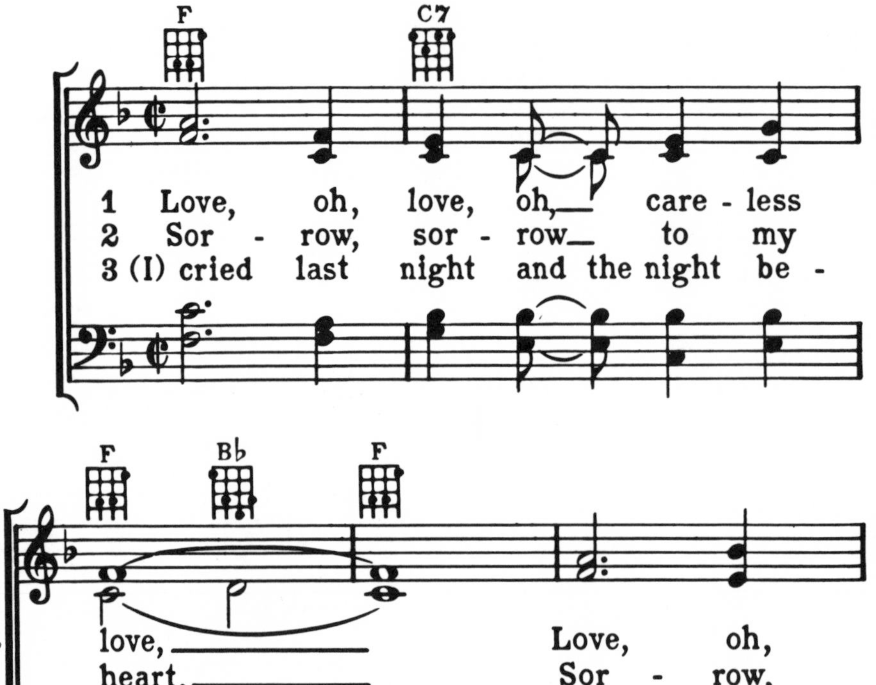
F
C7
1 Love, oh, love, oh,— care - less
2 Sor - row, sor - row— to my
3 (I) cried last night and the night be -
F
B♭
F
love,——
heart,——
fore,——
Love, oh,
Sor - row,
(I) cried last
C
G7
C7
love, oh, care-less love,—— Oh, well it's
sor - row to my heart,—— Oh, well it's
night and the night be - fore,—— Oh, well I

F
F7
F7+
love, oh, love, oh,
sor - row, sor - row
cried last night and the
Bb
Bbm6
F
care - less love, You see what
to my heart, Since my true
night be - fore, Going to cry to -
C7
F
Bb
F
care - less love has done.
love and I did part.
night and cry no more.

FLOW GENTLY, SWEET AFTON

Robert Burns — **James E. Spilman**

This Scottish song was set to music, at least in America, by a Philadelphian, James E. Spilman, in 1838. In Scotland and the British Commonwealth it usually is titled *Afton Water*, with a tune by Alexander Hume. The interval of a sixth, in the sixth and twelfth measures, is common to both melodies. Spilman's tune is used for *Away In A Manger* also.

A D
1. Flow gen - tly, sweet Af - ton, a - mang thy green
2. How loft - y, sweet Af - ton, thy neigh - bor - ing
3. Thy crys - tal stream, Af - ton, how love - ly it
A E7 A E7 A B7
braes; Flow gen - tly, I'll sing thee a song in thy
hills, Far marked with the cours - es of clear-wind - ing
glides, And winds by the cot where my Ma - ry re -
E7 A D
praise; My Ma - ry's a sleep by thy mur - mur - ing
rills! There dai - ly I wan - der, as morn ris - es
sides! How wan - ton thy wa - ters her snow - y feet
A E7 A D A E
stream, Flow gen - tly, sweet Af - ton, dis - turb not her
high, My flocks and my Ma - ry's sweet cot in my
lave, As, gath - 'ring sweet flow - 'rets, she stems thy clear

A E B7
dream. Thou stock-dove, whose ech - o re - sounds from the
eye. How pleas - ant thy banks and green val - leys be -
wave! Flow gen - tly, sweet Af - ton, a - mang thy green
E
hill, Ye wild whist - ling black - birds in
low, Where wild in the wood - lands the
braes, Flow gen - tly, sweet riv - er, the
B7 E7 A
yon thorn - y dell, Thou green - crest - ed
prim - ros - es blow! There oft, as mild
theme of my lays; My Ma - ry's a
D A
lap - wing, thy scream - ing for - bear, I
eve - ning creeps o - ver the lea, The
sleep by thy mur - mur - ing stream, Flow
E7 A D A E7 A
charge you, dis - turb not my slum - ber - ing fair.
sweet - scent - ed birk shades my Ma - ry and me.
gen - tly, sweet Af - ton, dis - turb not her dream.

IN THE GLOAMING

Meta Orred | Annie F. Harrison

A new word was added to the lexicon of popular songs when Meta Orred and Annie F. Harrison wrote In the Gloaming and introduced it in England in 1877. The song has been given the consideration of an art song, appearing on many concert programs. Sigmund Spaeth says that it "definitely belongs among the better products of popular music."

F
C7
C♯dim
Dm
1. In the gloam - ing oh,— my dar - ling!
2. In the gloam - ing oh,— my dar - ling!

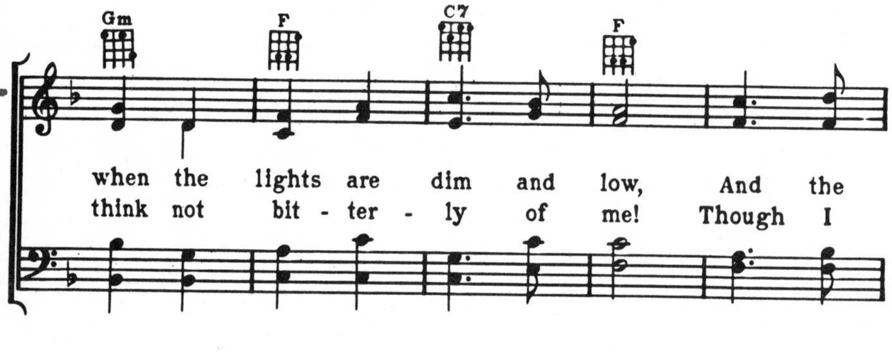
Gm
F
C7
F
when the lights are dim and low, And the
think not bit - ter - ly of me! Though I

C7
C♯dim
Dm
Gm
C7
qui - et shad - ows, fall - ing, soft - ly come and
passed a - way— in si - lence, left you lone - ly,

F F7 B♭ F7
soft - ly go, When the winds are sob - bing
set you free, For my heart was crushed with
B♭ G7 F B♭ F C7
faint - ly with a gen - tle, un - known woe,
long - ing; what had been could nev - er be.
F C7 C♯dim Dm Gm C7
Will you think of me and love me As you did once
It was best to leave you thus, dear, Best for you and
1. F 2. Dm Fdim G7
long a - go?
best for me. It was best to leave you
F G7 C7 F
thus, Best for you and best for me.

SHINE ON, HARVEST MOON

Nora Bayes and Jack Norworth

When Nora Bayes introduced this song in Ziegfeld's "Follies of 1908" she was already, as vaudeville and musical comedy star, perhaps the most popular songstress of her time. It was said she could make a hit of any song she sang, and she did probably make as many hits as any other woman singer. But this one, which she wrote in collaboration with her husband "in real life," Jack Norworth, was the song inextricably associated with her for the rest of her life and its title was selected as the title of a film biography of Miss Bayes made many years later.

E7+5
E7
Shine on, shine on har - vest
A7
F#m
A7
D7
moon up in the sky I ain't
G
D7
had no lov - in' since Jan - u - a - ry, Feb - ru - a - ry,

Gdim D7 G E7+5 E7
June or Ju - ly Snow time
ain't no time to stay out - doors and
Gdim D7
spoon, So shine on, shine on har - vest
G C9 G
moon for me and my gal.

THE ROSARY

ROBERT CAMERON ROGERS | ETHELBERT NEVIN

ETHELBERT NEVIN, born in Pittsburgh, has often been likened to Stephen C. Foster. Indeed, there are striking similarities in their lives and careers. Both encountered resistance from their families in becoming musicians. Both wrote mostly in miniature. Both died in their late thirties, Foster an alcoholic, Nevin a hopeless neurotic. Both wrote songs that are deathless masterpieces. THE ROSARY, written in 1896, is not a religious song, although Rogers' poem does create such a mood. It would be hard to name a song written in America that has exceeded it in popularity.

E♭ B7 Fm7 B♭7
The hours I spent with thee, dear heart,—
E♭ B7 Fm7 B♭7 E♭7
Are as a string of pearls to me;— I count them o-ver ev-'ry
A♭ B♭9 B♭7 E♭
one a-part, My ro-sa-ry, my ro-sa-ry!
B7 Fm7 B♭7
Each hour a pearl, each pearl a pray'r,—

Eb B7 Fm7 Bb7
To still a heart in ab - sence wrung;—
Eb7 Ab C G
I tell each bead un-to the end,—And there a cross is hung!—
Eb B7 Fm7 Bb7 Eb B7
Oh mem-o - ries that bless and burn,— Oh bar-ren gain, and bit-ter
Fm7 Bb7 Eb7 Ab
loss:— I kiss each bead, and strive at last to learn to kiss the
F9 F7 Eb Bb7 Eb
cross, sweet-heart! To kiss the cross.—

JEANIE, WITH THE LIGHT BROWN HAIR

STEPHEN C. FOSTER

STEPHEN FOSTER married Jane McDowell, the daughter of a Pittsburgh physician, in 1850. He was thinking of her when he wrote JEANIE, WITH THE LIGHT BROWN HAIR. After the Fosters' daughter was born, the songwriter-poet, though he seems never to have stopped loving his wife and daughter, proved ill adapted to domestic life. In the last unhappy years of his life, when he was separated from them, the words of this song were his favorites.

Ab
Eb
I dream of Jean - ie with the
I long for Jean - ie with the
Ab
light brown_ hair, Borne like a va - por,
day - dawn_ smile, Rad - iant in glad - ness,
Eb
F7
Bb7
Eb
on the sum - mer air; I see her trip-ping where the
warm with win - ning guile; I hear her mel - o - dies, like
F7
Bb7
Eb
bright streams play, Hap - py as the dai - sies that
joys gone_ by, Sigh - ing round my heart o'er the

B♭ F7 B♭7
dance on her way. Man-y were the wild notes her
fond hopes that die; Sigh-ing like the night wind and
E♭ A♭ E♭ G7
mer-ry voice would pour, Man-y were the blithe birds that
sob-bing like the rain, Wail-ing for the lost one that
F7 B♭7
war-bled them o'er; Ah!
comes not a-gain; Ah! I
E♭
dream of Jean-ie with the light brown hair,
A♭ E♭ A♭ E♭ B♭7 E♭
Float-ing like a va-por, on the soft sum-mer air.

SWEET GENEVIEVE

GEORGE COOPER HENRY TUCKER

AFTER HIS association with Stephen C. Foster, the versatile Cooper collaborated with innumerable composers. He became very well known and successful, writing many popular songs, but in spite of his success he always needed money. He sold SWEET GENEVIEVE for five dollars, to Henry Tucker, who wrote the music. The poem had been written after the tragic death of Cooper's wife Genevieve, soon after their marriage. He never loved again.

G D7
1. Oh Gen - e - vieve, I'd give the world To
2. Fair Gen - e - vieve, my ear - ly love The
G G7
live a - gain the love - ly past. The rose of youth was
years but make thee dear - er far. My heart shall nev - er,
C Cm G D7 G
dew im-pearl'd But now it with - ers in the blast. I
nev - er rove, Thou art my on - ly guid - ing star. For
G7 C G G7 C
see thy face in ev - 'ry dream; My wak-ing thoughts are
me the past has no re - gret; What - e'er the years may

G B7 Em
full of thee. Thy glance is in the star - ry beam That
bring to me, I bless the hour when first we met, The
G6 A7 F♯7 B7 D7
falls a - long the sum - mer sea.
hour that gave me love and thee.
CHORUS
G D7
Oh, Gen - e - vieve, Sweet Gen - e - vieve, The
G G7
days may come, the days may go, But still the hands of
C Cm G D7 G
mem - 'ry weave The bliss - ful dreams of long a - go.

I'LL TAKE YOU HOME AGAIN, KATHLEEN

THOMAS P. WESTENDORF

THIS MOST IRISH of songs was not written in Ireland, but in Plainfield, Indiana, by an American of German descent, who originally came from Virginia. He wrote it for his wife, to whom he was very devoted; but her name, Jennie, did not fit the music very well, so he used Kathleen instead. The song has been universally accepted as Irish.

F C7 G#dim F
I'll take you home a - gain, Kath - leen, A -
C7 F
cross the o - cean wild and wide, To
C7 G#dim F
where your heart has ev - er been, Since
C G7 C C7
first you were my bon-nie bride. The ros - es all have left your
F C7
cheek, I've watched them fade a - way and

F Dm
die; Your voice is sad when-e'er you
A7 G7 C7
speak, And tears be-dim your lov-ing eyes.
CHORUS
F C7 G♯dim F
Oh! I will take you back a-gain, To
C7 F F7
where your heart will feel no pain, And when the fields are fresh and
B♭ G♯dim F C7 F
green, I'll take you to your home a-gain.

MY WILD IRISH ROSE

CHAUNCEY OLCOTT

ALTHOUGH IT IS a "popular song" in every sense, this has many of the characteristics of the great folk songs. It has been sung by three generations of Americans and is known to almost everyone; many will be surprised to learn that it is not a genuine folk song. It was published in 1899, when recent heavy Irish immigration had created a demand for Irish songs; this was the first of the quasi-traditional ones and so is historic. Olcott, a matinee idol of that era, introduced the song in his own show.

C G7 C
My wild I - rish rose,—— The
F C C#dim G7
sweet - est flow'r that grows,— You may search ev - 'ry -
C C#dim G7 C D7
where, but none can com - pare With my wild I - rish

G7 C G7 C
rose.___ My wild I - rish rose,___
F C C#dim
— The dear - est flow'r that grows,___ And some-
G7 C C#dim C
day for my sake, she may let me take The
F D7 G7 C
gloom from my wild I - rish rose.___

THE ROSE OF TRALEE

C. MORDAUNT SPENCER

CHARLES W. GLOVER

AN IRISH SONG with a sweet simplicity that is reminiscent of Thomas Moore, this long-time favorite came with the Irish to the New World. Glover himself was never in America, so far as is known, but many of his songs became popular here. Tralee is the county seat of County Kerry, Ireland.

Bb
Eb
1. The pale moon was ris-ing a - bove the green
2. The cool shades of eve-ning their man-tle were
Bb
F7
Bb
C7
moun - tain, The sun was de - clin - ing be - neath the blue
spread - ing, And Ma - ry, all smil - ing, was lis-t'ning to
F7
Bb
Eb
sea, When I strayed with my love to the pure crys - tal
me; The moon thro' the val-ley her pale rays was
Bb
F7
Bb
Eb
Bb
foun-tain That stands in the beau - ti - ful vale of Tra - lee.
shed-ding, When I won the heart of the Rose of Tra - lee.

Bb D7 Gm Eb7
She was love - ly and fair as the rose of the
D7 Gm D7 Gm D7
sum - mer, Yet 'twas not her beau - ty a - lone that won
Gm F7 Bb Eb
me. Oh, no, 'twas the truth in her eyes ev - er
Bb F7 Bb F7 Bb
dawn - ing That made me love Ma - ry, the Rose of Tra - lee.

JUANITA

Mrs. Caroline Norton *Spanish Melody*

Spanish folk song is represented here, with its rhythmic three-four lilt. The early settlers of California sang it in their mother tongue, and Mrs. Norton's verse, in English, gave it a permanent place as one of America's favorites. Caroline Norton was a granddaughter of Richard Brinsley Sheridan, the Irish dramatist. All efforts to trace the composer have failed, and we must consider the melody a folk song. No song is more universally included in songbooks and collections, especially those intended for use in schools.

D
A7
1. Soft o'er the foun-tain, Ling-'ring falls the
2. When in thy dream-ing, Moons like these shall
D
A7
south-ern moon; Far o'er the moun-tain,
shine a - gain, And day-light beam-ing
D
Breaks the day too soon! In thy dark eye's
Prove thy dreams are vain, Wilt thou not, re -

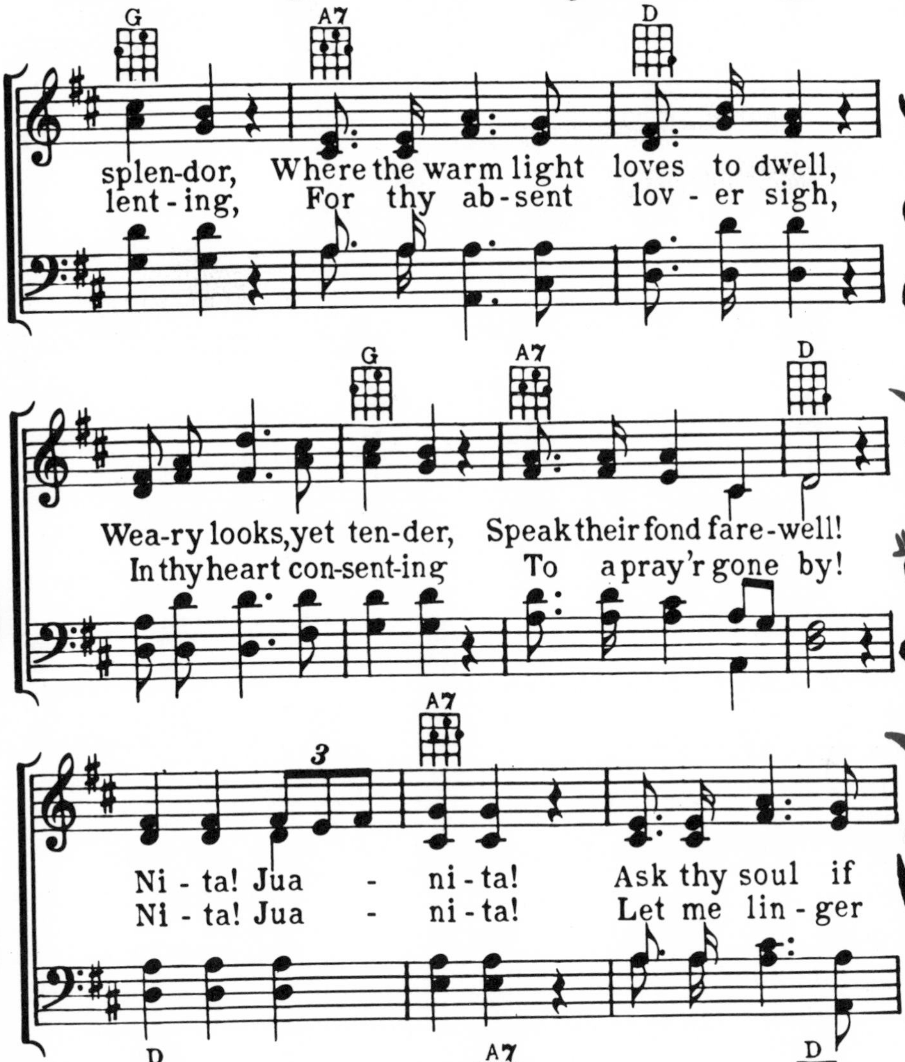
G A7 D
splen-dor, Where the warm light loves to dwell,
lent-ing, For thy ab-sent lov-er sigh,
G A7 D
Wea-ry looks, yet ten-der, Speak their fond fare-well!
In thy heart con-sent-ing To a pray'r gone by!
A7
3
Ni - ta! Jua - ni - ta! Ask thy soul if
Ni - ta! Jua - ni - ta! Let me lin - ger
D A7 D
3
we should part! Ni-ta! Jua - ni-ta! Lean thou on my heart.
by thy side! Ni-ta! Jua - ni-ta! Be my own fair bride!

ANNIE LAURIE

WILLIAM DOUGLASS LADY JOHN SCOTT

S. J. ADAIR FITZGERALD, the historian, tells of an old lady who heard ANNIE LAURIE sung in 1854. She was a descendant of Douglass of Fingland, and she said that he was desperately in love with Annie Laurie when he wrote the song, "but," she added, "he did na get her after all." Annie Laurie married the Ferguson of Craigdarrock, whose house, five miles away, could be seen from Maxwelton House, where she was born in 1682. Lady John Scott altered and polished the song, and possibly wrote the third verse.

C
1. Max - wel - ton's braes are
2. Her brow is like the
3. Like dew on th'gow - an
F C Am7 D7
bon - nie, Where ear - ly fa's the
snow-drift, Her throat is like the
ly - ing Is th' fa' o'her fair - y
G7 C
dew, And 'twas there that An - nie
swan; Her face, it is the
feet, And like winds in sum - mer

F C G7 C
Lau - rie Gie'd me her prom - ise
fair - est That e'er the sun shone
sigh - ing, Her voice is low and
G7 C
true; Gie'd me her prom-ise true, Which
on; That e'er the sun shone on, And
sweet; Her voice is low and sweet, And she's
Am Dm E7 G♯dim Am Cmaj7 F
ne'er for - got will be,
dark blue is her e'e,
a' the world to me,
And for bon-nie An-nie
C G7 C G7 C
Lau-rie, I'd lay me doon and dee.

SWEET ADELINE

RICHARD GERARD (R. G. HUSCH) HARRY ARMSTRONG

THIS SONG, PUBLISHED IN 1903 and the undisputed theme song of barbershop quartets for some forty years, is historic in at least three other ways: It pioneered the "repeat" or "echo" lyric (Sweet Adeline, my Adeline); it acquired, undeservedly, the stigma of being a "drunken" song; and it evidenced the irrational vagaries of public taste in matters of title. Originally titled *Down Home in Old New England*, it could not find a publisher. As *You're the Flower of My Heart, Sweet Rosalie*, it failed. With Rosalie changed to Adeline (in honor of Adelina Patti), it became an all-time hit.

G D7 G B7
(melody)
Sweet A - del - ine (Sweet A - del - ine) My A - del-
C E7 A7
ine (My A - del - ine) At night, dear
D7
heart, (At night dear heart) For you I

G D7
pine, (For you I pine,) In all my
G B7
dreams, (In all my dreams) Your fair face
C E7 A7 G♯ C♯dim
melody
beams, (Your fai_ face beams,) You're the
G E7 A7 D7 G G7 Edim Cm G
flow - er of my heart, Sweet A - del - ine. (My A - del - ine.)

DEAR OLD GIRL

RICHARD HENRY BUCK | THEODORE F. MORSE

THIS SONG IS A "MUST" for every male quartet. The lyricist, Buck, was among the best of his times; the composer, Morse, was one of the outstanding songwriters of the early years of this century. But of Morse's many successful songs, only this one has survived—making allowance for one odd exception. As David Ewen has pointed out, the one Morse production that *everyone* knows is the few words he added to a Gilbert and Sullivan march in *The Pirates of Penzance:* "Hail, hail, the gang's all here."

C Ebdim G7 Gbdim C Ebdim
Dear Old Girl the rob-in sings a - bove you Dear Old
G7 Gbdim C Am
Girl, it speaks of how I love you. When the blind-ing tears are
E7 F Ab7 Gbdim C Ab
fall-ing, Then I think of my lost pearl, And my brok-en heart is
C Am D7 G7 C Ab7 C
call-ing, Call-ing for you Dear_ Old Girl._____

I LOVE YOU TRULY

CARRIE JACOBS BOND

THIS BEAUTIFUL SONG is known wherever English is spoken. It is almost a standard part of American wedding ceremonies, usually as a solo sung after the service. Mrs. Bond, who turned to songwriting when she was widowed, was the only woman on the original list of those rated AA (highest) when the American Society of Composers, Authors and Publishers (ASCAP) was formed. The General Federation of Women's Clubs placed her among the first fifty women of this century.

Ab Bbm7 Eb7 Bbm7 Eb7 Ab
1. I love you tru - ly, tru - ly dear,
2. Ah, love 'tis some-thing to feel your kind hand,
Bbm7 Eb7 Bbm7 Eb7 Ab C7
Life with its sor - row, Life with its tear,
Ah, yes, 'tis some-thing by your side to stand,
Fm C7 Fm Bb9 Bb9 Fm7 Abm6 Fdim
Fades in - to dreams when I feel you are near,
Gone is the sor - row, Gone doubt and fear,
Ab Bbm7 Eb7 Ab
For I love you tru - ly, tru - ly dear.
For you love me tru - ly, tru - ly dear.

OH, PROMISE ME

CLEMENT SCOTT — REGINALD DEKOVEN

THE OPERETTA *Robin Hood,* of which OH, PROMISE ME is a part, has been a permanent success, often revived; but if Scott and DeKoven had never written anything but the one song, their fame would have been assured. It has been sung so consistently at weddings that it is treated almost as part of the service, in which respect it has few competitors.

G C G
1. Oh, prom - ise me that some-day you and I Will
2. Oh, prom - ise me that you will take my hand, The
D7 G7 C Cm G
take our love to - geth - er to some sky Where
most un - worth - y in this lone - ly land, And
Am F F7 Am
we can be a - lone, and faith re - new, And
let me sit be - side you, in your eyes, —

C Am6 B7 D7 G
find the hol - lows where those flow - ers grew, — Those
See - ing the vi - sion of our para - dise, —
D7
first — sweet — vi - o - lets of ear - ly spring, Which
Hear - ing God's mes - sage while the or - gan rolls Its
Em Am7 Em B7
come in whis - pers, thrill us both, and sing Of
might - y mu - sic to our ver - y souls; No
C B7 Em Cm6 Eb7
love un - speak - a - ble that is to be;
love less per - fect than a life with thee;
Oh,
G D7sus D7 G
prom - ise me! Oh, prom - ise me!

BELIEVE ME, IF ALL THOSE ENDEARING YOUNG CHARMS

Thomas Moore *Traditional*

Most authorities have said that the tune is English, *My Lodging Is On The Cold Ground*, but Edward Bunting insists that it is Irish, and points to the repeated use of the submediant, typical of Irish music. Moore, at any rate, wrote it to what he knew as "*As fada armso me* (Long am I here)." The alma mater of Harvard College, *Fair Harvard*, is sung to the same tune.

Eb
1. Be - lieve me, if all those en -
2. It is not while beau - ty and
Ab Eb Bb7
dear - ing young charms, Which I gaze on so fond - ly to -
youth are thine own, And thy cheek un-pro-faned by a
Eb
day, Were to change by to - mor - row and
tear, That the fer - vor and faith of a
Ab Eb Bb7
fleet in my arms, Like fair - y gifts fad - ing a -
soul can be known, To which time will but make thee more

Eb
Bb7
Eb
way,— Thou wouldst still be a - dored— as this
dear;— No, the heart that has tru - ly loved—
Ab
Eb
Bb
mo - ment thou art, Let thy love - li - ness fade as it
nev - er for - gets, But as tru - ly loves on to the
Eb
Bb7
Eb
will;— And a - round the dear ru - in each
close;— As the sun - flow - er turns on her
Ab
Eb
Bb7
Eb
wish of my heart Would en - twine it - self ver - dant - ly still.—
god, when he sets, The same look which she turn'd when he rose.—

LONG, LONG AGO

THOMAS HAYNES BAYLY

THIS SONG, so widely known and loved, was published in London, in 1843, as *The Long Ago*. The original title was changed by the public and is no longer used or remembered. Bayly was a successful songwriter during his lifetime, but of his songs only LONG, LONG AGO has survived. He was a poet rather than a musician, and most of his songs were set to music by others; but this melody he wrote himself, and it has an indestructible quality that has furnished a basis for many, more ephemeral, popular songs.

F
1. Tell me the tales that to me were so dear,
2. Do you re-mem-ber the paths where we met,
3. Tho' by your kind-ness my fond hopes were raised,
C7
F
Long, long a-go, Long, long a-go;
Sing me the songs I de-
Ah, yes, you told me you
You, by more el-o-quent
C7
F
light-ed to hear,
ne'er would for-get,
lips have been praised,
Long, long a-go, long a-go.

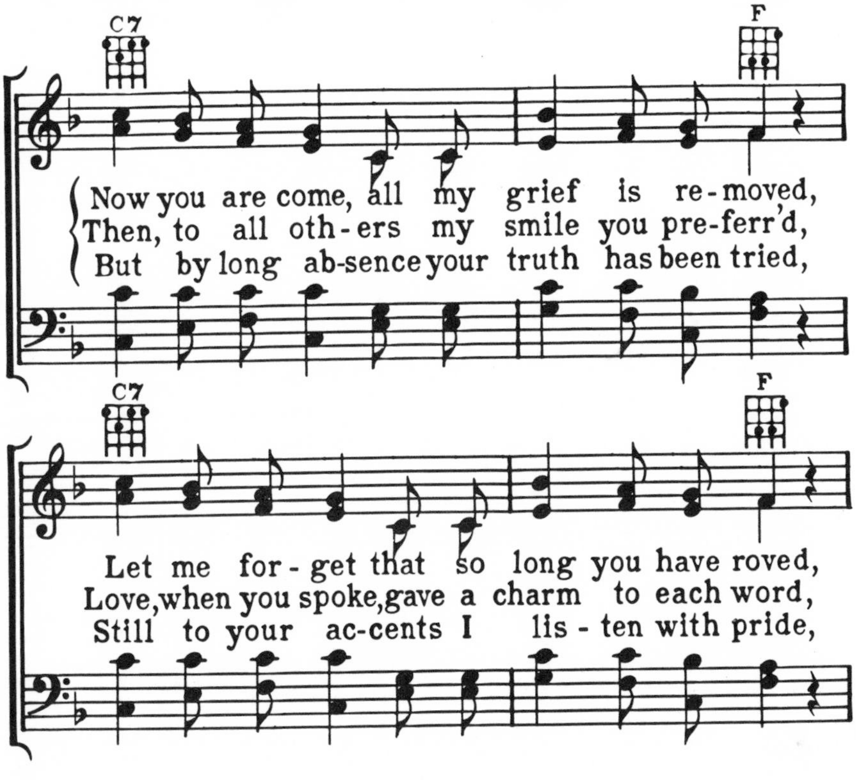
C7
F
Now you are come, all my grief is re-moved,
Then, to all oth-ers my smile you pre-ferr'd,
But by long ab-sence your truth has been tried,
C7
F
Let me for-get that so long you have roved,
Love, when you spoke, gave a charm to each word,
Still to your ac-cents I lis-ten with pride,
Let me be-lieve that you love as you loved,
Still my heart treas-ures the prais-es I heard,
Blest as I was when I sat by your side,
C7
F
Long, long a-go, long a-go.

SILVER THREADS AMONG THE GOLD

Eben E. Rexford | **Hart Pease Danks**

Rexford was the editor of a farmers' weekly, in which he sometimes printed verses he had written. When Danks, a successful composer, seemed attracted, Rexford sold him a number of verses for three dollars. One of these was Silver Threads Among The Gold. It became one of the most successful songs of all time, but the composer, like Stephen Foster, died in a furnished room, separated from those he loved, and in dire want. He left unfinished something he had started to write: "It is hard to die alone and . . ."

Bb
F7
Bb
1. Dar - ling, I am grow - ing old,
2. Love can nev - er - more grow old,
F7
Bb
Sil - ver threads a - mong the gold
Locks may lose their brown and gold;
F7
Bb
Shine up - on my brow to - day,
Cheeks may fade and hol - low grow,

F7 Bb
Life is fad - ing fast a - way.
But the hearts that love will know.
F7 Bb
But, my dar - ling, you will be, will be
Nev - er, nev - er win - ter's frost and chill,
(Refrain) Dar - ling, I am grow - ing old,
F C7 F C7 F7 Bb F7
Al-ways young and fair to me.
Yes, my dar-ling, you will
Sum-mer's warmth is in them still,
Nev - er win-ter's frost and
Sil - ver threads a-mong the gold,
Shine up - on my brow to -
Bb F7 Bb Eb Bb
Repeat for refrain
be Al - ways young and fair to me.
chill, Sum - mer's warmth is in them still.
day, Life is fad - ing fast a - way.

WHEN YOU AND I WERE YOUNG, MAGGIE

GEORGE W. JOHNSON — JAMES AUSTIN BUTTERFIELD

"THIS SONG has a real story, which has become so garbled through the years that it should be straightened out once and for all," writes Sigmund Spaeth in *A History of Popular Music*. This is the story: Johnson was a Canadian schoolteacher. At a little mill by a creek in Canada, he used to meet one of his pupils, Maggie Clark. They were deeply in love, and in 1865 they were married and went to live in Cleveland, Ohio, where Johnson had taken a position as a teacher. But Maggie died the same year, and Johnson's poem proved to be only a dream of what might have been. Butterfield, a teacher of music, set Johnson's poem to music and it was published in 1866. The song, simple and unpretentious and full of sincerity, is loved by the whole world.

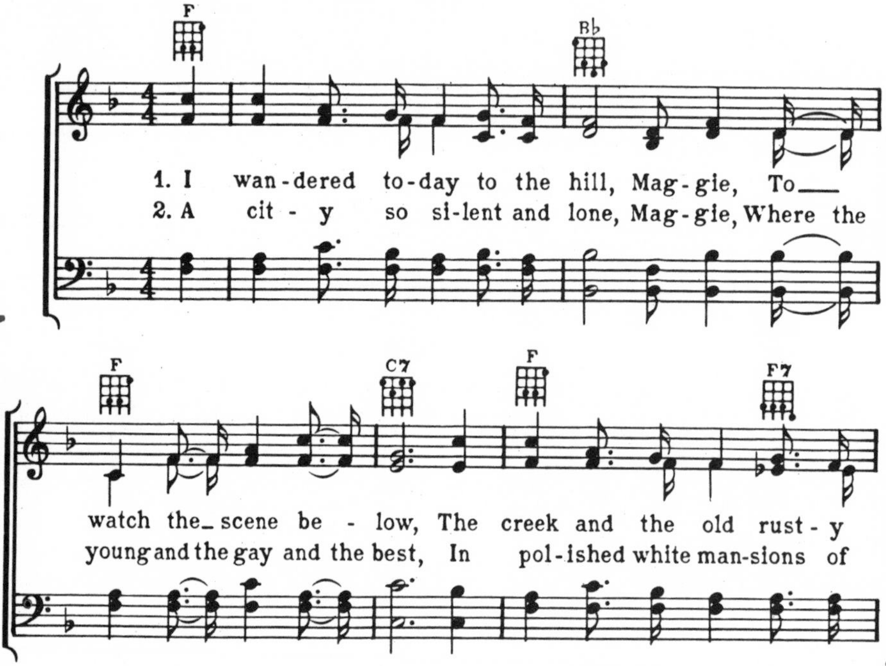
F
B♭
1. I wan-dered to-day to the hill, Mag-gie, To
2. A cit - y so si-lent and lone, Mag-gie, Where the
F
C7
F
F7
watch the scene be - low, The creek and the old rust - y
young and the gay and the best, In pol-ished white man-sions of
B♭
F
C7
F
mill, Mag-gie, Where we sat in the long, long a - go.
stone, Mag-gie, Have each found a place of rest,

B♭
The green grove is gone from the hill, Mag-gie, Where first the dai-sies sprung; The old rust-y mill is still, Mag-gie, Since you and I were young.
Is built where the birds used to play, Mag-gie, And join in the songs that were sung, For we sang just as gay as they, Mag-gie, When you and I were young.
Chos. And now we are a-ged and gray, Mag-gie, The tri-als of life near-ly done, But to me you're as fair as you were, Mag-gie, When you and I were young.
F C G7
C F C7 F F7
B♭ F C7 F
D. S. for Chorus

LOVE'S OLD SWEET SONG

C. Clifton Bingham | James L. Molloy

The first publication of this sweet song, with its ineffable nostalgic mood, was in England in 1884. Within a year it had swept the world, and this in a day before radio or phonograph records were available to create overnight saturation. Not too much is known about Bingham, but Molloy was a composer of wide scope, writing operettas and songs of considerable success. Love's Old Sweet Song far overshadowed most other popular songs of the period, and probably set a new standard for songs of the type.

F
C7
Once in the dear dead days be-yond re-call,
F
C7
When on the world the mists be-gan to fall, Out of the dreams that
F
Dm7
G7
C7
rose in hap-py throng, Low to our hearts love sang an old sweet song
Gm
Dm
And in the dusk, where fell the fire-light gleam,

G9 Am F6 C G7 C7
Soft - ly it wove it - self in - to our dream.
CHORUS
F C7 F
Just a song at twi-light, when the lights are low,
A7 Dm G7 C7
And the flick-'ring shad-ows soft - ly come and go;
F C7 F F7
Tho' the heart be wea-ry, sad the day and long, Still to us at
B♭ Am C7 F B♭ F C7 F
twi-light comes love's old song, Comes love's old sweet song.

WHEN YOU WERE SWEET SIXTEEN

JAMES THORNTON

JIM THORNTON was a vaudevillian, teamed with Charles Lawlor. Jim's wife Bonnie became a famous singer and helped to popularize his songs. Many of these were great successes in their time, but all are forgotten except WHEN YOU WERE SWEET SIXTEEN, written in 1898. It is said that Bonnie always waited at the stagedoor on payday to commandeer her husband's salary before he could spend it on liquor. Thornton "took the cure" several times, with complete failure. Then he simply stopped drinking. WHEN YOU WERE SWEET SIXTEEN was revived in 1944 and reached the position of No. 1 in nationwide popularity.

C
E7
I love you, as I ne - ver loved be -
F
A7
Dm
Dm7
G7
fore, Since first I met you
G+7
C
C♯dim
G7
on the vil - lage green; Come

C E7 F A7
to me, or my dream of love is o'er,
Dm F#dim C E7 C
I love you as I loved you When you were
D9 Dm7
sweet When you were sweet
(when you were sweet,) (when you were
G7 G9 add 11 C C7 F C
Six - teen.
sweet,)

LOCH LOMOND

ANONYMOUS

LOCH LOMOND lies between the counties of Dumbarton and Stirling, in Scotland, and not far from the city of Glasgow. Not much is known about the song. Early Scottish editions bore the credit line, "By a lady," and the wide variety of scales found in the folk music of the Scots makes it very difficult to place it in a specific period. It may be of comparatively recent origin, or quite ancient.

G G+ C D7
1. By yon bon-nie banks, And by yon bon-nie braes, Where the
2. 'Twas then that we part - ed In yon sha-dy glen On the
3. The wee bird-ies sing And the wild flowers spring, And in
G C G7 C G
sun shines bright on Loch Lo - mond, Where
steep, steep side of Ben Lo - mond, Where
sun-shine the wa - ters are sleep-ing, But the
Em G C6 D7
me and my true love were ev - er wont to gae On the
in pur-ple hue_ the Highland hills we view And the
bro-ken heart it kens_ Nae sec-ond Spring again Though the

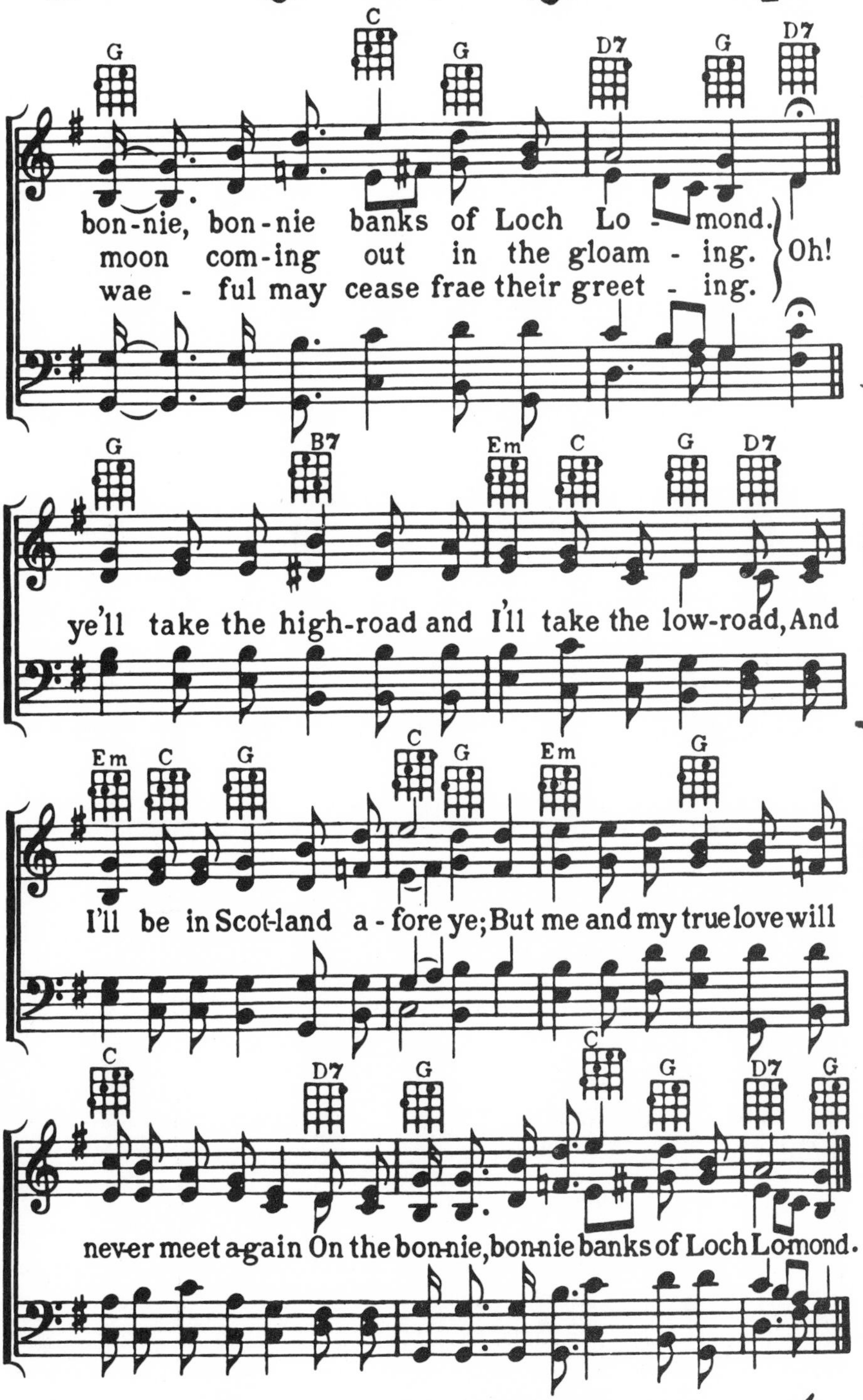
G C G D7 G D7
bon-nie, bon-nie banks of Loch Lo - mond.
moon com-ing out in the gloam - ing. Oh!
wae - ful may cease frae their greet - ing.
G B7 Em C G D7
ye'll take the high-road and I'll take the low-road, And
Em C G C G Em G
I'll be in Scot-land a - fore ye; But me and my true love will
C D7 G C G D7 G
nev-er meet a-gain On the bon-nie, bon-nie banks of Loch Lo-mond.

ALL THROUGH THE NIGHT

Attributed to David Owen — *Welsh air: Ar Hyd y Nos*

The people of Wales, with their long tradition of group singing, have given us this, one of the most beautiful of their folk songs. An English version beginning:

"Here beneath a willow weepeth
Poor Mary Ann"

was written by Mrs. Constance Opie. The tune is ancient and of unknown origin.

Ab Db Ab Bb7 Eb Ab
1. Sleep, my child, and peace at-tend thee,
2. While the moon her watch is keep-ing
Db Eb7 Ab Db Ab
All through the night, Guard-ian an-gels
All through the night, While the wea-ry
Bb7 Eb Ab Db Eb7 Ab
God will send thee, All through the night;
world is sleep-ing, All through the night;

Eb7
Soft the drow-sy hours are creep-ing, Hill and vale in
O'er thy spir-it gen-tly steal-ing, Vi-sions of de-
Ab Db Ab
slum-ber steep-ing, I my lov-ing
light re-veal-ing, Breathes a pure and
Bb7 Eb Ab Db Eb7 Ab
vig-il keep-ing All through the night.
ho-ly feel-ing All through the night.

SWEET AND LOW

ALFRED TENNYSON | JOSEPH BARNBY

JOSEPH BARNBY was a musical prodigy, and later became conductor of the Albert Hall Choral Society, succeeding Gounod in 1871. He wrote hundreds of hymns and four-part songs, his harmonizations being distinctive and well in advance of his time. He was knighted in 1892. The poem is one of the several lyrics, by some considered Tennyson's best, in *The Princess.*

C D♯dim C F C G D7
1. Sweet and low, sweet and low, Wind of the west - ern
2. Sleep and rest, sleep and rest, Fa-ther will come to thee
D7sus G C D♯dim C D7
sea; — Low, low, — breathe and blow,
soon; — Rest, rest on moth - er's breast,
G C6 Bm D7 G
p
Wind of the west - ern sea; —
Fa - ther will come to thee soon; —

G7 C F♯dim C
O - ver the roll - ing wa - ters go,
O - ver the wa - ters go.
Fa-ther will come to his babe in the nest,
Fa - ther will come to his babe,
G7 C D♯dim C
Come from the dy - ing moon and blow,
Come from the moon and blow,
Sil - ver sails all out of the west,
Sil - ver sails out of the west,
Am E7 F A♭7 C G7
Blow him a-gain to me, While my lit-tle one,
Un-der the sil-ver moon, Sleep, my lit-tle one,
C Cm G7 B♭m6 C7 F Fm C
while my pret-ty one sleeps.
sleep my pret-ty one, sleep.

CRADLE SONG
(Wiegenlied)

German from
Des Knaben Wunderhorn JOHANNES BRAHMS

THIS LITTLE SONG is also known as "Brahms' Lullaby." It was published by Karl Simrock, of Berlin, in 1868, and reached America the same year, being No. 4 in Brahms' *Fünf Lieder*, Opus 49. Much of the lyric so clearly suggests an English equivalent that several English versions, independently produced, are almost word-for-word the same. Mrs. Natalia Macfarren's English version was the first to have circulation in America.

D
Lul - la - by and good -
Gu - ten A - bend, gut'
A7
night, with ros - es be - dight,_ With_
Nacht, mit Ro - sen be - dacht,_ Mit_
flow - ers round thy head, Be thou co - zy in thy
Nelk - lein be - deckt schlupf' un - ter die

D D7 G D
bed. Lay thee down now and rest, May thy
Deck'; Mor - gen früh, wenn Gott will, wirst du
A7 D D7 G
slum-bers be blest; Lay thee down now and
wie - der ge - weckt; Mor - gen früh, wenn Gott
D A7 D
rest, May thy slum - bers be blest.
will, wirst du wie - der ge - weckt.

SONGS MY MOTHER TAUGHT ME

English: Natalia Macfarren
German: Adolph Heyduk

Anton Dvorâk

This song, by the great Bohemian composer of the symphony *From the New World*, has a place on the concert stage and also in the repertoire of every quartet and glee club. It has the sentimental appeal of a popular song, and in her translation, Mrs. Macfarren has captured the poetry of the original German text. The song was published in America in 1880, before Dvorâk's stay in the United States.

Bb Gm Cm F7 F+
Songs my mother taught_ me, In the days long
Als die al - te Mut - ter mich noch lehr-te
Bb Eb C7 F7 F#dim
van - ished; Sel - dom from her eye - lids
sin - gen, trä -nen in den Wim - pern
Gm Eb Bb Gm
Were the tear-drops ban - ished. Now I teach my
gar so oft ihr hin - gen. Jetzt, wo ich die

Cm F7 F+ B♭
chil - dren Each mel - o - dious meas - ure.
Klei - nen sel - ber üb im San - ge,
E♭ C7 F7 F♯dim G7 C7
Oft the tears are flow - ing, Oft they flow
rie-selt's in den Bart oft, rie-selt's oft
F7 B♭
from my mem - 'ry's treas - ure.
von der brau - nen Wan - ge.

AULD LANG SYNE

Robert Burns

Attributed to
William Shield

Auld Lang Syne is a *strathspey*, a dance from the region of Spey, in Scotland. Burns adapted the traditional words and William Shield used the tune in one of his operas. The form in which we now know the song has become an institution for New Year's Eve. *Bohunkus*, using the same tune, has always been popular in collegiate circles, and Princeton used the tune for *Old Nassau.*

G
1. Should auld ac - quaint - ance
2. We twa hae paid - l't
3. And there's a hand, my
D7 G G7
be for - got, And nev - er brought to
i' the burn, From morn - in' sun to
trust - y fier, And gie's a hand o'
C G
min'? Should_ auld ac - quaint - ance
dine; But_ seas be - tween us
thine; And we'll tak a right guid -

PAIDL'T, paddled FIER, friend WILLIE WAUGHT, friendly draught
BURN, brook

D7 Em D7 G
be for-got, And auld_ lang_ syne?
braid hae roar'd Sin' auld_ lang_ syne.
wil - lie waught For auld_ lang_ syne.
CHORUS
G D7 G
For auld_ lang_ syne, my dear, For
G7 C G
auld_ lang_ syne, We'll tak a cup o'
D7 Em D7 G
kind-ness yet For auld_ lang_ syne.

HOME SWEET HOME

John Howard Payne — Sir Henry Rowley Bishop

Both England and America can justly claim this song, for it was written jointly by Payne, an American, and Bishop, who was conductor of the London Philharmonic Society in 1814. Payne was a vagabond of sorts, and it has been said that "the man who wrote Home Sweet Home never had a home of his own." This is not far from true, but when Payne died he was representing his country as consul to Tunis. The tune, which Bishop had included in a collection as *Sicilian Air,* was assumed by others to be a folk song. It was only through a legal investigation that he proved his claim as composer. The complete song first appeared in London, in 1823, as part of an opera, *The Maid of Milan.*

Eb
1. 'Mid_ pleas - ures and pal - a - ces_
2. An_ ex - ile from home_ splen-dor
Bb7
Eb
though_ we may roam, Be it ev - er so
daz - zles in vain; Oh,_ give_ me my
Bb7
Eb
hum - ble There's no_ place like home. A
low - ly thatched cot - tage a - gain. The

Ab Eb Bb7 Eb
charm_from the skies seems to hal - low us there, Which,
birds_ sing-ing gai - ly that come_ at my call, Give me
Ab Eb Bb7
seek_ through the world, is not met_ with else-
them_ with that peace of mind dear - er than
Eb Bb7 Cm Bb7 Eb
where. Home! home!_ sweet, sweet home!
all. Home! home!_ sweet, sweet home!
Ab Eb Bb7 Eb
D. C.
There's no_ place like home, Oh, there's no_ place like home.

MY OLD KENTUCKY HOME, GOODNIGHT

Stephen C. Foster

Kentucky has made this its state song, and there is a state shrine at Bardstown, Ky., where Foster's relatives, the Rowans, lived, and where the song was believed to have been written; but the investigations of John Tasker Howard have shown that Foster wrote the song while on tour, and may never have been in Kentucky. The great success of Mrs. Stowe's *Uncle Tom's Cabin*, with its Kentucky setting, undoubtedly inspired this song and its title; the song, like the book, was published in 1852.

G
C
G
1. The sun shines bright in the old Ken-tuck - y home, 'Tis
young folks roll on the lit - tle cab - in floor, All
2. They hunt no more for the 'pos - sum and the coon, On the
day goes by like a shad - ow o'er the heart, With
3. The head must bow and the back will have to bend, Wher-
few more days for to tote the wea - ry load, No
A7
D7
sum - mer, we're care - free and gay; The
mer - ry, all hap - py and bright; By'n
mead - ow, the hill and the shore; They
sor - row where all was de - light; The
ev - er we ev - er may go; A
mat - ter, 'twill nev - er be light; A
G
C
G
Em
corn - top's ripe and the mead - ow's in the bloom, While the
by hard times comes a - knock - ing at the door, Then my
sing no more by the glim - mer of the moon, On the
time has come when we know we have to part, Then my
few more days, and the trou - ble all will end, In the
few more days till we tot - ter on the road, Then my

1.
G
D7
G
1. birds make— mu - sic all the day; The
2. bench by the old— cab - in door; The
3. field where the su - gar - canes— grow; A
2.
G
D7
G
old Ken - tuck - y home, good - night!
old Ken - tuck - y home, good - night!
old Ken - tuck - y home, good - night!
CHORUS
G
C
G
B7
Em
C
Weep no more my la - dy, Oh, weep no more to -
G
C
G
Em
Cm6
day! We will sing one song for the old Ken-tuck - y home, for the
G
D7
G
old Ken - tuck - y home far a - way.

THE OLD FOLKS AT HOME

(Swanee River)

Stephen C. Foster

Foster wanted a good two-syllable name for a southern river, to finish a song. He consulted his brother, who produced an atlas and began to look at the maps. Stephen waited, and finally his brother said:

"How about this one? Suwannee River?"

Thus the song was finished, in 1851, and became Foster's most successful work. But he spelled the name wrong, "Swanee," and so it has remained. The real river is the Suwannee, in Florida, which empties into the Gulf of Mexico.

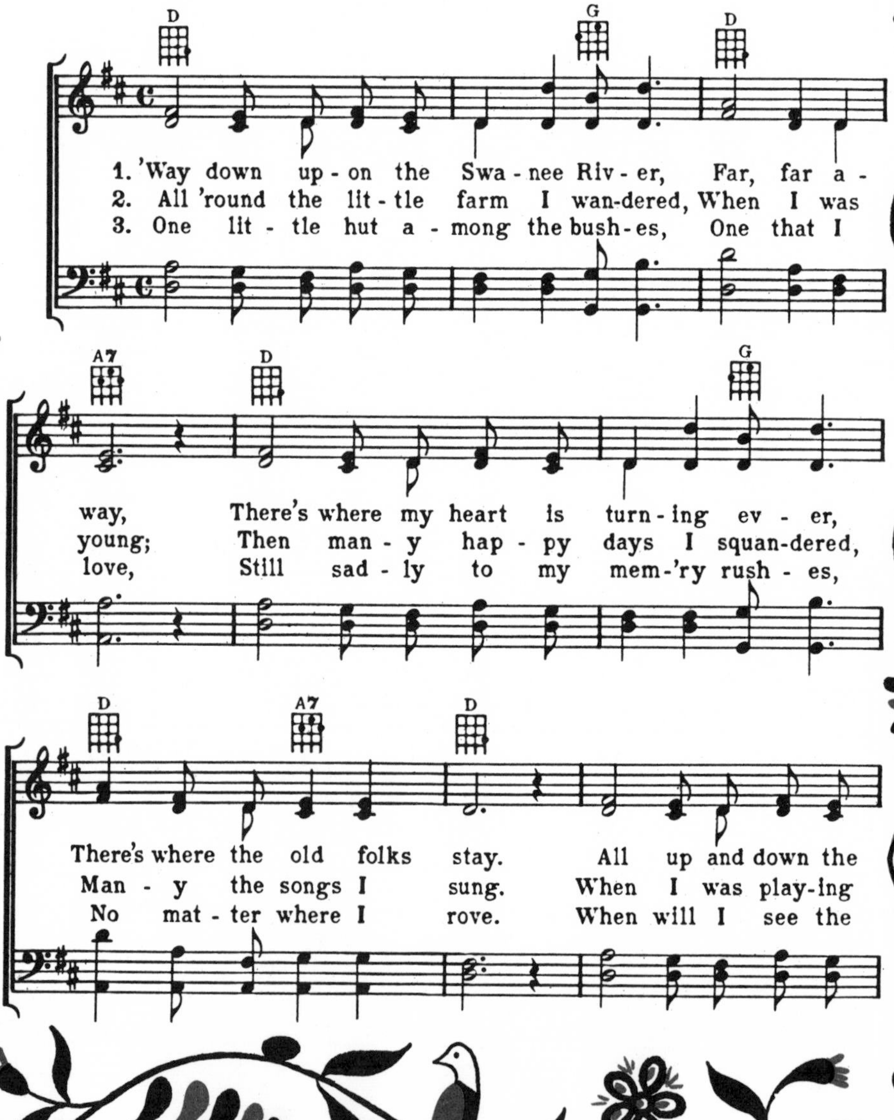
D
G
D
1. 'Way down up - on the Swa - nee Riv - er, Far, far a -
2. All 'round the lit - tle farm I wan-dered, When I was
3. One lit - tle hut a - mong the bush - es, One that I
A7
D
G
way, There's where my heart is turn - ing ev - er,
young; Then man - y hap - py days I squan-dered,
love, Still sad - ly to my mem-'ry rush - es,
D
A7
D
There's where the old folks stay. All up and down the
Man - y the songs I sung. When I was play-ing
No mat - ter where I rove. When will I see the

G D A7 D
whole cre - a - tion, Sad - ly I roam, Still long-ing for the
with my broth - er, Hap - py was I; Oh, take me to my
bees a - hum-ming All 'round the comb? When will I hear the
G D A7 D
old plan - ta - tion, And for the old folks at home.
kind old moth - er, There let me live and_ die.
ban - jo tum-ming, Down in my good old_ home?
CHORUS
A7 D G D
All the world is sad and drear - y, Ev - 'ry - where I roam;
G D A7 D
Oh! la - dies, how my heart grows wea - ry, Far from the old folks at home.

ON THE BANKS OF THE WABASH

Paul Dresser

This is the official song of the State of Indiana. Dresser, a giant in size (300+ pounds) and a giant in songwriting in his times, wrote both words and music, notwithstanding reports that his more famous younger brother, novelist Theodore Dreiser, helped him. Dreiser was the original name, which Paul simplified. Though Paul Dresser wrote hundreds of songs, of which some dozens were hits, he died penniless. This song, the chief survivor, deserves its immortality if only for its simple nostalgic appeal.

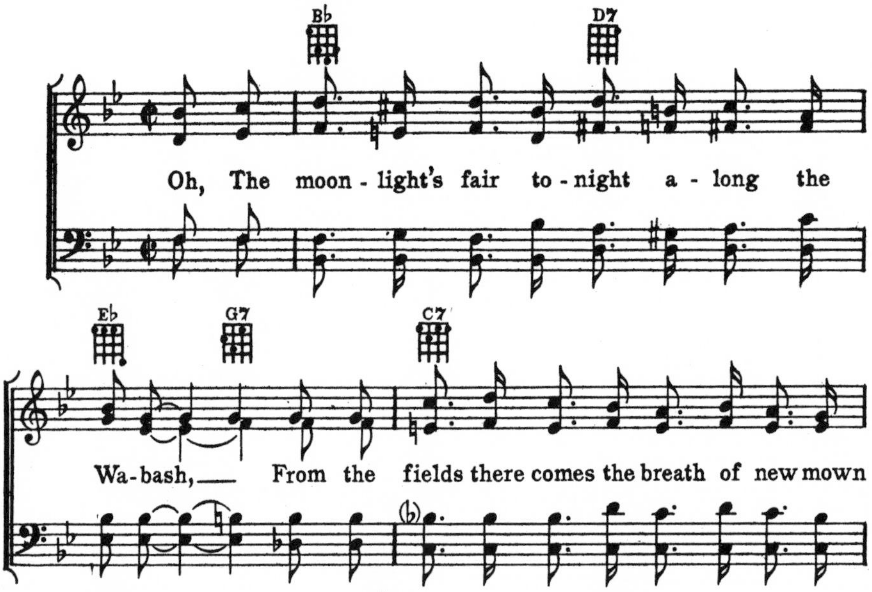
Bb D7
Oh, The moon-light's fair to-night a-long the
Eb G7 C7
Wa-bash, From the fields there comes the breath of new mown
F7 Bb D7
hay Thru the syc-a-mores the can-dle lights are
Eb Edim Bb D7 Gm C7 F7
gleam-ing, On the Banks of the Wa-bash, far a-way.
(Far a-way.)

WAIT TILL THE SUN SHINES, NELLIE

ANDREW B. STERLING

HARRY VON TILZER

THE SIMPLICITY and harmonic construction of this song have long established it in the repertory of all barbershop quartets, most of whose members probably believe it older than it is (1905). Harry von Tilzer (born Harry Gumm) perhaps wrote more neo- and quasi-folksongs than any other American songwriter. Sterling wrote the words for many of the standard songs of the early 1900s. In 1906, when the San Francisco disaster occurred, "Frisco" was often substituted for "Nellie" in singing this song.

Bb D7 Eb Gdim Bb F7
Wait till the sun shines, Nel - lie, And the clouds go
Bb Gdim Bb Eb Gdim Bb D7 G7 C7
drift - ing by We'll be so hap - py Nel - lie Don't you
F7 Bb D Eb Gdim Bb F7 Gdim
cry Down lov - ers' lane we'll wan - der, sweet - heart you and
D7 G7 C7 F7 Bb
I, Wait till the sun shines, Nel - lie Bye and Bye.

DAISY BELL
(On A Bicycle Built for Two)

Harry Dacre

When Harry Dacre came to America from England there was already a wave of bicycle songs in progress, and the bicycle "built for two," the tandem bike, was to be seen everywhere. Dacre was unacqainted with the New York publishers (though he had written successful songs in England) and could not place his song, written in 1892. Katie Lawrence, an English singer, introduced it in London, and it became immediately and permanently popular. For community sings it is sure to be included, and as it was written in the 'nineties, at the height of the bicycle craze, there is no better musical theme for that period.

G
C
Dai - sy, Dai - sy, Give me your
G
D7
G
an - swer, do! I'm half cra -
Em
A7
D7
zy, All for the love of you! It

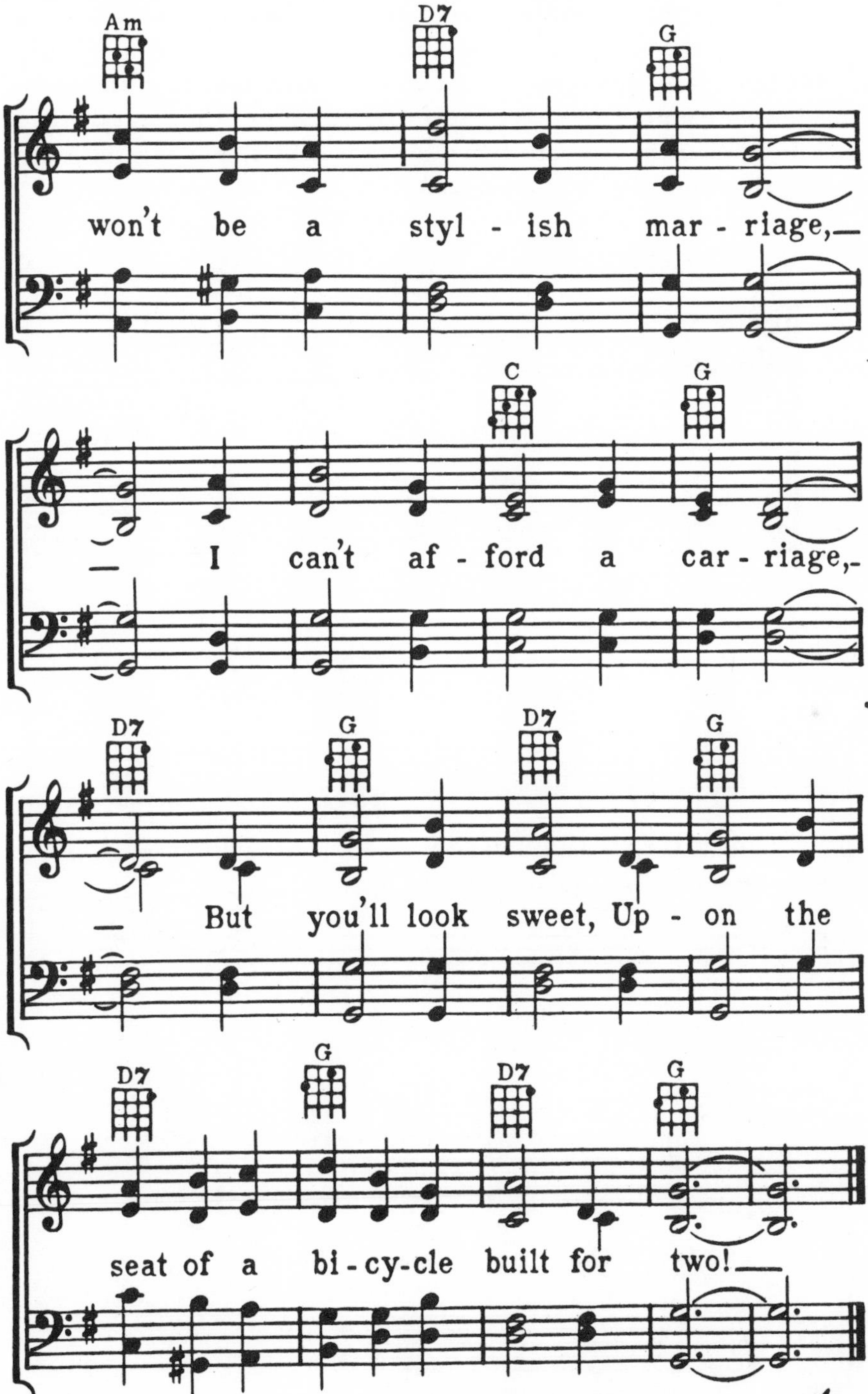
Am D7 G
won't be a styl - ish mar - riage, —
C G
— I can't af - ford a car - riage, —
D7 G D7 G
— But you'll look sweet, Up - on the
D7 G D7 G
seat of a bi - cy - cle built for two! —

AFTER THE BALL

CHARLES K. HARRIS

MANY WRITERS might have been discouraged after a first performance such as befell AFTER THE BALL, when the singer forgot the words. But Harris believed in his song, and when no publisher seemed interested he published it himself, a fact later regretted by every publisher to whom Harris had offered it. A famous singer, J. Aldrich Libby, introduced it in the revue *A Trip to Chinatown*, and it was featured by John Philip Sousa at the Chicago World's Fair in 1893. Sales exceeded five million copies, placing the song among the most popular of all time.

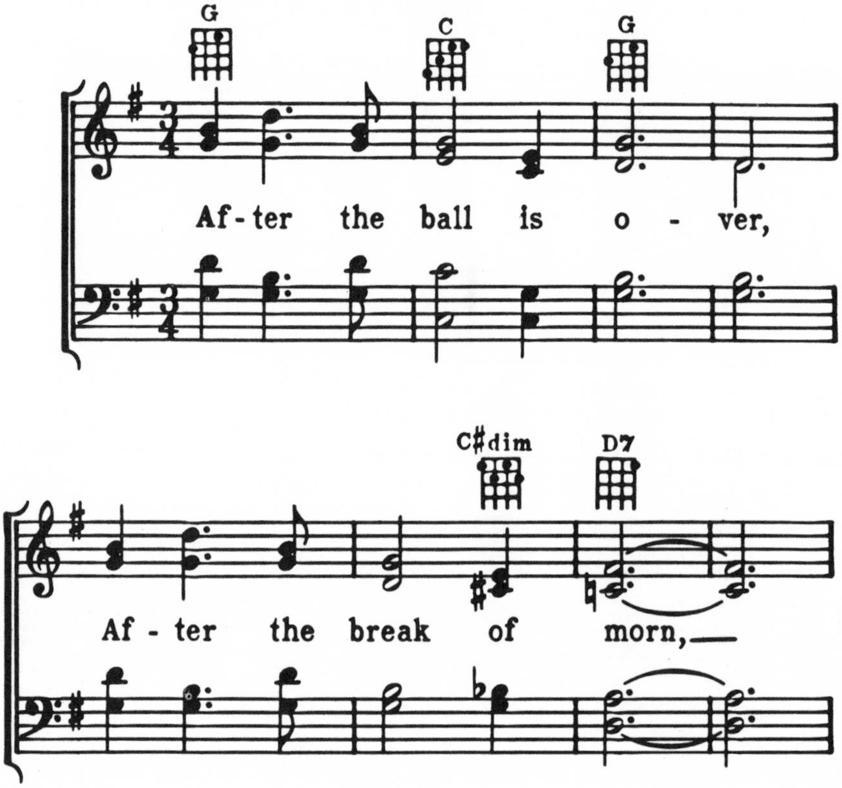
G C G
Af - ter the ball is o - ver,
C♯dim D7
Af - ter the break of morn,—
Am E7 Am E7 Am
Af - ter the danc - ers' leav - ing,

D7 G E#dim D7 G
After the stars are gone; Man-y a
C G E7
heart is ach - ing, If you could read them
A7 D D7 G
all: Man-y the hopes that have van -
E7 A7 D7 G
ished, Af - ter the ball.

THE BAND PLAYED ON

JOHN E. PALMER

CHARLES B. WARD
JOHN E. PALMER

THE SONG about "Casey and the Strawberry Blonde" was the subject of a newspaper promotion in 1895, when the New York *World* gave it a publicity campaign. Charles B. Ward wrote no fewer than four songs in which the word "band" appeared in the title; but both words and music of THE BAND PLAYED ON were written by Palmer. Ward bought it outright, "doctored" it and published it himself. In 1946 a motion picture was founded upon the song.

Bb
Bbmaj7
Bb6
Ca-sey would waltz with the straw-ber-ry
Bb
Bb6
F7
Cm7
F7
blonde, And the Band Played On, He'd glide o'er the
(Played on,)
Bb
floor with the girl he a-dored, And the Band Played

Bb F7
On, But his brain was so load-ed he
(and on)
Bb7 Eb G7 Dm7 G7
near-ly ex plod-ed, The poor girl would shake with a-
Cm Eb E♮dim
larm, He mar-ried the girl with the
(a - larm)
Bb D7 Gm C7 F7 Bb
straw-ber-ry curls, And the Band Played On.

THE SIDEWALKS OF NEW YORK
(East Side, West Side)

JAMES W. BLAKE CHARLES B. LAWLOR

CHARLES B. LAWLOR (vaudeville partner of Jim Thornton, who wrote *When You Were Sweet Sixteen*) was in the store where Blake worked as a hat salesman. Lawlor hummed his new tune for Blake, who wrote down the words while on the job. This was in 1894, and ever since there has been no other musical signature for New York, and to some extent big cities in general. Alfred E. Smith used it as a theme song during his presidential campaign in 1928.

G D7 G C
East side, West side, all a -
G C C#dim
round the town,— The tots play "Ring - a -
G E7 A7
ros - ie," "Lon - don Bridge is fall - ing

D7 G D7
down!" Boys and girls to-
to-
G G7 C G
geth-er, Me and Ma-mie Rorke, We
geth - er,
C C♯dim G E7
trip the light fan-tas-tic on the
A7 D7 G
side-walks of New York.

THE MAN ON THE FLYING TRAPEZE

George Leybourne **Alfred Lee**

When this famous song was first published, it was by three different publishers, all in 1868. None of them credited the writers, and it was some years later that they were recognized. Some collections, even dated in the 1950s, failed to credit the writers, perpetuating the omission. The song was revived through its use in the motion picture *It Happened One Night,* the outstanding film of 1934.

A
A7
1. Oh, once I was hap - py but
2. Now the young man by name was Señ -
3. Some months af - ter that I went
Chorus: He flies thro' the air with the
Last Chorus: She floats thro' the air with the
D
E7
now I'm for - lorn, Like an old
or Bon - i Slang, Tall, big and
in - to a hall, To my sur -
great - est of ease, This dar - ing young
great - est of ease, You'd think her a
A
coat that is tat - ter'd and torn.
hand - some, as well made as Chang. When -
prise I found there on the wall A
man on the fly - ing tra - peze, His
man on the fly - ing tra - peze, She
A7
D
Left in this wide world to fret and to
e'er he ap - peared the hall loud - ly
bill in red let - ters that my heart did
move - ments are grace - ful; all girls he does
does all the work while he takes his

B7 E7 A
Fine
mourn, Be - trayed by a maid in her teens.
rang With o - va - tion from ev - 'ry - one there.
gall, That she was ap - pear - ing with him.
please, And my love he's pur - loin - ed a - way.
ease, And that's what's be - come of my love!
F♯m
Now this girl that I lov'd she was hand - some,
He'd smile from the bar on the peo - ple be -
He'd taught her gym - nas - tics and dressed her in
C♯7
And I tried all I knew her to please;
low, And one night he smiled on my love.
tights, To help him to live at his ease;
F♯m
But I nev - er could please her one quar - ter so
She winked back at him and she shout - ed "Bra -
He made her as - sume a mas - cu - line
C♯dim B9 B7(♭5) E7(6) E7
D.S. for Chorus
sfz
well, As the man on the fly - ing tra - peze! Oh!
vo!" As he hung by his nose up a - bove. Oh!
name, And now she goes on the tra - peze, Oh!
sfz

LITTLE BROWN JUG

Attributed to
JOSEPH E. WINNER

THIS SONG has been called "the wettest ever written," which is undoubtedly true. It is perhaps for that reason that Winner, who probably wrote both words and music in 1869, published it under the name of Eastburn. At that time were gathering the temperance forces that later were to become an organized movement (W.C.T.U.). We can guess that Winner, using excellent judgment, played it safe.

C
F
1. My wife and I lived all a-lone, In a
2. If I'd a cow that gave such milk, I'd
3. 'Tis you who makes my friends and foes, 'Tis
G7
C
G7
C
lit - tle log house we called our own;
clothe her in the fin - est silk,
you who makes me wear old clothes;
F
She loved whis - key and I loved rum, I
I'd feed her the choic - est hay, And
Here you are so near my nose, So

G7
C
F
C
tell you we had lots of fun.
milk her for - ty times a day.
tip her up and down she goes.
F
CHORUS
Ha! ha! ha! you and me,
G7
C
G7
C
Lit-tle brown jug how I love thee! Ha! ha! ha!
F
Cdim
G7
C
F
C
you and me, Lit-tle brown jug how I love thee!

JINGLE BELLS

J. S. PIERPONT

IF EVER A SONG could turn back time to the days before the automobile and the super-highway, it would be this one. Even the youngest can experience a sleigh-ride through the magic of this music. Written in 1857, it has been a winter "standard" ever since; and who, hearing it played, can resist the impulse to tap on his glass? Sleigh-bells were placed upon the horses as a warning, for otherwise the approaching sleigh made hardly a sound.

G
Dash - ing thro' the snow In a
C
D7
one horse o - pen sleigh, O'er the fields we go,
G
Laugh-ing all the way; Bells on bob - tail ring,
C
D7
Mak - ing spir - its bright; What fun it is to ride and sing a

(Tinkle on glasses)
G
sleigh-ing song to-night! Jin-gle bells! Jin-gle bells!
C G
Jin-gle all the way! Oh, what fun it is to run In a
A7 D D7 G
one horse o-pen sleigh, Oh! Jin-gle bells! Jin-gle bells!
C
Jin - gle all the way! Oh, what fun it
G D7 G
is to run In a one horse o - pen sleigh!

ALOHA OE

QUEEN LYDIA LILIUOKALANI

ALOHA OE is not the national anthem of the Hawaiian Islands, but it has become so well known to the rest of the world that it is the song heard for gatherings and festivities not affairs of state. When a steamer docks at Honolulu the band is there to play ALOHA OE, and when the visitor departs it is to the same strain. *Aloha,* in the Hawaiian language, means farewell, or love, or greeting, or just best wishes; and also it has meanings that cannot be expressed in any other language. Liliuokalani wrote it in 1878, partly in Hawaiian and partly in English. The melody is similar to that of an earlier song, *The Rock Beside the Sea,* by Charles Converse, but that may be coincidence.

A
D
Proud-ly swept the rain cloud by the
Ha - a - heo e ka u - a i - na
A
E7
cliff,_ As on_ it glid - ed_through the
pa - li, Ke ni - hi a - e - la i - ka - na
A
D
trees,_ Still_ fol - low-ing with grief our
he - le, E ha - ha - i a - na i - ka

A D B7 E7
love song, Borne to sea with the flow-ers on the
li - ko, Pu - a a - hi - hi le - hu - a o
A D A
breeze._ Fare-well to thee, fare-well to thee! Thou
u - ka A - lo - ha oe, A - lo - ha oe, E ke
E7 A
charm-ing one who dwells a-mong the bow-ers; One
o - na - o - na no - ho i - ka li - po; One
D A E7 A
fond em-brace before I now depart, Un-til we meet a-gain.
fond em-brace, a - ho - i a - e au, Un-til we meet a-gain.

LA PALOMA

SEBASTIAN YRADIER

YRADIER published most of his songs in Paris, where he served as singing master to the Empress Eugenie. He was a Spaniard and his songs were of typical Spanish color; Bizet, believing that his *El Areglito* was a folk song, used the theme for the Habanera in *Carmen*. LA PALOMA was published in the United States in 1877. All attempts to trace the author of the beautiful English words have been to no avail.

C
G7
The day that I left my home for the roll - ing
(And) ere I de-part - ed I went fond leave to
Cuan - do sa - li de la Ha - ba - na, vál - ga - me
(Yu) - na lin - da Gua - chi - nan - ga a - llá voy
sea, I said, "Moth - er dear, oh,
take Of Ni - na, who wept as
dios! Na - die me ha vis - to sa -
yo Que se vi - no tras de
pray to thy God for me." And
if her poor heart would break.
lir si no fui yo. Yu-
mi que si se - ñor.
1. 2.
Ni - na, if I should die and o'er o - cean's
O - pen thy lat - tice, dear - est, for it will
Si a tu ven - ta na llé - ga u - na pa
Cuen - ta la tus a mor - es bien de mi

G7
foam, Soft - ly a white dove
be My faith - ful soul that
lo - ma, trá - ta - la con ca -
vi - da, co - ró - na - la de
C
1.
on a fair eve should come.
lov - ing comes back to thee!
ri - ño que es mi per so - na.
flo - res que es co - sa mi - a.
2.
Oh, a life on the sea, Sing - ing joy - ous and
¡Ay! chi - ni - ta que sí! ¡Ay! que da - me tu a -
G7
ad lib.
free! Ah! none are so hap - py
mor! ¡Ay! que ven - te con - mi - go chi - ni - ta,
C
a tempo
none are so gay as we!
a - don - de vi - vo yo.

CIELITO LINDO

English version by
JAMES MOREHEAD

CARLOS FERNANDEZ

THIS MAGNIFICENT SONG was popular in California through its tenancy by Spain and Mexico. It remained very popular among Spanish-speaking peoples, and then suddenly, in 1923, became a "hit" song in the United States. A pattern of syncopation that is not exactly like that of any other song, and an engaging lilt, assure it permanent popularity. All along the Mexican border there are hundreds of people who know the words of CIELITO LINDO in Spanish, even though they do not speak a word of the language and have no idea what they are singing.

Bb
F7
Bb
Moun-tains high_ seem to hide the sky_
De la Sie - rra Mo - re - na, Cie-
F7
Bb
F7
_ When the clouds hang low_ on the ceil-ing;_
li - to Lin - do, vie_ nen ba-jan-do,_
Nev - er mind,_ for it's clear be - hind,_
Un par de o - ji - tos ne - gros Cie -

Bb
And the morn-ing light soon comes steal-ing.
li-to Lin-do de con-tra-ban-do.
Bb+
Eb
G7(b5)
C7
F7
Ay, Ay, Ay, Ay! Sing! have no
¡Ay Ay Ay Ay! Can-ta y no
Bb
Bdim
F7
sor-row; Al-though to-day skies are dark and gray,
llo-res, Por-que can-tan-do se a-le-gran, Cie-
Bb
They'll be blue a-gain by to-mor-row.
li-to Lin-do los co-ra-zo-nes.

LA CUCARACHA

Mexican Folk Song

La Cucaracha (the cockroach) in Mexico is idiomatically applied to an old maid. During the Mexican Revolution of 1914-1917, the dictator Venustiano Carranza was so called by the forces of the revolutionists Pancho Villa and Emiliano Zapata. The song (based upon an ancient Spanish folk song) consists of a series of "dichos," or epigrammatic quatrains of folk origin and development, and includes allusions to Mexican political history. The English words, of unknown origin, are not easy to sing and do not rhyme, but they do constitute a translation.

G
Cuan - do u - no quie - re a u - na,
1. When a fel low loves a maid - en
2. All the girls from Mex - i - co
3. One thing makes me laugh most heart - y:
4. Fel - low needs an au - to - mo - bile
E7
Am
Y es - ta u - na no lo quie - re,
And that maid - en does - n't love him,
Are as pret - ty as a flow - er,
Pan - cho Vi - lla with no shirt on;
If he un - der - takes the jour - ney
D7
Es lo mis - mo que si un cal - vo
It's the same as when a bald man
And they talk so ver - y sweet - ly,
Now the Car - ran - zis - tas "beat it,"
To the place at which Za - pa - ta

G
En la ca - lle en - cuen - tra un pei - ne.
Finds a comb up - on the high - way.
Fill your heart quite up with love.
Be - cause Vi - lla's men are com - ing.
Or - dered the fa - mous con - ven - tion.
CHORUS
La cu - ca - ra - cha, La cu - ca - ra - cha,
The cu - ca - ra - cha, The cu - ca - ra - cha,
C♯dim
D7
Ya no quie - re ca - mi - nar, Por - que no
Does - n't want to trav - el on, Be - cause she
tie - ne, Por - que le fal - ta,
has - n't, Oh, no, she has - n't
G
Ma - ri - hua - na que fu - mar.
Ma - ri - hua - na for to smoke.

THE LORELEI

HEINRICH HEINE
Translated by JAMES MOREHEAD

FRIEDRICH SILCHER

HEINE CAPTURED the mood of an old German myth with such perfection that it found universal acceptance. Silcher, a composer who spent many years as musical director of the University of Tübingen, in Germany, in 1852 produced an ideal complement of Heine's poem. It is strophic in form, and has often been erroneously considered a folk song. The English translation by Emma Lazarus is faithful but not "singable"; in the English version used here the essentials of the story are told in two stanzas.

D
G
1. Oh, tell me the rea-son I sor - row, While
2. The Lor - e - lei, combing her tress-es That
1. Ich weiss nicht was soll es be - deu - ten, Dass
D
A7
D
tear-drops glist in my eye? From whence the sad leg-end I
dim the gold of the comb Her song of the sir-en ad-
ich so trau - rig bin; Ein Mär-chen aus al - ten
G
D
A7
D
bor - row, The tale of the Lor - e - lei? Then
dress - es Each boat seek-ing ha - ven and home. En-
zei - ten, Das kommt mir nicht aus dem Sinn. Die

A
D
lis - ten, while soft - ly the Rhine flows, And
tranced by her voice sweet - ly call - ing, They
Luft ist kühl und es dun - kelt, Und
A
E7
A
A7
wea - ry birds seek their rest; In
heed not the wind nor the wave; But
ru - hig fliesst der Rhein; Der
D
G
glo - ry, the sun in the sky glows, And
soon are in treach - er - y fall - ing To
Gi - pfel des Ber - ges fun - kelt Im
D
A7
D
sinks a - way in the west.
death in a wa - ter - y grave.
A - bend - son - nen - schein.

DARK EYES
(Otchi Tchorniya)

English version by
ALBERT MOREHEAD

ANONYMOUS

THIS RUSSIAN FOLK SONG probably originated in Spain in the 16th century or earlier, and was introduced into Russia by the gypsies who wandered through Spain, Hungary, and the Balkans. OTCHI TCHORNIYA is now a great favorite in America. The Russian words here given are those commonly sung by Russian-speaking Americans. The transliteration is by Princess Alexandra Kropotkin.

Adim
Cm
G7
Eyes of dark - est hue,
O - tchi tchor - ni - ya,
Cm
Eyes where beau - ty lies,
O - tchi yas - ni - ya,
G7
Eyes where pas - sion burns, Love - ly,
O - tchi jgut - chi - ya, E pre -

Cm
Fm6
love - ly eyes! And I love you so,
kras - ni - ya! Kak lu - blu ya vas,
Cm
Yet I fear you too, For my
Kak bo - yus ya vas, Znat ou -
G7
Cm
heart was lost When I first saw you.
vi - del vas Ya v'ne - do - bry tchas.

O SOLE MIO

Translated by
JAMES MOREHEAD

EDUARDO DI CAPUA

AMONG AMERICANS of Italian descent particularly, and among all generally, O SOLE MIO remains in high favor. The moving and climatic "Ma n'a—tu sole," at the start of the chorus, is most effective vocally, lending itself perfectly to the Neapolitan tenor timbre. Di Capua wrote many other songs which enjoy permanent popularity, both in Italy and America. The tune, with a new sentimental lyric *(There's No Tomorrow)*, was a popular song of 1951.

F
What is more love - ly than a day of
Neapolitan: Che bel - la co - sa 'na iur na ta'e
Bb
C7
sun - shine, When clouds have passed a - way and all the
so - le, N'a - ria se - re - na dop - po 'na tem -
F
flow'rs are gay? Just as the sun - shine
pe - sta, Pe' ll'a - ria fre - sca
Bb
warms the sum - mer ros - es, Bathed in your
pa - re già 'na fe - sta, Che bel - la

F
C7
F
wondrous love my heart re - pos - es.
co - sa 'na iur - na - ta'e so - le!
CHORUS
a tempo
C7
You are my sun - shine, my light, my love!
Ma n'a - tu so - le cchiu bel lo ohi ne',
F
Your eyes re - cap - ture the skies a - bove,
'O so - le mi - o sta 'n fron - te a te!
B♭m
F
And fill my soul with rap - ture,
'O so - le'o so - le mi - o
C7
F
My love - ly sun - shine, my light, my love!
sta 'n fron - te 'a te, sta 'n fron - te a te!

SANTA LUCIA

Teodoro Cottrau

When Teodoro Cottrau wrote his gentle melody, he must have envisioned the beautiful Bay of Naples, his "home of fair poesy." A natural duet, Santa Lucia has always been an international favorite, both vocally and instrumentally. It is a *barcarolla,* or boatman's song, and typically Italian. The first edition was dated 1849, in Naples.

C
G7
Now 'neath the sil - ver moon
Here balm - y zeph - yrs blow,
(Neapolitan) Sul ma - re luc - ci - ca
C
O - cean is glow - ing, O'er the calm
Pure joys in - vite_ us, And as we
l'a - stro d'ar - gen - to, pla - ci - da é
G7
C
bil - low Soft winds are blow-ing.
gen - tly row All things de - light us.
l'on - da, pro-spero é il ven - to.

F
Hark, how the sailor's cry Joy - ous - ly
Home of fair Po - e - sy, Realm of pure
Ve - ni-te al - l'agi - le bar - chet - ta
C
G7
ech-oes nigh. San - ta_ Lu - ci - a!
Har-mo - ny, San - ta_ Lu - ci - a!
mi - a San - ta_ Lu - ci - a!
1.
C
2.
C
San-ta Lu - ci - a! San-ta Lu - ci - a!
San-ta Lu - ci - a! San-ta Lu - ci - a!

AU CLAIR DE LA LUNE

AUTHOR UNKNOWN
Translated by "C. F. M."

JEAN-BAPTISTE LULLY

LULLY, who died in Paris in 1687, is known as the founder of French Grand Opera. He was a musical giant who can be compared with Gluck and Wagner; he was a director, composer, stage-manager; he composed ballets, masques, symphonies, masses, choral works; he was a man of tremendous energy. But had he written nothing except AU CLAIR DE LA LUNE, his fame would have been assured. Little children never fail to learn it, along with their ABCs.

B♭ F7
1. "At thy door I'm knock - ing,
2. Pier - rot cried in an - swer
1. Au clair de la lu - ne,
2. Au clair de la lu - ne,
B♭ F7 B♭
By the pale moon-light, Lend a pen, I
By the pale moon-light, "In my bed I'm
Mon a - mi Pier - rot; Prê - te - moi ta
Pier - rot ré - pon - dit: "Je n'ai pas de
F7 B♭ F7 B♭
pray thee, I've a word to write;
ly - ing, Late and chill the night;
plu - me, Pour é - crire un mot.
plu - me, Je suis dans mon lit.

F
C7
Gut - ter'd is my can - dle,
Yon - der at my neigh - bor's
Ma chan - delle est mor - te,
Va chez la voi - si - ne,
F
C7
F7
B♭
Burns my fire no more, For the love of
Some-one is a - stir; Fire is fresh - ly
Je n'ai plus de feu; Ou - vre moi ta
Je crois qu'elle y est Car dans sa cui-
F7
B♭
F7
B♭
heav - en, O - pen now the door!"
kin - dled, Get a light from her.
por - te, Pour l'a - mour de Dieu.
si - ne On bat le bri - quet."

ALOUETTE
(Gentle Skylark)

French-Canadian Folk Song

No "GANG" SONG has more appeal than this one, attested to by the fact that people sing it out lustily even when they have no idea what the words mean. It has been a long-time favorite in Canada, and spread all over the United States, to England, France, and probably everywhere else. An American version, in 1931, became nationally popular.

CHORUS
G
D7
A - lou - et - te, gen - tille A - lou -
1-6
Fine
et - te, A - lou - et - te, je te plu - me - rai. rai.
SOLO
CHORUS
SOLO
Je te plu - me - rai la tête, Je te plu - me - rai la tête. Et la
2. le cou, Je te plu - me - rai le cou.
3. les ailes, Je te plu - me - rai les ailes.
4. les pattes, Je te plu - me - rai les pattes.
5. le dos, Je te plu - me - rai le dos.
6. la queue, Je te plu - me - rai la queue.
tête, Et la tête! A - lou - ette, A - lou - ette! Ah!

SEA, WESTERN AND FOLK SONGS

A LIFE ON THE OCEAN WAVE

EPES SARGENT — HENRY RUSSELL

EPES SARGENT wrote the words in 1838 after a stroll on the Battery, in New York City, and took the manuscript to his publisher. "This is not a song at all," said the publisher, and he turned it down. But Sargent's friend Henry Russell was of a different opinion. A few days later he wrote the lively tune that ever since has kept the song in permanent popularity. It was a favorite of the Hutchinsons, a famous band of family singers.

G
1. A life on the o - cean wave, A_
2. Once more on the deck I stand Of my
3. The land is no long-er in view, The
D7
home on the roll-ing deep, Where the
own_ swift-glid-ing craft, Set_
clouds have be - gun to frown, But_
scat - tered wa - ters rave, And the
sail! fare - well to the land, The
with a stout ves-sel and crew We'll

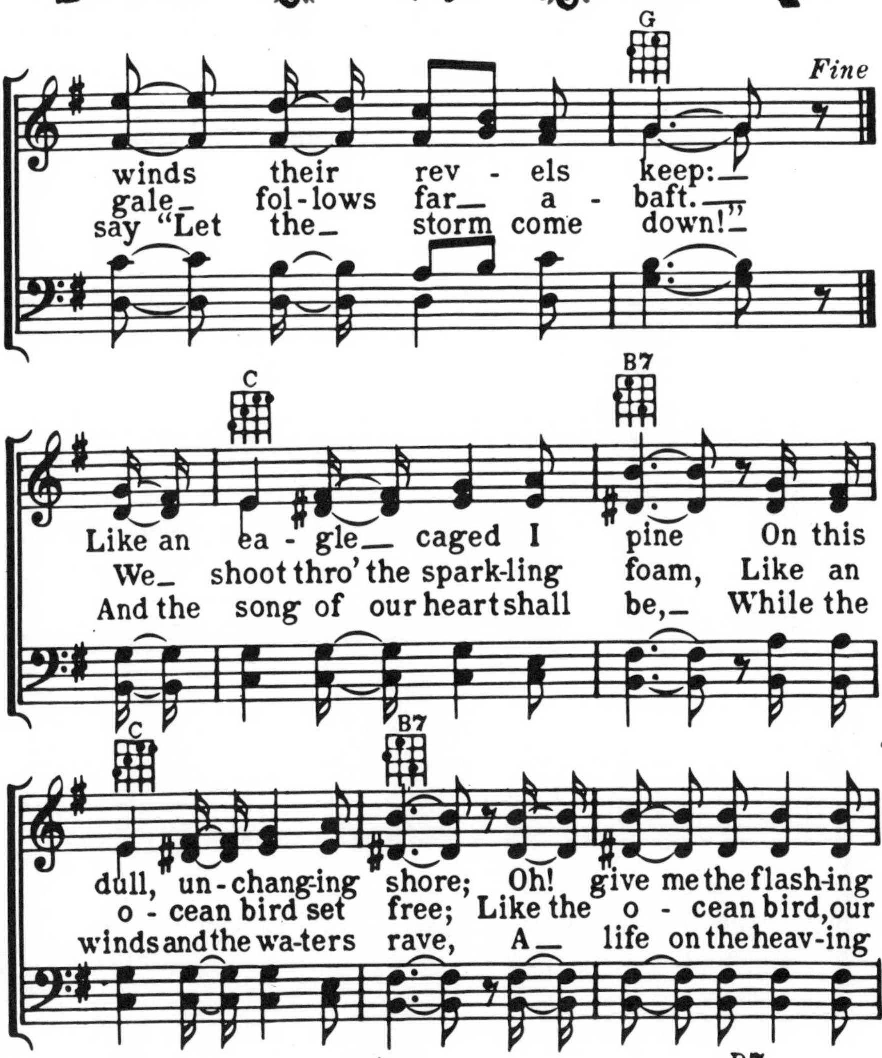
G
Fine
winds their rev - els keep:
gale fol - lows far a - baft.
say "Let the storm come down!"
C
B7
Like an ea - gle caged I pine On this
We shoot thro' the spark-ling foam, Like an
And the song of our heart shall be, While the
C
B7
dull, un - chang-ing shore; Oh! give me the flash-ing
o - cean bird set free; Like the o - cean bird, our
winds and the wa-ters rave, A life on the heav-ing
Em
G♯dim
D7
Sing first verse in D. C.
brine, The spray and the tem - pest roar!
home We'll find far out on the sea!
sea, A home on the bound-ing wave!

BLOW THE MAN DOWN

ANONYMOUS

WHEN A SAILING SHIP weighs anchor, every man in the crew is affected by the excitement of departure. Sails are set, and the pull on the halyards finds the sailors singing to a lively rhythm. This is one of the best known of the chanteys. It was originally called the *Black Ball Liner Song.* The Black Ball Line was a line of packets sailing between New York and Liverpool, and this chantey was sung in heavy hauling. BLOW THE MAN DOWN has always been directly identified with "Jack Tar," as between the lines we can hear the boast of the professional seaman, who recognizes in his mate singing and working beside him a brother sailor, a man like himself.

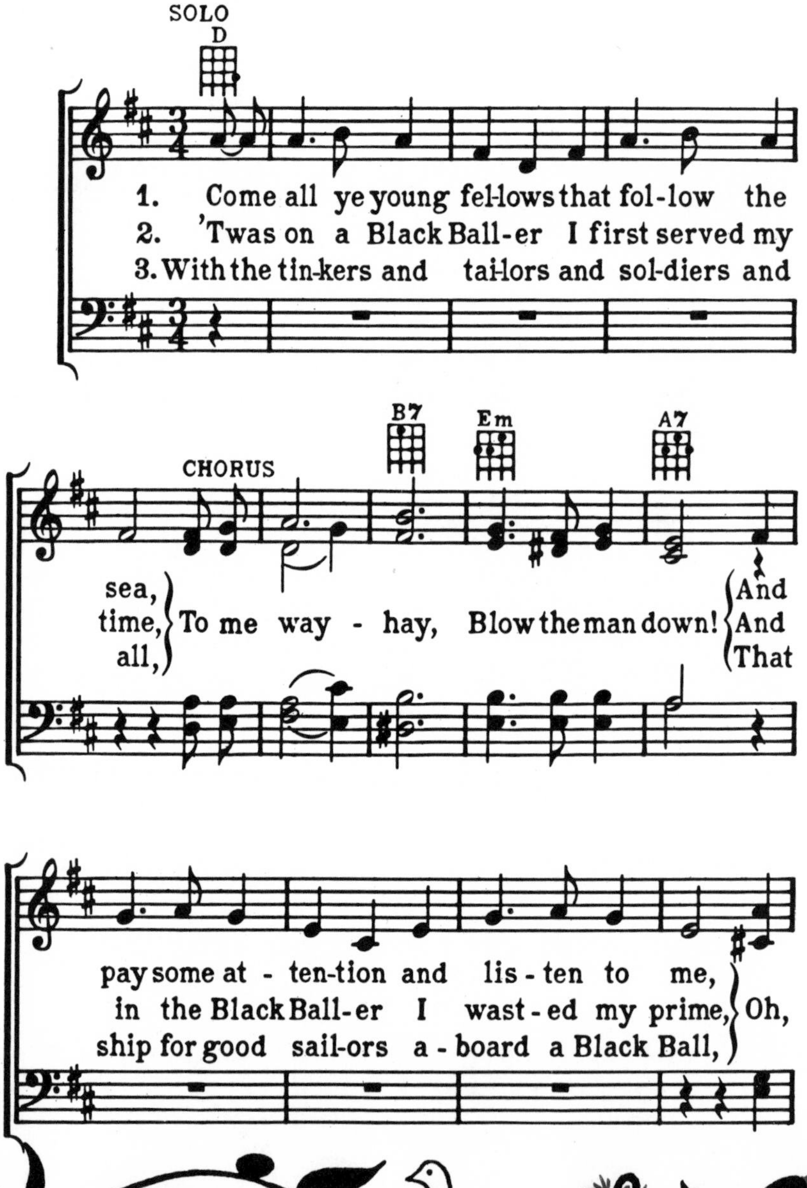
SOLO
D
1. Come all ye young fel-lows that fol-low the
2. 'Twas on a Black Ball-er I first served my
3. With the tin-kers and tai-lors and sol-diers and
B7
Em
A7
CHORUS
sea,
time,
all,
To me way - hay, Blow the man down!
And
And
That
pay some at - ten-tion and lis - ten to me,
in the Black Ball-er I wast - ed my prime,
ship for good sail-ors a - board a Black Ball,
Oh,

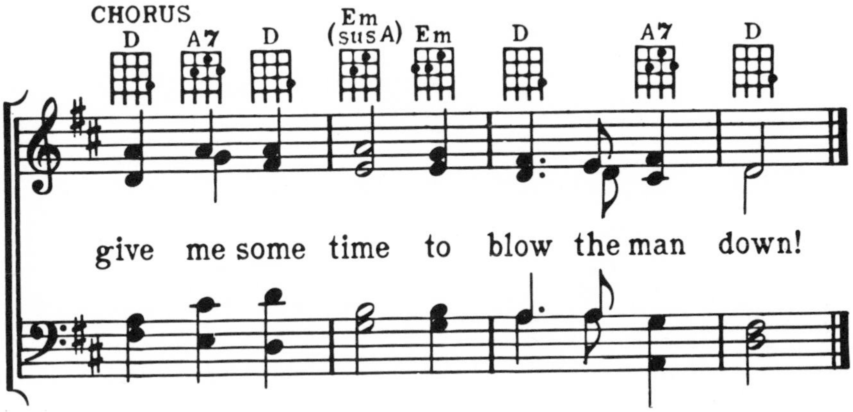
CHORUS
D A7 D Em (sus A) Em D A7 D
give me some time to blow the man down!

4. 'Tis when a Black Baller's preparing for sea,
To me way-hay, blow the man down!
You'd split your sides laughing, the sights you would see,
Oh, give me some time to blow the man down.

5. 'Tis when a Black Baller is clear of the land,
To me way-hay, blow the man down!
The crew musters aft at the word of command,
Oh, give me some time to blow the man down!

6. 'Tis larboard and starboard, on the deck you will sprawl,
To me way-hay, blow the man down!
For 'Kicking Jack Williams' commands the Black Ball,
Oh, give me some time to blow the man down!

The BLACK BALL LINE was a famous line of packets between New York and Liverpool.

NANCY LEE

FREDERICK E. WEATHERLY | STEPHEN ADAMS

A ROLLICKING and joyous ditty, NANCY LEE has always been a favorite with school children, even before they grasp the metaphorical "guiding star" of the sailor in the song. Weatherly and Adams (whose real name was Michael Myabrick) also wrote the famous sacred song *The Holy City*. NANCY LEE appeared in *Gems of English Song*, a collection published in Boston in 1875; but the song may be older.

Eb
Of all_ the wives as e'er you know,___ Yeo -
Bb7
Eb
ho!_ lads, ho! Yeo - ho!_ yeo - ho! There's none_like Nan-cy Lee, I
Cm7
Gm
D7
Gm
trow,___ Yeo - ho!_ lads,_ ho!_ yeo - ho! See
Bb7
Eb
Bb7
F
there she stands and waves her hands, up-on_ the quay, An' ev-'ry day when

I'm a-way, She'll watch_ for_ me, An' whis-per low, when
tem-pests blow, for Jack_ at sea, Yeo-ho!_ lads,_ho!_ yeo-ho!
The_ sail-or's wife the sail-or's star_ shall be, Yeo-
ho!_ we_ go a-cross_the sea,_The sail-or's wife the sail-or's
star_ shall be, The sail-or's wife his star shall be.

MY BONNIE LIES OVER THE OCEAN

ANONYMOUS

SIGMUND SPAETH *says:* "If people cannot be persuaded to sing *My Bonnie*, particularly when on the water, there is really no hope for them." Originally the jumps, or intervals, on "Bring back" went downward instead of upward. People didn't like it that way, and changed it, as is their prerogative with a folk song.

C
F
1. My Bon - nie lies o - ver the
2. Last night as I lay on my
3. O blow, ye winds, o - ver the
C
Am
o - cean, My Bon - nie lies o - ver the
pil - low, Last night as I lay on my
o - cean, And blow ye winds o - ver the
G7
C
F
sea, My Bon - nie lies o - ver the
bed, Last night as I lay on my
sea, O blow, ye winds, o - ver the

C
F
o - cean, O bring back my
pil - low, I dream'd that my
o - cean, And bring back my
G7
C
F
Bon-nie to me.
Bon-nie was dead. Bring back, bring
Bon-nie to me.
G7
C
back, bring back my Bon-nie to me, to me: Bring
F
D7
G7
C
back, bring back, O bring back my Bon-nie to me.

HOME ON THE RANGE

Cowboy Song

John A. Lomax called this song "the cowboy's national anthem," and when it became known that it was the favorite of Franklin D. Roosevelt, the song became a "hit." Several claimants to a copyright on it immediately appeared. Some claims seemed well documented, and in one case a $500,000 lawsuit was instituted against publishers and recording companies. The matter at length reached the United States Senate and in at least one instance the controversy was recorded in the Congressional Record, but indisputably several versions are in the public domain.

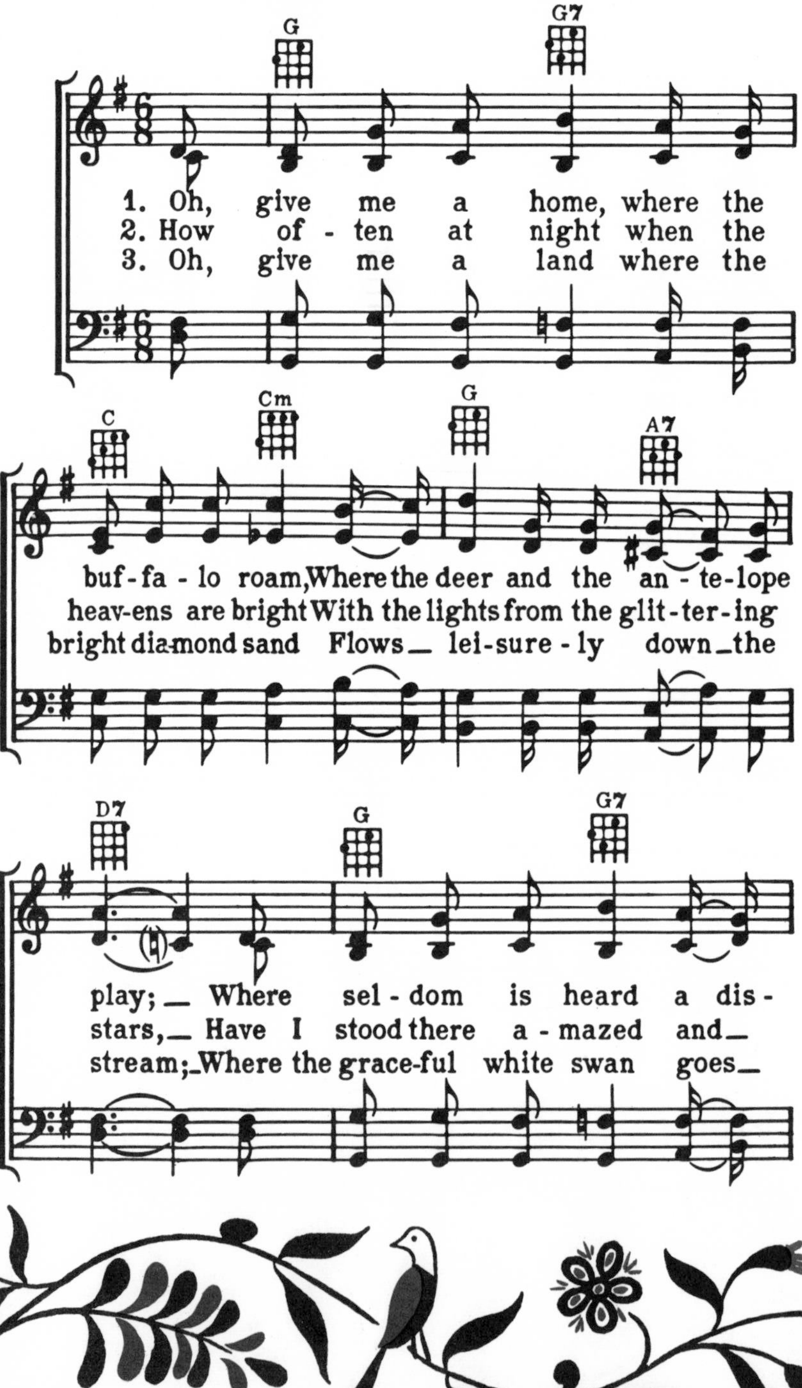
G
G7
1. Oh, give me a home, where the
2. How of - ten at night when the
3. Oh, give me a land where the
C
Cm
G
A7
buf-fa - lo roam,Where the deer and the an - te-lope
heav-ens are bright With the lights from the glit-ter-ing
bright diamond sand Flows_ lei-sure - ly down_the
D7
G
G7
play; _ Where sel - dom is heard a dis -
stars,_ Have I stood there a - mazed and_
stream;_Where the grace-ful white swan goes_

C Cm G D7 G
cour-ag-ing word, And the skies are not cloud-y all day.
asked as I gazed If their glo-ry exceeds that of ours.
glid-ing a-long Like a maid in a heav-en-ly dream.
CHORUS
G D7 G
Home, home on the range, Where the
Em A7 D D7 G G7
deer and the an-te-lope play; Where sel-dom is heard a dis-
C Cm G D7 G
cour-ag-ing word, And the skies are not cloud-y all day.

WHOOPEE-TI-YI-YO!

Adapted by James Morehead *Cowboy Song*

The lilt is unmistakably Irish; and "sure" there were plenty of Irish among those who settled the West; but except for the flavor of the tune, here is an American folk song of the first rank. Somehow it has escaped the usual mutilation, and nearly all versions are the same, except for an occasional elaboration at the start of the chorus. No other Western folk song presents a more vivid picture of life on the open range.

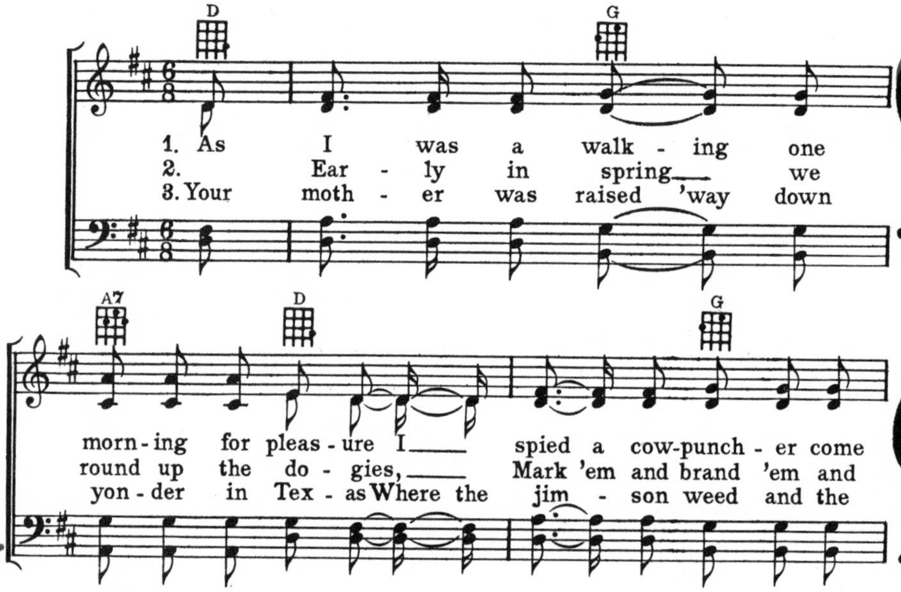
D G
1. As I was a walk - ing one
2. Ear - ly in spring we
3. Your moth - er was raised 'way down
A7 D G
morn - ing for pleas - ure I spied a cow-punch - er come
round up the do - gies, Mark 'em and brand 'em and
yon - der in Tex - as Where the jim - son weed and the
A7 D G
rid - ing a - long; His hat was throwed back and his
cut off their tails; Then we load up the
sand - spurs grow; But we're gon - na feed you on
A7 D
spurs was a jin - gle, And
old chuck wag - on,
prick - ly pears and chol - la,* Till you're

*Pronounced 'Choy-a'

G
A7
D
as he ap-proached he was sing-ing this song:
Hitch up our hors-es and start up the trail,
read-y to hit out for old I-da-ho,
CHORUS
A7
D
Whoo-pee, ti-yi-yo, Git a-long, lit-tle dog-ies, It's
A7
D
your mis-for-tune, And none of my own; Whoo-pee
A7
D
ti-yi-yo, Git a-long, lit-tle dog-ies, For you
A7
D
know Wy-o-ming will be your new home!

O BURY ME NOT ON THE LONE PRAIRIE

Cowboy Song

THIS POIGNANT appeal is also known as *The Dying Cowboy.* Other melodies are used, including some of Indian origin, and the standard tune, here given, occasionally appears with other words, as in the song *Ol' Texas.* Every cowhand knows and understands this song, which is the essence of true poetry.

F
1. "O bu - ry me not
2. "O bu - ry me not
3. "It mat - ters not,
on the lone prai - rie!"
on the lone prai - rie!
so I've been told,
C7
These words came low
Where coy - otes howl
Where the bod - y lies

F
— and — mourn-ful - ly — From the pal - lid
— and the wind blows free, — In a nar-row
— when the heart grows cold, — Yet grant, O
lips — of a youth who lay —
grave — just — six by three —
grant — this — wish to me, —
C7
— On his dy - ing bed —
— O — bury me not —
— O — bury me not —
F
— at the close of day. —
— on the lone prai - rie!" —
— on the lone prai - rie!" —

THE OLD CHISHOLM TRAIL

Cowboy Song

IF EVER a song could properly be called a cowboy song it is this one. It literally smells of saddle leather and the trail. Jesse Chisholm was a real man, an Indian trader and interpreter, who (in 1866, according to the Columbia Encyclopedia) found a route over which to drive Texas longhorns from San Antonio and the South to the nearest railroad at Abilene, Kansas, a distance of 800 miles. Back in the 1870s they still called it "Jesse Chisholm's Trail."

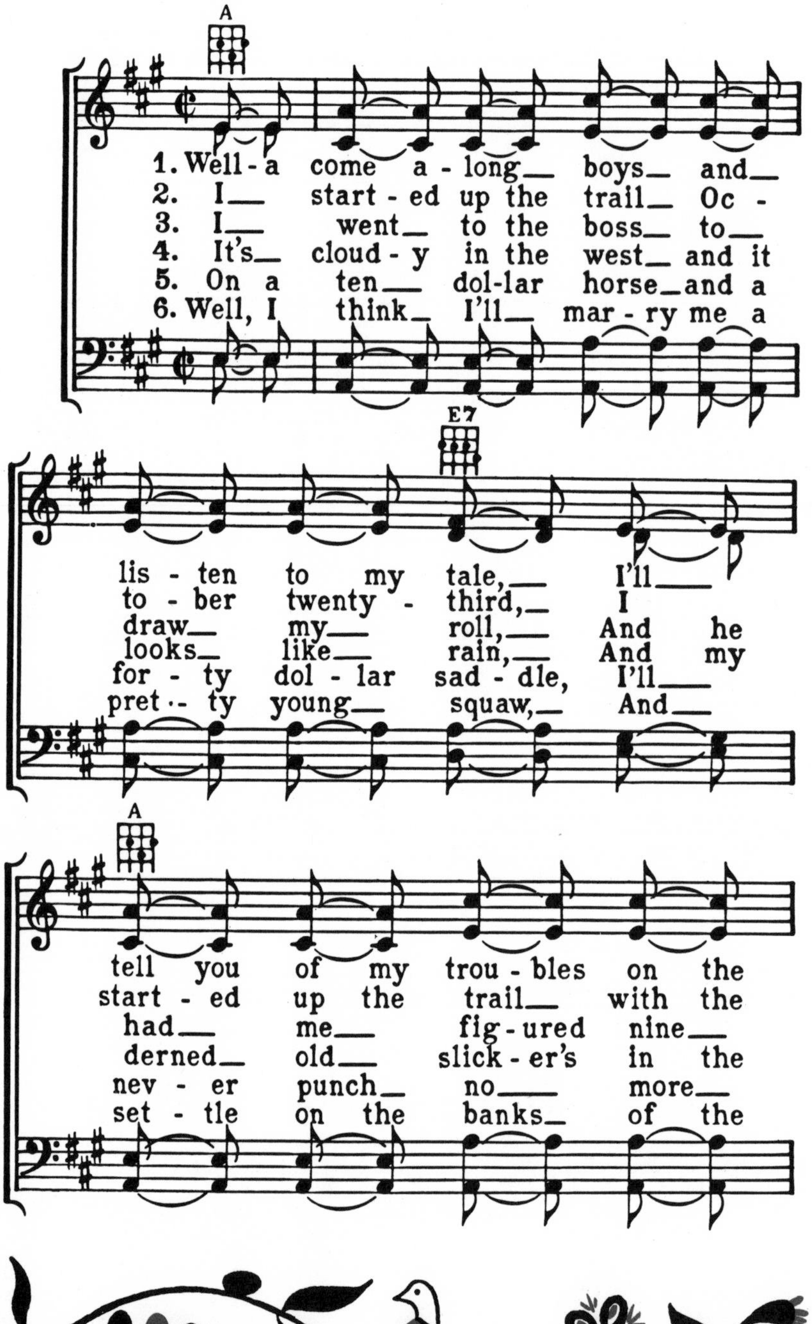
A
1. Well-a come a - long_ boys_ and_
2. I_ start - ed up the trail_ Oc -
3. I_ went_ to the boss_ to_
4. It's_ cloud - y in the west_ and it
5. On a ten_ dol-lar horse_and a
6. Well, I think_ I'll_ mar - ry me a
E7
lis - ten to my tale,_ I'll_
to - ber twenty - third,_ I
draw_ my_ roll,_ And he
looks_ like_ rain,_ And my
for - ty dol - lar sad - dle, I'll_
pret - ty young_ squaw,_ And_
A
tell you of my trou - bles on the
start - ed up the trail_ with the
had_ me_ fig - ured nine_
derned_ old_ slick - er's in the
nev - er punch_ no_ more_
set - tle on the banks_ of the

E7
Old Chis - holm Trail,
Z U herd,
dol - lars in the hole,
wag - on a - gain,
Tex - as cat - tle,
old Choc - taw,
CHORUS
A E7
Com - a - ti - yi - yip - ee yip - ee
A E7 A E7 A E7
yay, yip - ee yay, Com-a - ti - yi yip-ee yip-ee yay - ay -
A D A E7 A
ay! (Yell: EEE-YOW!) Com-a - ti - yi-yip - ee yip - ee yay!

RED RIVER VALLEY

Cowboy Song

THIS IS A SONG that "went West" in the 1890s, when that was the thing to do. It went along with the young men who were going that way, and who were leaving sweethearts behind, as they are wont to do. It was then *In the Bright Mohawk Valley*, a New York State popular song by James Kerrigan, but it donned cowboy garb and emerged with a new set of words. Folk singers of the past fifty years have rubbed away the more pretentious form of the original song, and it now has simplicity and sweetness that goes right to the heart.

G
D7
1. From this valley they say you are
2. I have prom-ised you, dar-ling, that
3. As you go to your home by the
Refrain: Come and sit by my side if you
G
E7
go-ing; I will miss your bright eyes and sweet
nev-er Shall the words from my lips cause you
o-cean, May you nev-er for-get those sweet
love me, Do not has-ten to bid me a-

A7 D7 G G7
smile,_ For they say you are tak-ing the
pain,_ And I swear I will love you for-
hours_ That we spent in the Red Riv-er
dieu,_ But re - mem - ber the Red Riv - er
C F♯7
sun - shine___ That___
ev - er___ If you
Val - ley,___ And the
Val - ley,___ And the
G D7 G
D. S.
bright-ened our path - way a - while.
on - ly will love me a - gain.
love we ex - changed 'mid the flowers.
cow - boy who loved you so true.

ACROSS THE WIDE MISSOURI
(Shenandoah)

ANONYMOUS

ALWAYS considered a sea chantey—and indeed it is generally sung by sailors—this song undoubtedly had an inland origin. Shenandoah was an Indian chief, according to the song, but the "wide Missouri" is far from the Shenandoah Valley of Virginia. Also, who ever heard of a chantey sung to such a slow tempo? Where is its "lively rhythm," to which the sailors can haul on the halyards? No one can satisfactorily explain these shortcomings of *Shenandoah* (usually pronounced "Shenandore"), but the song seems to have flourished just the same. When the words and music go together so beautifully, what difference does it make?

E♭
1. Oh, Shen - an-doah, I long to
2. Oh, Shen - an-doah, I love your
3. Oh, Shen - an-doah, I'm bound to

A♭
hear you,
daugh - ter,
leave you,
Way— hay, you roll - ing

Eb Ab Eb
(Oh, Shen-an-doah, I long to
riv-er! {Oh, Shen-an-doah, I love your
(Oh, Shen-an-doah, I'll not de-
hear you,
daugh-ter, } Way hay, we're bound a-
ceive you,)
Ab Eb Bb7 Eb
way, 'Cross the wide Mis-sou-ri!

BARB'RY ALLEN

Adapted by JAMES MOREHEAD

Elizabethan Folk Song
Appalachian Mountain Version

THIS IS ONE of the oldest and best-known folk songs of the English-speaking world. There are versions galore of the Scottish tune, hundreds of them in the Southern states alone. The version here given is from the Appalachian Mountains of eastern Tennessee. Note the use of the ancient Gaelic (pentatonic) scale.

G
1. 'Twas_ in the mer - ry
2. He___ sent his ser - vant
3. She was slow - ly, slow - ly,
4. He___ turned his face un -
D7
month of May, When_ green buds they were
to the town, To the place where she was
get - ting up, And_ slow - ly, slow - ly,
to the wall, And_ death was in him
G
swell - ing;_ Sweet_ Wil-liam on his
dwell - ing;_ "My___ mas-ter has a
go - ing;_ And the on - ly words she
well - ing;_ "A_ - dieu, a - dieu, to

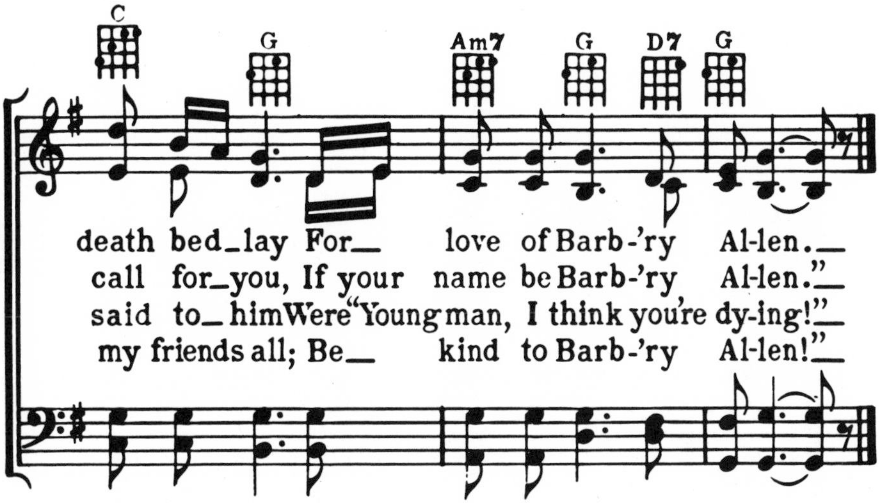
C G Am7 G D7 G
death bed_lay For_ love of Barb-'ry Al-len._
call for_you, If your name be Barb-'ry Al-len."_
said to_him Were "Young man, I think you're dy-ing!"_
my friends all; Be_ kind to Barb-'ry Al-len!"_

5. When she got in two miles of town
She heard the death-bells ringing.
They rang so clear as if to say:
"Hard-hearted Barb'ry Allen!"

6. "Oh, mother, mother, come make my bed,
"And make it both soft and narrow;
"For Sweet William died for love,
"And I will die for sorrow!"

7. "Oh, father, father, come dig my grave,
"And dig it both deep and narrow;
"For Sweet William died today,
"And I will die tomorrow!"

8. Barb'ry Allen was buried in the old Church tomb,
Sweet William was buried beside her;
Out of William's heart a red rose grew,
Out of Barb'ry Allen's a briar.

9. They grew and grew to the old Church tomb,
Till they could grow no higher;
At the end they tied a true-lover's knot,
And the rose wrapped 'round the briar.

THE BLUE-TAIL FLY

Anonymous

A popular minstrel song of the 1840s. Dan Emmett, who wrote *Dixie,* adapted it and published a version under his name, but the tune is older, and a true folk song. In his Pulitzer Prize poem *John Brown's Body,* Stephen Vincent Benét recognizes it as a popular song of Union soldiers in the Civil War. Burl Ives restored *The Blue-Tail Fly* to popularity in recent times.

G
1. When I was young I___
2. And when he rides in the
3. One day he ride a -
4. The po - ny run, he___
5. They laid him un - der a
C
D7
used to wait On mas - ter and hand
af - ter - noon, I'd fol - low with a
round the farm, The flies so num - 'rous
jump, he pitch, And threw old mas - ter
'sim - mon tree; His ep - i - taph is
G
him his plate, And pass the bot - tle when
hick - 'ry broom; The po - ny, he___ was
they did swarm. One chanced to bite him
in the ditch. He died and the ju - ry
there to see: "Be - neath this stone I'm

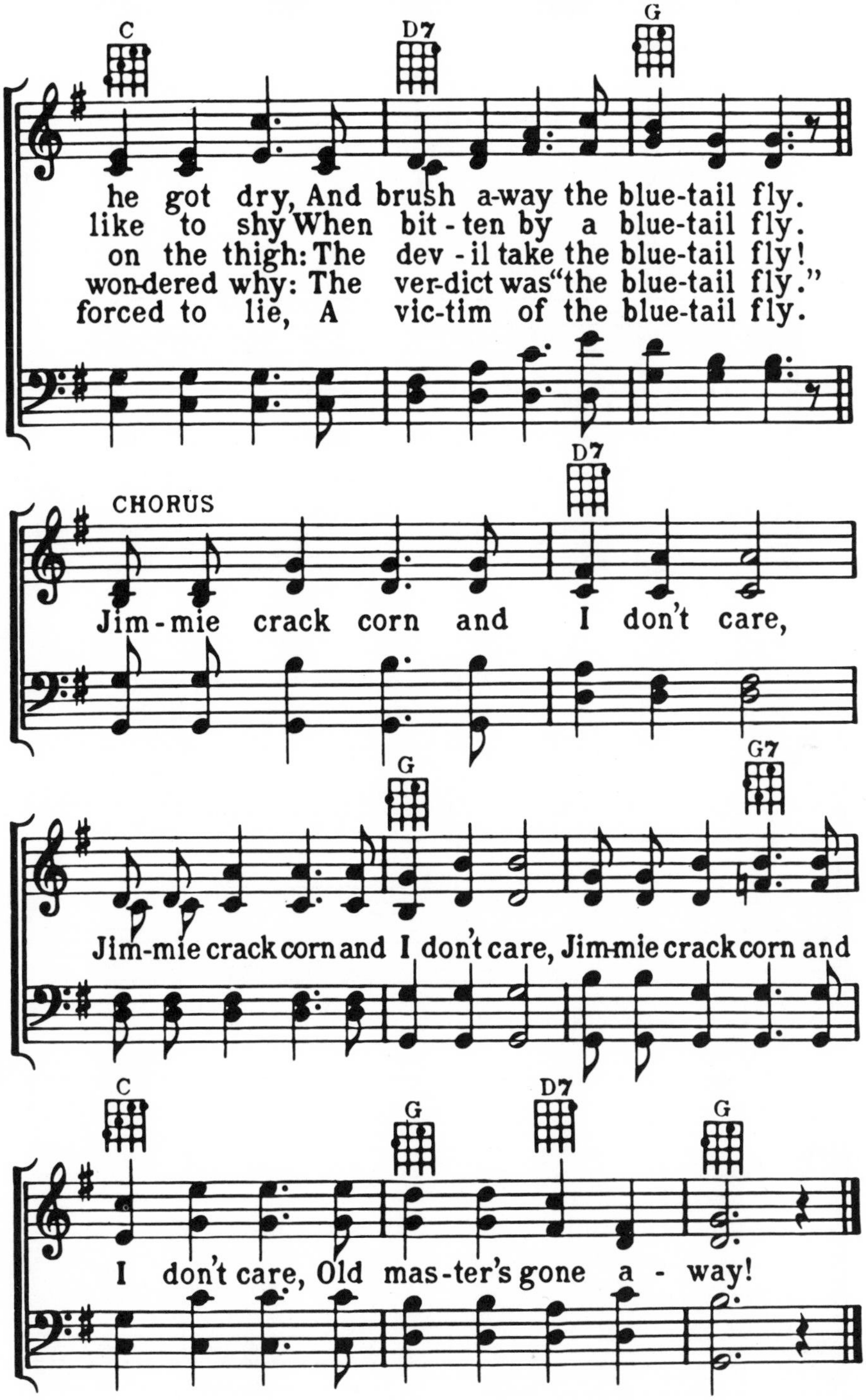
C
D7
G
he got dry, And brush a-way the blue-tail fly.
like to shy When bit-ten by a blue-tail fly.
on the thigh: The dev-il take the blue-tail fly!
won-dered why: The ver-dict was "the blue-tail fly."
forced to lie, A vic-tim of the blue-tail fly.
CHORUS
D7
Jim-mie crack corn and I don't care,
G
G7
Jim-mie crack corn and I don't care, Jim-mie crack corn and
C
G
D7
G
I don't care, Old mas-ter's gone a-way!

DOWN IN THE VALLEY

Cowboy Song

Birmingham Jail is the name by which it is known throughout the South and Southwest, but many versions have been altered to fit the region, and often a local jail is substituted. The first two stanzas are seldom altered. Most printed versions give the second line of the first stanza as:

"Hang your head over
Hear the wind blow"

—but the editors have never heard the line in actual use.

G
1. Down in the val - ley,
2. Ros - es love sun - shine,
3. Write me a let - ter,
D7
val - ley so low,
vi - 'lets love dew,
send it by mail,
Late in the eve - ning hear that train
An - gels in heav - en know I love
Send it in care of Bir-ming-ham

G
blow. Hear that train blow-
you. Know I love you
jail. Bir-ming-ham jail
D7
ing, hear that train blow,
dear, know I love you,
house, Bir-ming-ham jail,
Late in the eve - ning,
An - gels in heav - en
Send it in care of
G
hear that train blow.
know I love you.
Bir - ming - ham jail.

THE FOGGY, FOGGY DEW

ANONYMOUS

ACCORDING TO Carl Sandburg, this song is a condensed novel of real life. He cites as endorsers to this view Sinclair Lewis, Sherwood Anderson, and D. W. Griffith. Griffith (according to Sandburg) once wired from New York to a friend in Chicago: "Send verses Foggy Dew stop tune haunts me..."

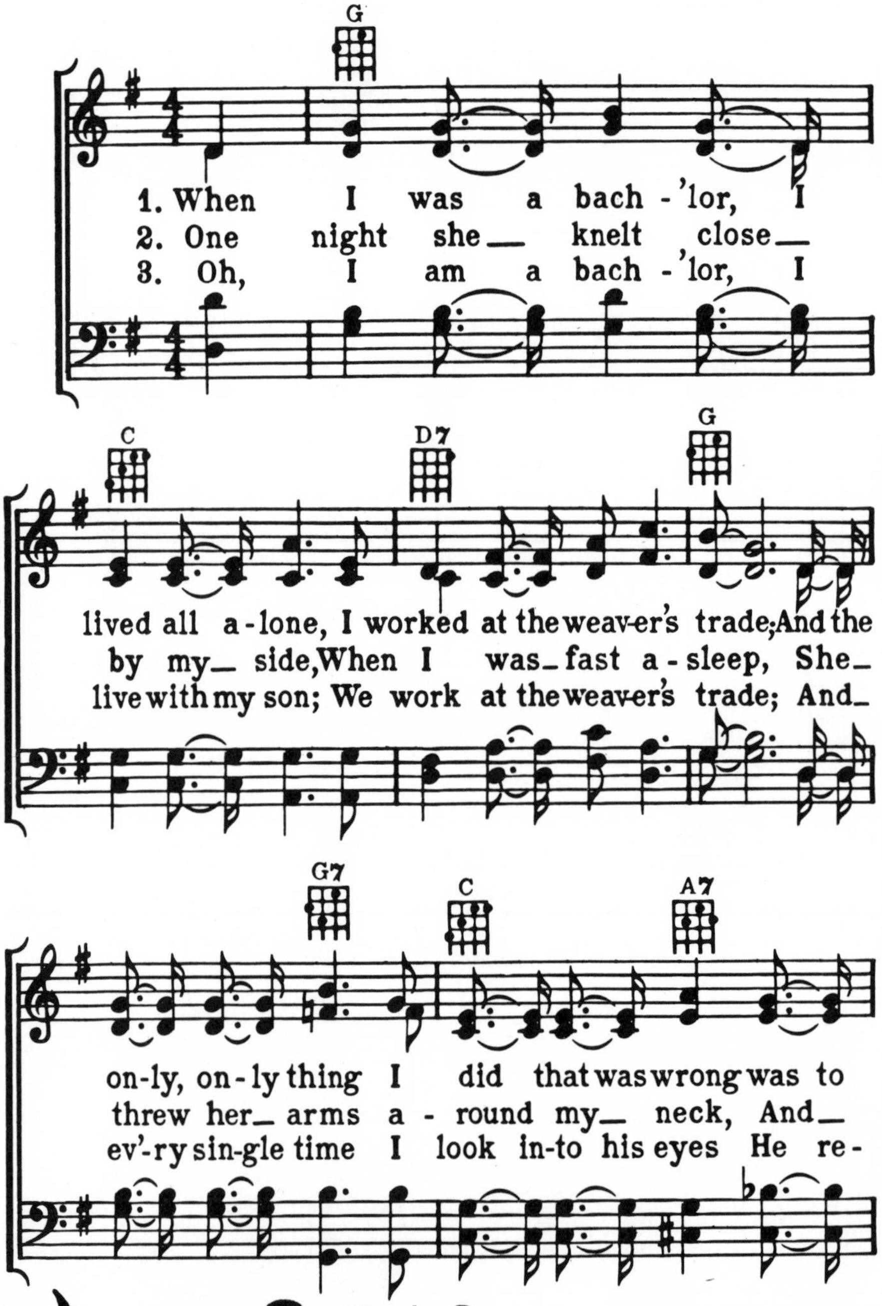
G
1. When I was a bach - 'lor, I
2. One night she_ knelt close_
3. Oh, I am a bach - 'lor, I
C
D7
G
lived all a - lone, I worked at the weav-er's trade; And the
by my_ side, When I was_ fast a - sleep, She_
live with my son; We work at the weav-er's trade; And_
G7
C
A7
on-ly, on-ly thing I did that was wrong was to
threw her_ arms a - round my_ neck, And_
ev'-ry sin-gle time I look in-to his eyes He re-

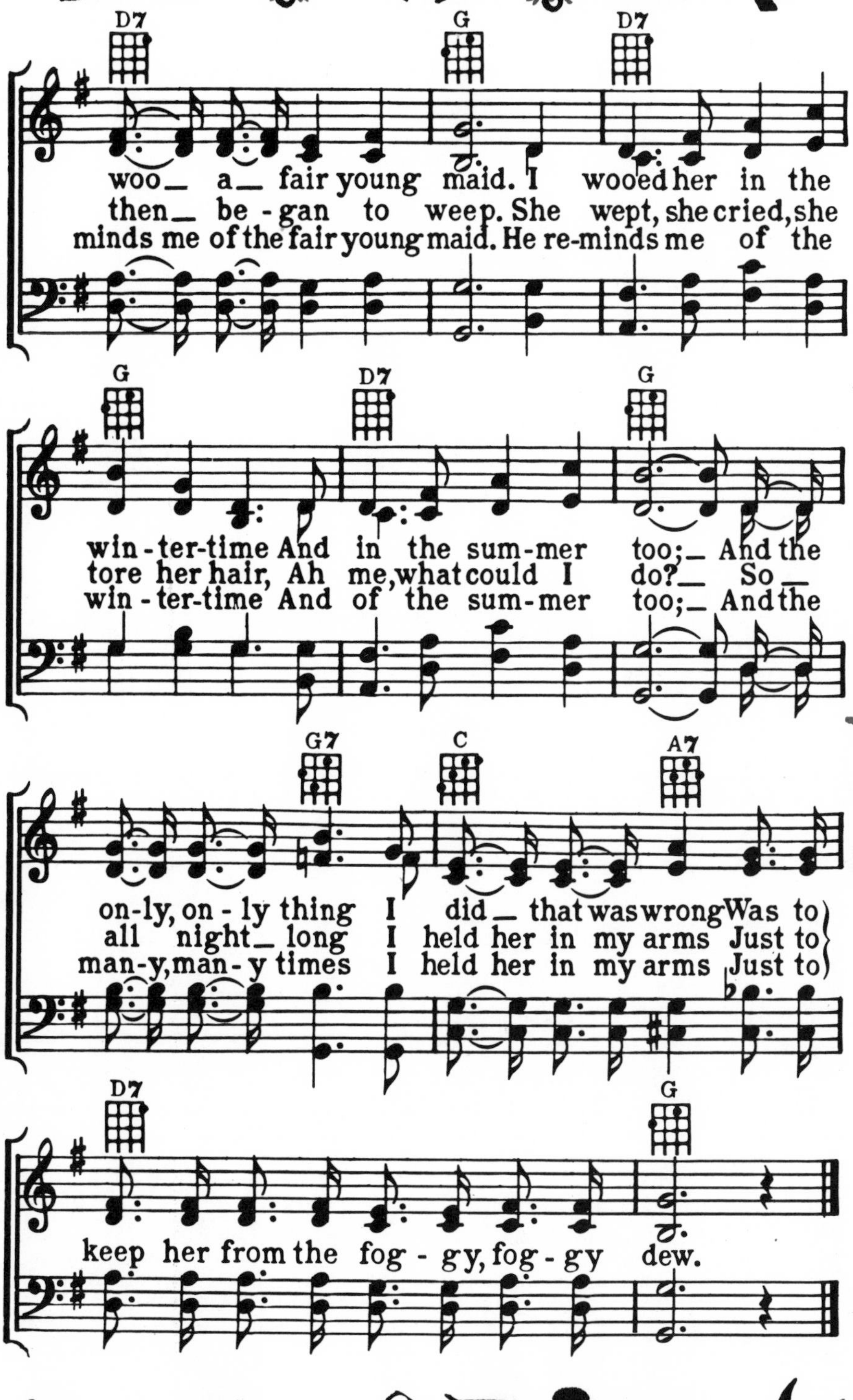
D7 G D7
woo_ a_ fair young maid. I wooed her in the
then_ be-gan to weep. She wept, she cried, she
minds me of the fair young maid. He re-minds me of the
G D7 G
win-ter-time And in the sum-mer too;_ And the
tore her hair, Ah me, what could I do?_ So_
win-ter-time And of the sum-mer too;_ And the
G7 C A7
on-ly, on-ly thing I did_ that was wrong Was to
all night_ long I held her in my arms Just to
man-y, man-y times I held her in my arms Just to
D7 G
keep her from the fog-gy, fog-gy dew.

TURKEY IN THE STRAW

Adapted by JAMES MOREHEAD — ANONYMOUS

THIS SONG is as American as Thankgiving turkey, though its ancestry may be vaguely Irish. There must be a thousand verses, and at least six complete titles are on record. Notably, *Old Zip Coon* has the same tune. It is a square-dance tune that can be counted upon to furnish a climax, and several hifalutin arrangements have thrust it into the concert halls. Lists of favorite American tunes invariably include TURKEY IN THE STRAW.

D7
G
Well, I had an old_ hen_ and she
Well, I hitched_ up the wa - gon and I
Well, if frogs_ had_ wings_ and_
had a wood - en leg, Just the best old_ hen_ that_
drove_ down the road, With a two horse_ wa - gon and a
snakes_ had_ hair And_ au - to - mo - biles_ went a -
D7
ev - er laid an egg; Well, she
four_ horse_ load; Well, I
fly - ing thro' the air; Well, if
G
laid_ more_ eggs than an - y hen_ on the farm, But an-
cracked my_ whip_ and the lead_ horse sprung, And I
wa - ter - mel - ons grew_ on a huckle - ber - ry vine,

D7
G
oth - er lit - tle drink_ wouldn't_ do her an - y harm.
said_ "Good - bye"_ to the wag - on_ tongue.
We'd_ have_ win - ter in the sum - mer_ time.
CHORUS
G
Tur - key in the hay, in the hay, hay, hay!
C
Tur - key in the straw, in the straw, straw, straw!
G
D7
Pick 'em up, shake 'em up, an - y way at all, And_
G
D7
G
hit up a tune called_ 'Tur - key in the straw.'

BUFFALO GALS

ANONYMOUS

THE FIRST published copy was by Cool White, a minstrel man, in 1844. It began, "Lubly Fan, woncha come out tonight?" From then on, as the song went on tour, the title was always changed to fit the locale, becoming "Jimtown Gals," "New York Gals," etc. BUFFALO GALS sounds best of all; and the public with unerring finality, determined the title. As *Dance With A Dolly,* with a partly new lyric, the song was a "hit" in 1944.

D
Buf - fa - lo gals, won-cha come out to-night,
A7
D
Come out to-night, come out to-night? Buf-fa-lo gals won-cha
B7
Em
A7
D
come out to-night, And dance by the light of the moon? I

CHORUS
G A7 G A7 D
danced with the gal with the hole in her stock-in' And her
A7 D
heel kep' a-rock-in' and her toe kep' a-knock-in', I
G A7 G A7 D
danced with the gal with the hole in her stock-in'; And we
B7 Em A7 D
danced by the light of the moon.

HAND ME DOWN MY WALKING CANE

Adapted by JAMES MOREHEAD — AUTHOR UNKNOWN

THOUGH THIS SONG is quite as well known as the great majority of folk songs in the United States, it has avoided appearing in print, and is not included in any of dozens of popular collections. We present a version from the Southern states.

F
1. Hand me down
2. I got drunk
3. The beans was tough
4. Come here baby
5. If I had listened
hand me
I got
beans was
come here
I had
C7
F
my walk - ing cane, Hand me
and I got in jail, I got
and the meat was fat, The beans was
and go my bail, Come here
to what ma - ma had said If I had
down
drunk
tough
baby
listened
walk - ing cane
got in jail
meat was fat
go my bail
ma - ma said
C7
F
down my walk - ing cane,
drunk, and I got in jail.
tough and the meat was fat,
baby and go my bail,
listened to what ma - ma had said,

F7
B♭
Hand me down my walk - ing
I got drunk and I got in
The beans was tough and the meat was
Come here ba - by and go my
If I had listened what ma - ma had
B♭m6
cane I'm go - ing a -
jail and there was - n't no -
fat and oh, my
bail and get me
said I'd be sleep - ing
F
way on the mid - night train;
bod - y for to go my bail,
Lord I could - n't eat that,
out of this bug - gy old jail;
now on a feath - er bed,
CHORUS
C7
F
And all my sins are tak - en a - way, Tak - en a - way!

JOHN HENRY

Adapted by James Morehead *Work Song, Southern U.S.A.*

Throughout the South there are tall tales about big John Henry. Of the countless versions, all tell essentially the same story: John Henry races against a steam drill, "beats it down," and dies in the effort. The version here given is strictly a "steel-driving" rhythm, accented by the ring of the sledge on the drill.

G
Em
1. John Hen - ry said to his
2. John Hen - ry said to his
3. John Hen - ry drove in the
4. Laid old John Hen - ry on the
G
Cap - tain: "Cap - tain, when you
Cap - tain: Says "A man ain't
moun - tain, Drove till his
cool - ing board, Looked at him
(M - m - m)
C
G
go to town, Bring me back a
noth-in' but a man! 'Fore I let that
ham-mer caught on fire; Ver - y last
good and long; Ver - y last

Em
G
nine pound sledge, unh, And
steam drill beat me down, I'll
words I hear old John Hen-ry say: "A
words I hear his good wife say: "My
C7
G
I'll drive that steel right down, (Lord, Lord!) And
die with my ham-mer in my hand, (Lord, Lord!) I'll
cool drink of wa-ter 'fore I die, (Lord, Lord!) A
man he is dead and gone, (Lord, Lord!) My
C7
Am7
G
I'll drive that steel right down."
die with my ham-mer in my hand!"
cool drink of wa-ter 'fore I die!"
man he is dead and gone."

ON TOP OF OLD SMOKY

ANONYMOUS

"THE LITTLE MOHEE" is sung to the same tune, which comes from the Kentucky Mountains. In 1951 OLD SMOKY suddenly became a "hit" song, reaching No. 1 in popularity in the United States, and sold more than a million phonograph records and nearly as many copies of sheet music. OLD SMOKY could be any high mountain in the 48 states, for the song was first popular when wagon-trains labored across roadless wilderness. The song itself got to Kentucky from England.

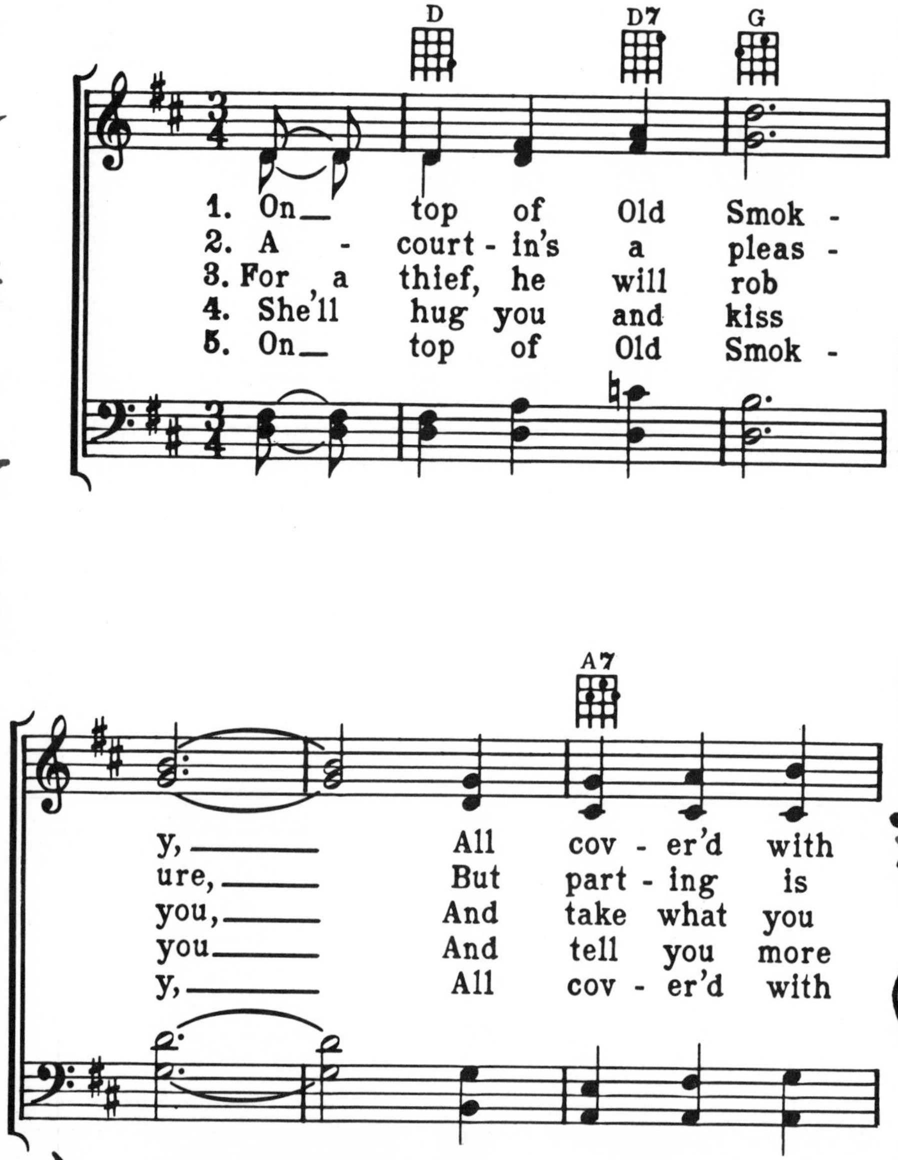
D
D7
G
1. On__ top of Old Smok -
2. A - court - in's a pleas -
3. For a thief, he will rob
4. She'll hug you and kiss
5. On__ top of Old Smok -
A7
y, ______ All cov - er'd with
ure, ______ But part - ing is
you, ______ And take what you
you ______ And tell you more
y, ______ All cov - er'd with

D
A7
D
snow, I lost my true
grief, And a false heart - ed
have, But a false heart - ed
lies Than the cross ties on the
snow, I lost my true
A7
lov - er, Come a -
lov - er Is
lov - er Will
rail - road, Or the
lov - er, Come a -
D
court - in' too slow.
worse than a thief.
send you to your grave.
stars in the skies.
court - in' too slow.

SHE'LL BE COMIN' 'ROUND THE MOUNTAIN

Anonymous

This "railroadin'" song of the 1890s was made from an old spiritual, *When the Chariot Comes.* Grading the roadbeds through the mountains, winding around and tunneling through the irregular terrain, the track gangs could sometimes see the awaited supply train "comin' 'round the mountain," almost half a day away.

B♭
1. She'll be com - in' 'round the
2. She'll be driv - in' six white
3. Oh, we'll all go down to
4. We'll be sing - in' "Hal - le -
moun-tain when she comes, (when she comes,) She'll be
hors - es when she comes, (when she comes,) She'll be
meet her when she comes, (when she comes,) Oh, we'll
lu - jah" when she comes, (when she comes,) We'll be
C7
F7
com - in' 'round the moun-tain when she comes, (when she
driv - in' six white hors - es when she comes, (when she
all go down to meet her when she comes, (when she
sing - in' "Hal - le - lu - jah" when she comes, (when she

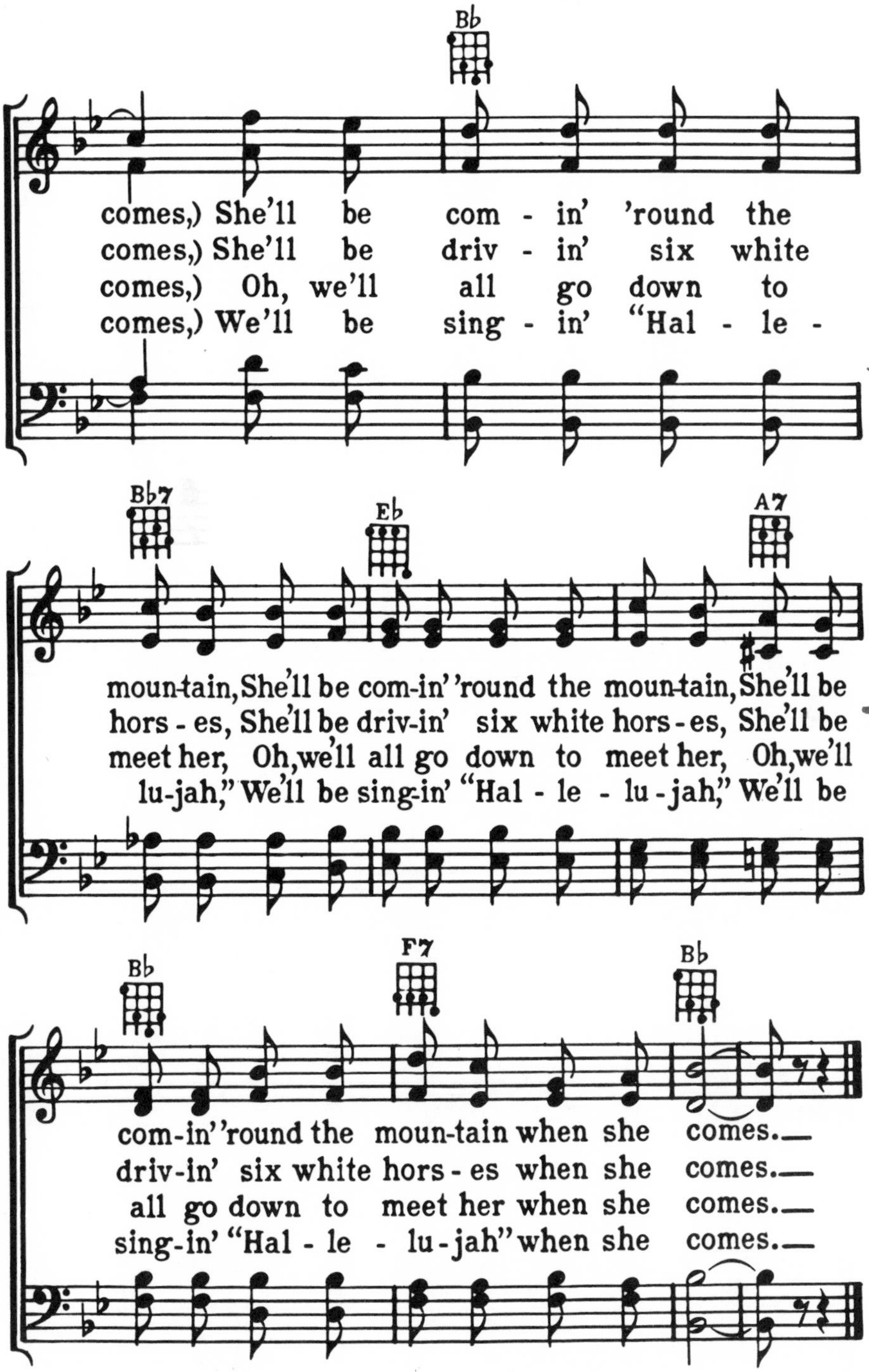
Bb
comes,) She'll be com - in' 'round the
comes,) She'll be driv - in' six white
comes,) Oh, we'll all go down to
comes,) We'll be sing - in' "Hal - le -
Bb7
Eb
A7
moun-tain, She'll be com-in' 'round the moun-tain, She'll be
hors - es, She'll be driv-in' six white hors - es, She'll be
meet her, Oh, we'll all go down to meet her, Oh, we'll
lu-jah," We'll be sing-in' "Hal - le - lu - jah," We'll be
Bb
F7
Bb
com-in' 'round the moun-tain when she comes.
driv-in' six white hors - es when she comes.
all go down to meet her when she comes.
sing-in' "Hal - le - lu - jah" when she comes.

I GAVE MY LOVE A CHERRY
(The Riddle)

ANONYMOUS

A TENDER Elizabethan song from the Kentucky mountains. Many of the songs sung by the people of this inaccessible area have been preserved almost intact for three hundred and more years, never written down but passed along from generation to generation. Often, the words have no modern meaning but are sung as they were in England during the 16th century.

G
Em
1. I gave my love a cher - ry that
2. How can there be a cher - ry that
3. A cher - ry, when it's bloom - ing, it
Am7
G
has no stone, I
has no stone? How
has no stone, A
D7
G
gave my love a chick - en that
can there be a chick - en that
chick - en, when it's pip - ping, it

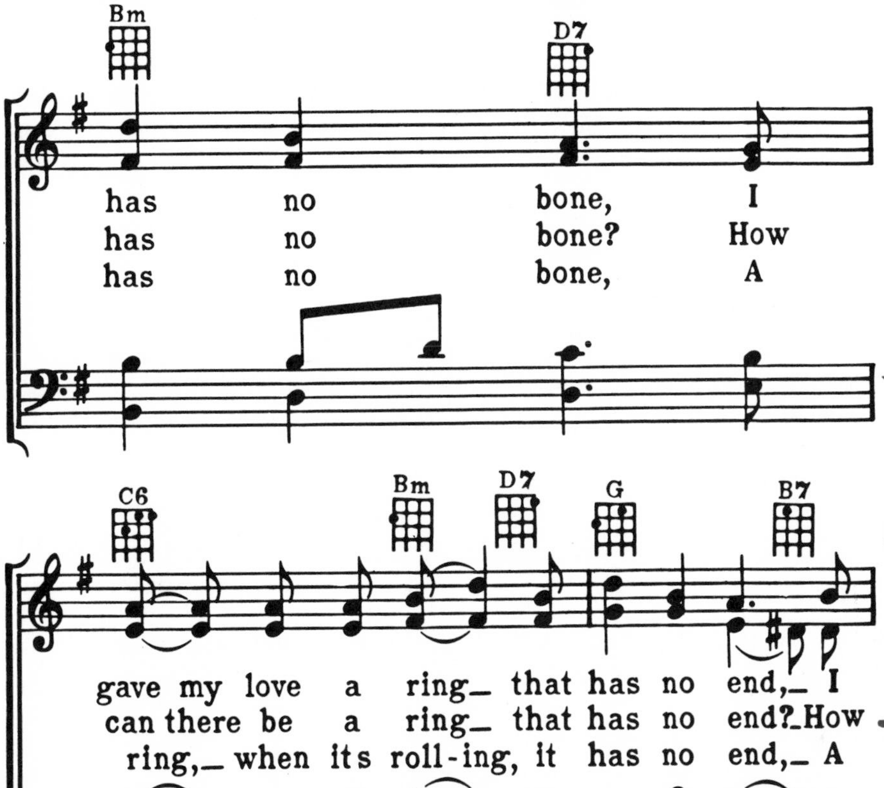
Bm
D7
has no bone, I
has no bone? How
has no bone, A
C6
Bm
D7
G
B7
gave my love a ring_ that has no end,_ I
can there be a ring_ that has no end?_How
ring,_ when its roll-ing, it has no end,_ A
Em
Em7
C6
G
Am7
D
gave my love a ba - by with no cry - en.
can there be a ba - by with no cry - en?
ba - by, when it's sleep - ing, has no cry - en.

KENTUCKY BABE

RICHARD HENRY BUCK — ADAM GEIBEL

HERE IS a true quartet classic, of which glee clubs and their audiences never tire. Its pianissimo ending is like an art song, and it is full of opportunities for nuance and effect. Adam Geibel, who wrote the melody in 1886, was blind from the age of nine days, but became a Doctor of Music and had his own publishing house. Buck also wrote the words of *Dear Old Girl*, another quartet favorite.

C
Am
C
Am
'Skeet-ers are a-hum-min' on the hon-ey-suck-le vine,
C
G7
Dm
G7
Sleep, Ken-tuck-y Babe; Sand-man is a-com-in' to this
Dm
G7
D7
G7
lit-tle one of mine, Sleep Ken-tuck-y Babe!
C
Sil-v'ry moon is shin-in' in the heav-ens up a-bove,

G7
Bob - o - link is pin - in' for his lit - tle la - dy love,
Fm7 G7 Fm7
You are might - y luck - y, Babe of old Ken - tuck - y,
G G+ CHORUS C Am
Close your eyes in sleep.— Fly a - way! Fly a - way Ken - tuck - y Babe,
C Am G9 G7
Fly a - way to rest, Fly a - way! Lay your lit tle curl - y head
C Ab7 C Ab7 C G7 C G7 C
On your mom-my's breast. Mmmm— Mmmm— Close your eyes in sleep.—

THERE IS A TAVERN IN THE TOWN

Attributed to
William H. Hills

In 1883 William H. Hills included this in a collection of college songs, and claimed copyright, but did not enter his name as author, composer, or arranger. The song is probably much older, and English in origin. It was revived in 1934 by Rudy Vallee, a popular singer and orchestra leader.

C
There is a tav-ern in the town, (in the town) And
G G7 C
there my true love sits him down, (sits him down) And drinks his wine, as
F G7 C F C
mer-ry as can be, And nev-er, nev-er thinks of me! (thinks of me!)
G7
Fare thee well, for I must leave thee, Do not

C G7
let the part-ing grieve thee, and re-mem-ber that the best of friends must
C
part, (must part,) A-dieu, a-dieu, kind friends, a-dieu, (yes, a-dieu) I
G G7
can no lon-ger stay with you, (stay with you) I'll
C C7 F
hang my harp on a weep-ing wil-low tree, And
G7 C F C
may the world go well with thee. (well with thee.)

I'VE BEEN WORKIN' ON THE RAILROAD

ANONYMOUS

NO ONE KNOWS the origin of this classic American work-song. The original version, known as *The Levee Sons,* changed to railroad vernacular in the 1890s. The verse is usually omitted, and there is a segue to "Dinah, won't you blow your horn?" further followed by "Someone's in the kitchen with Dinah." *The Eyes of Texas Are Upon You* is set to this tune.

G C A7
1. Oh, I was born in Mo - bile town, I'm
2. I used to have a dog named Bill, A -
3. That li'l ol' dog set up and beg, A -
D7 G
work - in' on the lev - ee. All
work - in' on the lev - ee. He
work - in' on the lev - ee. Till
G C A7
day I roll the cot - ton down, A -
run a - way, but I'm here still, A -
I give him a chick - en leg, A -
D7 G
work - in' on the lev - ee.
work - in' on the lev - ee.
work - in' on the lev - ee.

CHORUS
G G7 C Cm
I've been work - in' on the rail - road All the live - long
G
day; I've been work - in' on the rail - road, Just to
A7 D7
pass the time a - way. Don't you hear the whis - tle
G C B7
blow - ing, Rise up so ear - ly in the morn;
C G D7 G
Don't you hear the cap - tain shout - ing, "Di - nah, blow your horn!"

OH! SUSANNA

STEPHEN C. FOSTER

WHEN OH! SUSANNA was written, in 1848, Foster literally gave it away, not realizing its value; but its enormous success turned him to songwriting as a profession. Representative of this period in his career, he was slightly imitative, rather than original, following the styles of Dan Emmett and others. There is no doubt, however, that he improved such traditional material as came his way, as witness the lasting power of his songs. OH! SUSANNA is inextricably associated with the banjo, for which it is ideally suited.

G
1. I— come from A - la - ba - ma With my
2. I— had a dream the oth - er night, When
A7 D7 G
ban-jo on my knee, I'm goin' to Lou-'si - a - na, My—
all was dark and still, I thought I saw Su-san-na A -
D7 G
true love for to see;— It rained all day the
com - in' down the hill.— A buck-wheat cake was

A7
D7
G
night I left, The weather it was dry, The sun so hot I
in her hand, A tear was in her eye, Says I, "I'm com-in'
D7
G
froze to death, Su - san - na don't you cry.
from the south, Su - san - na don't you cry!"
CHORUS
C
G
D7
G
Oh! Su - san-na, Oh, don't you cry for me, I
D7
G
come from A - la - ba-ma, With my ban-jo on my knee.

AUNT DINAH'S QUILTING PARTY
(When I Saw Sweet Nellie Home)

FRANCIS KYLE **JAMES FLETCHER**

THIS SONG is known by many titles, including *The Quilting Party, I Was Seeing Nellie Home,* and the ones presented above, of which AUNT DINAH'S QUILTING PARTY is most commonly used; but WHEN I SAW SWEET NELLIE HOME is the real title, as first published in 1867. The harmonies seem made-to-order for barber-shop quartets, college boys favor it as well, and it is much parodied. Sigmund Spaeth points to the use of its melody in Cole Porter's *Old Fashioned Garden,* and the novelty song of 1923, *Yes! We Have No Bananas.*

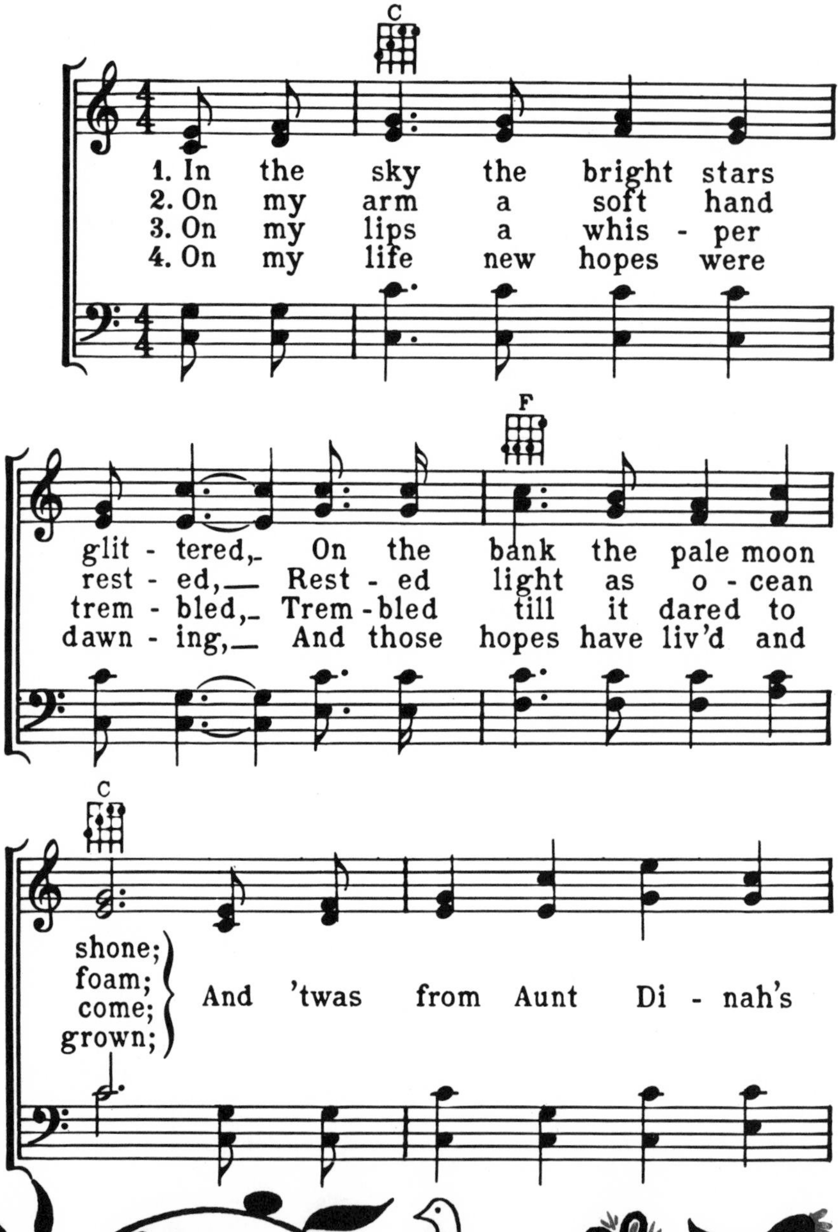
C
1. In the sky the bright stars
2. On my arm a soft hand
3. On my lips a whis - per
4. On my life new hopes were
F
glit - tered,_ On the bank the pale moon
rest - ed,_ Rest - ed light as o - cean
trem - bled,_ Trem - bled till it dared to
dawn - ing,_ And those hopes have liv'd and
C
shone; foam; come; grown;
And 'twas from Aunt Di - nah's

F
G7
C
quilt-ing par-ty, I was see-ing Nel-lie home.
CHORUS
C
I was see-ing Nel-lie home, I was
F
C
see-ing Nel-lie home; And 'twas from Aunt Di-nah's
F
G7
C
quilt-ing par-ty, I was see-ing Nel-lie home.

COCKLES AND MUSSELS
(Molly Malone)

Adapted and arranged by
JAMES MOREHEAD

ANONYMOUS

COCKLES AND MUSSELS, an Irish folk song also known as MOLLY MALONE, has been a "hit" several times, most recently because of its use in the motion picture *A Tree Grows in Brooklyn.* "Wheelbarrow," as used in the song, means a small cart.

G
1. In Dub-lin's fair cit-y, where
2. She was a fish-mon-ger, and
3. She died of a fe-ver, and
Am
D7
G
girls are so pret-ty, 'Twas there that I first met sweet
sure 'twas no won-der, Her fa-ther and moth-er were
no one could save her, And that's all I know of sweet
A7
D
D7
G
Mol-ly Ma-lone, As she wheel'd her wheel-
fish-mon-gers too; And they each wheel'd a
Mol-ly Ma-lone; Now her ghost wheels her

Am
D7
bar-row through streets broad and nar-row,
bar-row through streets broad and nar-row, Crying,
bar-row through streets broad and nar-row,
G
D7
G
"Cock-les and Mus-sels! a - live, a-live - oh!"
CHORUS
D7
G
G7
C6
D7
"A - live, a-live - oh! _ A - live, a-live - oh!" Cry-ing,
G
D7
G
"Cock-les, and Mus-sels, a - live,_ a-live - oh!"

COMIN' THROUGH THE RYE

Attributed to
ROBERT BURNS

Traditional

THE QUESTION IS, did Burns write the words? Or did he merely improve upon already existing lines, as he often did? In a collection of Scottish songs edited by Angus MacKay, about 1858, the song is listed as anonymous, with the suggestion that Burns altered the verses. As early as 1784 the tune appeared as *The Miller's Daughter,* a *strathspey* (Scottish dance) full of the "Scotch snap," or accented sixteenth note followed by a dotted eighth. In America, the first publication was about 1828.

Ab
Eb7
1. If a bod - y meet a bod - y
2. If a bod - y meet a bod - y
3. A-mang the train there is a swain I
Ab
Eb7
Ab
Com - in' thro' the rye,
Com - in' frae the town,
dear - ly love my - sel'; But
Eb7
If a bod - y kiss a bod - y,
If a bod - y greet a bod - y,
what's his name, or where's his hame, I

Ab Eb7 Ab
Need a bod - y cry?
Need a bod - y frown?
din - na choose to tell.
Ev-'ry las-sie
Eb7 Ab7
has her lad - die, Nane, they say, ha'e
Db Ab Eb7
I; Yet a' the lads they
Ab Eb7 Ab Eb7 Ab
smile on me, When com - in' thro' the rye.

THE CAMPBELLS ARE COMIN'

ANONYMOUS

THE SONG refers to the Campbell clan of Scotland, whose chieftains were the Earls, and later Dukes, of Argyll. It is martial music. The claymore of the second stanza is a two-handed sword, hung at the warrior's side; the pibroch of the third stanza is a warlike air played by the pipes for a marching army. Today a playing of THE CAMPBELLS ARE COMIN' summons up a picture of kilts and bonnets and other American imagery regarding the highland Scots.

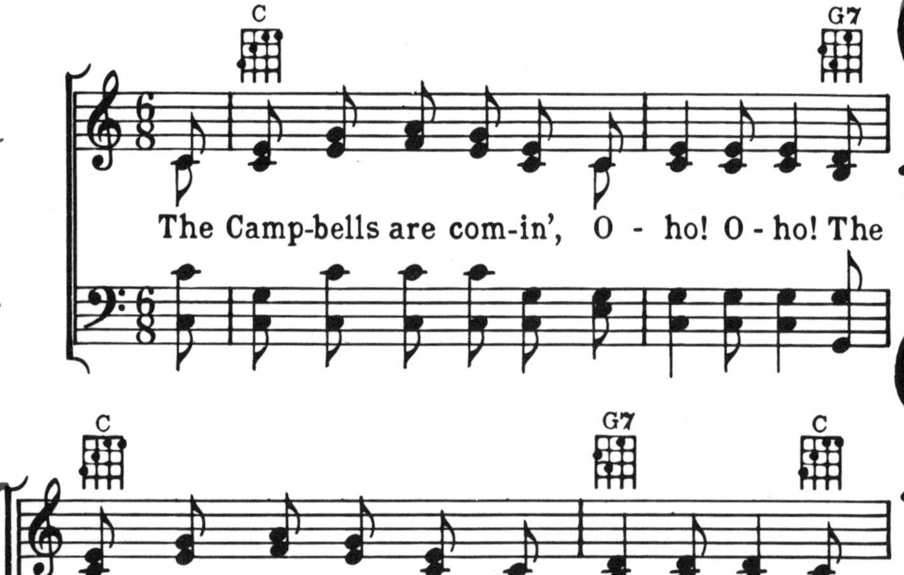
C
G7
The Camp-bells are com-in', O - ho! O - ho! The
C
G7
C
Camp-bells are com - in', O - ho! O - ho! The
C
C7
Camp-bells are com - in' From bon-nie Loch Lo-mond, The

F F♯dim C
Camp-bells are com - in', O - ho! O - ho!
C
1. The great Ar - gyle, he goes be - fore, He
2. With bon - net blue, auld Scot-ties pride, And
3. Hark! hark! the Pib - roch's sound I hear, Now
F G7 C
makes the guns and can-nons roar; With sound of trum-pet,
broad clay-more hung at their side, With plumes all nodding
bon-nie las - sie, din - na fear; 'Tis hon - or calls, I
C7 F F♯dim C
pipe and drum, And ban - ners wav - ing in the sun.
in the wind, They have not left a man be-hind.
must a - way, Ar - gyle's the word and ours the day.

THE CAMPTOWN RACES

STEPHEN C. FOSTER

SCHOLARS have found that this song of Foster's is not entirely original; that it resembles a folk song called *Hoodah Day,* the chantey *Sacramento,* and the spiritual *Roll, Jordan, Roll.* The resemblance consists mostly of a simple major chord, 1-3-5-8. Foster wrote the words, which is more important, and probably used a standard folk tune of his time. The song was published in 1850, the year of Foster's marriage. Sigmund Spaeth says: ". . . . if Stephen Foster could invent *O Susanna,* he could just as easily create *Camptown Races.*"

HARMONY
D
A7
SOLO
1. The Camp-town la - dies sing this song: Doo-dah!
2. The long-tail'd fil-ly and the big black 'hoss', Doo-dah!
3. Oh, see them fly-in' on a ten mile heat, Doo-dah!
SOLO
D
doo-dah! The Camp-town race track nine_ miles long,
doo-dah! They fly the track and they both_ cut_'cross,
doo-dah! Round the race track, then_ re - peat,
HARMONY
A7
D
SOLO
Oh! doo-dah day! I came down here_ with a
Oh! doo-dah day! The blind 'hoss' stick_ in a
Oh! doo-dah day! I keep my mon - ey in an

HARMONY
SOLO
A7
D
pock-et full of tin, Doo-dah! doo-dah! I'm
big_ mud hole, Doo-dah! doo-dah! Can't
old_ tow bag, Doo-dah! doo-dah! I'll
HARMONY
A7
D
go-in' back home with my hat caved in, Oh, doo-dah day!
touch the bot-tom with a ten foot pole Oh, doo-dah day!
bet my mon-ey on the bob-tail nag, Oh, doo-dah day!
CHORUS
A
Bm
G
D
Goin' to run all night, Goin' to run all day, I'll_
A7
D
bet my mon-ey on the bob-tail nag, Some-bod-y bet on the bay.

TAKE ME OUT TO THE BALL GAME

Jack Norworth | **Albert von Tilzer**

This is the official song of America's traditional national game, but the writers of it were not necessarily baseball fans when the song was published in 1908; that was an era when popular songs had topical themes. The original lyric had a "verse" in which Nelly Kelly begged her escort to take her out to the ball game. Albert was youngest of the famous Von Tilzer brothers, who made history in popular American music; Jack Norworth, a skilled songwriter, was husband of Nora Bayes and may have done more than merely collaborate in her biggest song, *Shine On, Harvest Moon.*

D
A7
Take me out to the ball - game,
D
A7
B7
Take me out to the park
Buy me some
Em
E7
pea-nuts and crack - er - jack I don't care if I

A7
D
nev - er come back, Let me root root root for the
A7
D7
home team, If they don't win it's a
G
B7
Em
Em6
Bb7
D
shame. For it's one, two, three strikes, "You're
E7
A7
D
out!" at the old ball - game.

SCHOOL DAYS

WILL D. COBB

GUS EDWARDS

THE FAMILIAR AND SUCCESSFUL SONGS he wrote are numerous, yet this simple and homely one is the classic contribution of Gus Edwards. Born in Germany in 1879, named Gustav Edward Simon, and brought to the United States as a child, he became a successful songwriter, publisher, vaudevillian and show producer in his early twenties. He wrote SCHOOL DAYS (1907) for a vaudeville act in which he introduced as children such later stars as Eddie Cantor, George Jessel, Groucho Marx, and many others. Cobb, a successful lyricist of those times, wrote several big songs with Edwards.

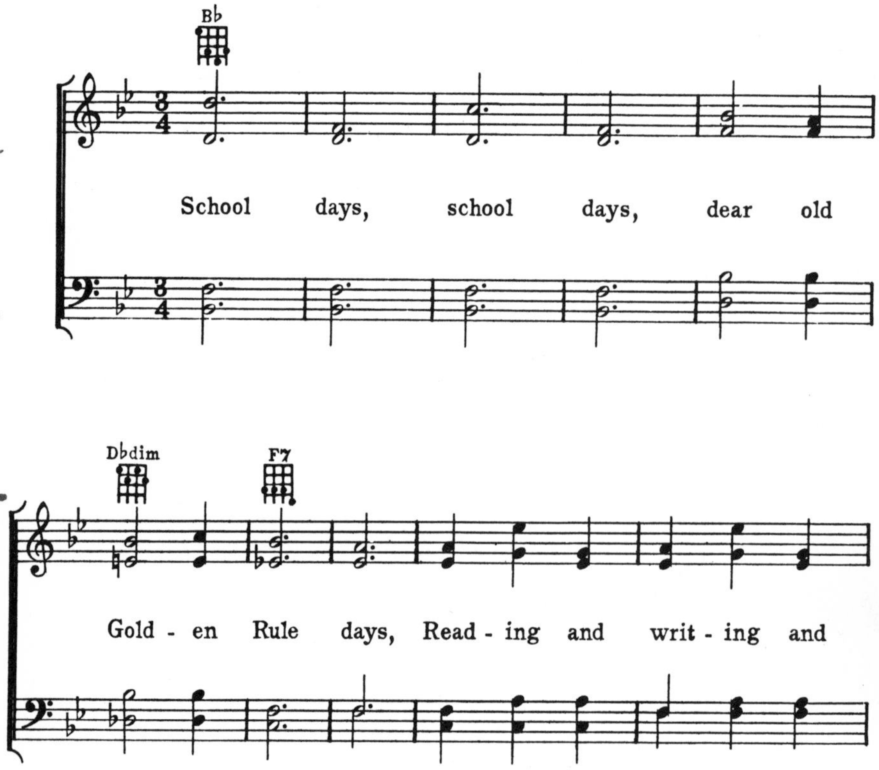
Bb
School days, school days, dear old
Dbdim
F7
Gold - en Rule days, Read - ing and writ - ing and
Bb
'rith - ma - tic, Taught to the tune of a

B♭6 B♭ G7 C7
hick - 'ry stick, You were my queen in cal - i -
B♭
co, I was your bash - ful bare - foot
E♭ Edim B♭
beau, And you wrote on my slate "I love you,
D7 Gm C7 F7 B♭
Joe," When we were a cou - ple of kids.

CASEY JONES

T. LAWRENCE SEIBERT — EDDIE NEWTON

There is no more American song. From our history in which railroads made America's greatness, this is the No. 1 railroad song. It is typical of the topical ballads that flourished before it was published (1909). There are forty-five versions and the Seibert-Newton one is not necessarily the first, but who knows? The incident is actual; John Luther Jones, called Casey because he came from Cayce, Kentucky, died as recounted in the ballad, taking a train called the Cannonball out of Memphis.

C G7 C G7 C
1. Come all you round-ers, if you want to hear a
2. Put in your wa-ter and sho-vel your coal, Put your
3. Ca-sey pulled up that Re-no hill He
4. Ca-sey said just be-fore he died "There's
G7 C D7 G7
sto-ry a-bout a brave en-gi-neer,
head out the win-dow watch them driv-ers roll, I'll
toot-ed for the cross-ing with an aw-ful shrill, The
two more roads that I'd like to ride, The
C G7 C G7 C
Ca-sey Jones was the round-er's name, On a
run her till she leaves the rail 'Cause I'm
switch-man knew by the en-gine's moan That the
fire-man said "What could that be?" "The
G7 C
six eight wheel-er boys, he won his fame. The
eight hours late with the West-ern mail." He
man at the throttle was Ca-sey Jones. He
South-ern Pa-ci-fic and the San-ta Fe." Mrs.

G7 C G7 C
call - er called Ca - sey at a half past four, He
looked at his watch and his watch was slow, He
pulled up with - in two miles of the place,
Jones sat on her bed a - sigh'n, Just re -
G7 C D7 G7
kissed his wife at the sta - tion door, He
looked at the wa - ter and the wa - ter was low, He
num - ber four stared him right in the face, He
ceived a mes - sage that Ca - sey was dy - ing, Said
C G7 C G7 C
mount - ed to the ca - bin with his or - ders in his hand, And he
turned to the fire - man and he said, "Boy, we're
turned to the fire - man said "Boy, you bet - ter jump, Cause there's
"Go to bed, chil - dren, hush your cry - in', Cause you
G7 C
took his fare - well trip to the Prom - ised Land.
goin' to reach Fris - co but we'll all be dead."
two lo - co - mo - tives that's a goin' to bump."
got an - oth - er pa - pa on the Salt Lake Line."

CHORUS
C F G7
Ca-sey Jones, mount-ed to the ca-bin (Well)
Ca-sey Jones, goin' to reach Fris-co (Well)
Ca-sey Jones, two lo-co-mo-tives (Yes)
Mrs. Ca-sey Jones, got an-oth-er pa-pa, Mrs.
C D7 G7
Ca-sey Jones, with his or-ders in his hand,
Ca-sey Jones, but we'll all be dead,
Ca-sey Jones, that's a-goin' to bump,
Ca-sey Jones, on the Salt Lake Line, Mrs.
C F G7
Ca-sey Jones, mount-ed to the cab-in and he
Ca-sey Jones, goin' to reach Fris-co, we're
Ca-sey Jones, two lo-co-mo-tives, There's
Ca-sey Jones, got an-oth-er pa-pa, 'Cause you
C G7 C
took his fare-well trip to the Prom-ised Land.
goin' to reach Fris-co but we'll all be dead."
two lo-co-mo-tives that's a goin' to bump."
got an-oth-er pa-pa on the Salt Lake Line."

HYMNS

GLORIA PATRI

H. W. GREATOREX

THIS IS ONE of the time-honored forms of doxology, or expression of praise of God. The *Gloria in excelsis* (glory [be to God] in the highest) and *Gloria Patri* (glory [be to] the Father) are accounted somewhat more formal than the Doxology shown on the front endpages of this book. The text of the *Gloria Patri* below is said to derive from St. Thomas Aquinas, can be traced to a Meissen Breviary of the early 16th century, and was rendered by Dr. John Mason Neale in 1851. It is sung in almost all Christian churches.

Glo - ry be to the Fa-ther, and to the
Son, and to the ho - ly_ Ghost; As it
was in the be - gin-ning, is now, and ev - er
shall be, world with-out end. A - men, A - men.

OUR GOD, OUR HELP IN AGES PAST

Isaac Watts — William Croft

St. Anne's, C.M.

In a time of crisis for the Church of England, Watts based his poem upon the 90th Psalm. The tune is named for the church where Croft was organist. The hymn appears in almost all hymn books (often with the beginning altered to "O God . . .") and is much used for New Year's Day. At St. Clement's Church in London it is rung daily on the bells.

1. Our God, our help in a-ges past, Our hope for years to come, Our shel-ter from the storm-y blast, And our e-ter-nal home!
2. Un-der the shad-ow of Thy throne Thy saints have dwelt se-cure; Suf-fi-cient is Thine arm a-lone, And our de-fence is sure.
3. Be-fore the hills in or-der stood, Or earth re-ceive her frame, From ev-er-last-ing Thou art God, To end-less years the same.
4. A thou-sand a-ges in Thy sight Are like an eve-ning gone; Short as the watch that ends the night Be-fore the ris-ing sun.
5. Time, like an ev-er roll-ing stream, Bears all its sons a-way; They fly, for-got-ten as a dream Dies at the ope-ning day.
6. Our God, our help in a-ges past, Our hope for years to come, Be Thou our guard while life shall last, And our e-ter-nal home!

HOLY, HOLY, HOLY!

REGINALD HEBER JOHN BACCHUS DYKES

Nicaea, **P.M.**

THIS WAS regarded by Tennyson as one of the finest of all hymns and it was sung at his burial in Westminster Abbey. It was adapted by Bishop Heber from the "cadence of the Apocalypse," REVELATION 4:8, "and they rest not day and night, saying Holy, holy, holy, Lord God Almighty, which was, and is, and is to come."

1. Ho - ly, Ho - ly, Ho - ly!
2. Ho - ly, Ho - ly, Ho - ly!
3. Ho - ly, Ho - ly, Ho - ly!
Lord God Al-might - y! Ear - ly in the
all the saints a - dore Thee, Cast - ing down their
tho' the dark-ness hide Thee, Though the eye of
morn - ing our song shall rise to Thee;
gold - en crowns a - round the glass - y sea;
sin - ful man Thy glo - ry may not see,

Ho - ly, Ho - ly, Ho - ly!
Cher - u - bim and ser - aphim
On - ly Thou art Ho - ly;
Mer - ci - ful and might - y!
fall - ing down be - fore Thee,
there is none be - side Thee,
God in three Per - sons,
Which wert and art, and
Per - fect in pow'r, in
bless - ed Trin - i - ty!
ev - er - more shall be.
love, and pur - i - ty.

A MIGHTY FORTRESS

Translated by
FREDERICK H. HEDGE | MARTIN LUTHER

Ein Feste Burg,
8.7.8.7.6.6.6.7.

KNOWN AS "the battle hymn of the reformation," this is a truly historic hymn. Meyerbeer incorporated it into his opera *Les Huguenots,* Wagner into *Der Kaisermarsch,* Mendelssohn in his *Reformation Symphony*. The famous chorale was sung in Boston in 1869 by a chorus of ten thousand voices, accompanied by a thousand-piece orchestra directed by Patrick S. Gilmore.

1. A might-y Fort-ress is our God, A
2. Did we in our own strength con-fide, Our
3. And tho' this world, with dev - ils filled, Should
Bul-wark nev - er fail - ing; Our Help-er He a -
striv-ing would be los - ing; Were not the right man
threat-en to un - do_ us; We will not fear for
mid the flood Of mor-tal ills pre - vail - ing.
on our side, The man of God's own choos - ing.
God hath will'd His truth to tri-umph through us.

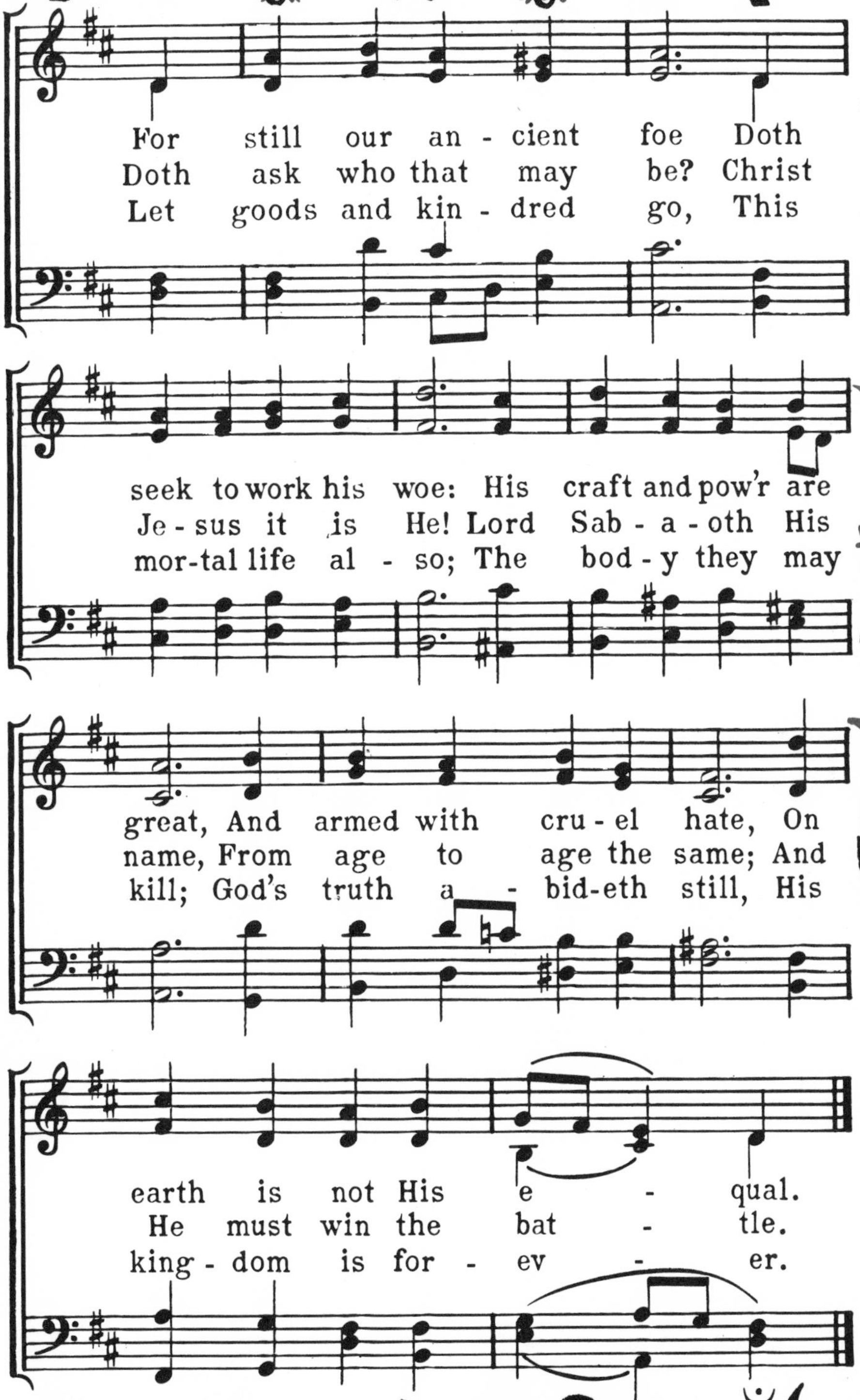
For still our an - cient foe Doth
Doth ask who that may be? Christ
Let goods and kin - dred go, This
seek to work his woe: His craft and pow'r are
Je - sus it is He! Lord Sab - a - oth His
mor-tal life al - so; The bod - y they may
great, And armed with cru - el hate, On
name, From age to age the same; And
kill; God's truth a - bid-eth still, His
earth is not His e - qual.
He must win the bat - tle.
king - dom is for - ev - er.

THE CHURCH'S ONE FOUNDATION

Samuel J. Stone — Samuel S. Wesley

Aurelia, 7s, 6s, D.

Written in 1866 during the "Colenso Controversy" in the Church of England, when the authenticity of the Pentateuch was questioned, this hymn is one of twelve based upon the articles of the Apostles' Creed. The Reverend Dr. Stone, who was then curate of Windsor, figured prominently in the controversy. The tune had previously been used for *Jerusalem the Golden*, from which it derives its name *Aurelia* (golden).

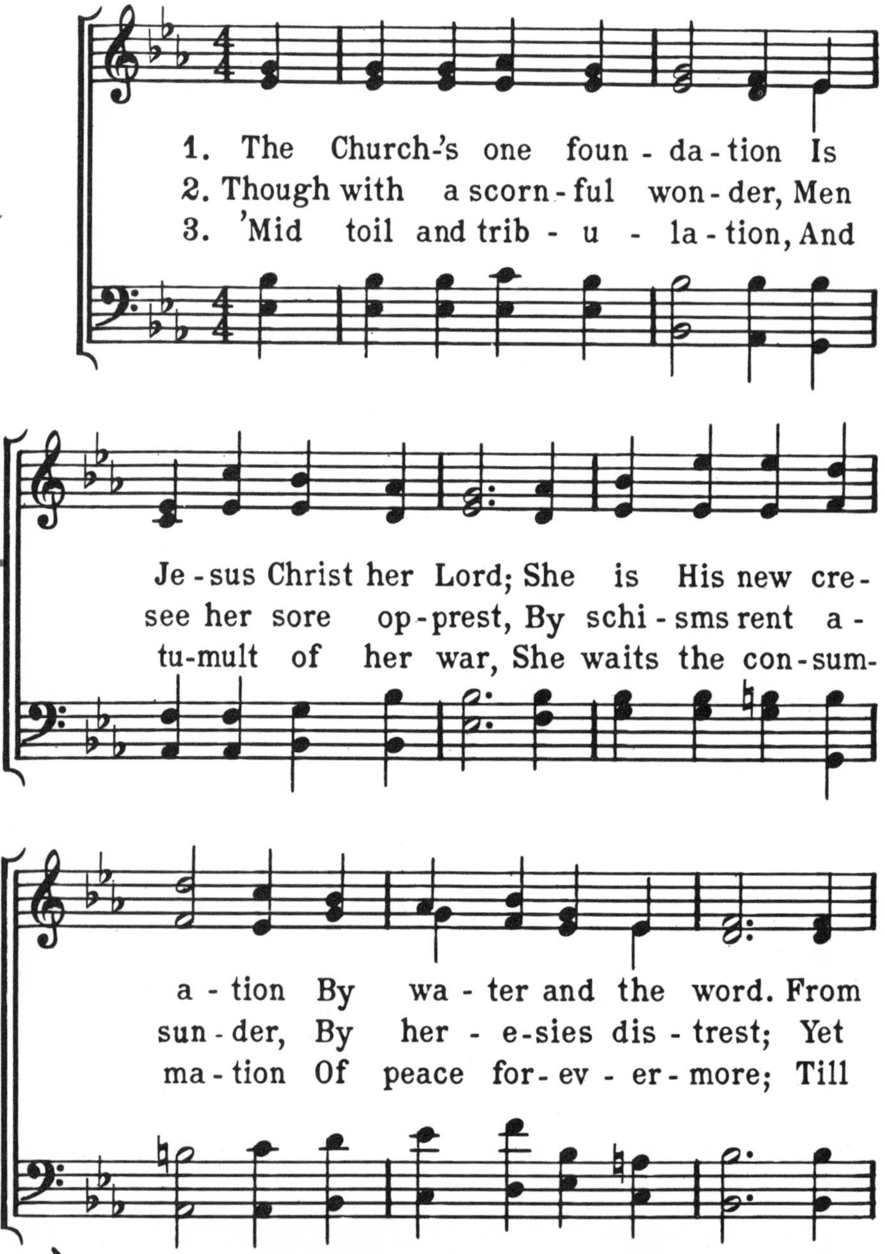

1. The Church's one foun - da - tion Is
2. Though with a scorn - ful won - der, Men
3. 'Mid toil and trib - u - la - tion, And
Je - sus Christ her Lord; She is His new cre -
see her sore op - prest, By schi - sms rent a -
tu-mult of her war, She waits the con - sum -
a - tion By wa - ter and the word. From
sun - der, By her - e-sies dis - trest; Yet
ma - tion Of peace for - ev - er - more; Till

heav'n He came and sought her To
saints their watch are keep - ing, Their
with the vi - sion glo - rious Her
be His ho - ly Bride; With
cry goes up "How long?" And
long - ing eyes are blest, And
His own blood He bought Her, And
soon the night of weep - ing Shall
the great Church vic - to - rious, Shall
for Her life He died.
be the morn of song.
be the Church of rest.

ANCIENT OF DAYS

WILLIAM CROSWELL DOANE | J. ALBERT JEFFREY

Albany, 11.10.11.10

WRITTEN in 1886 for the bicentenary in celebration of the chartering of the city of Albany, New York. The title is derived from DANIEL 7:9, "I beheld till the thrones were cast down, and the Ancient of days did sit."

1. An - cient of days, Who
2. O Ho - ly Fa - ther,
3. O Ho - ly Je - sus,
4. O Ho - ly Ghost, the
5. O Tri - une God, with
sit - test throned in glo - ry;
Who hast led Thy chil - dren
Prince of Peace and Sav - iour,
Lord and the Life - Giv - er,
heart and voice a - dor - ing,
To Thee all knees are bent, all voic - es pray;
In all the a - ges, with the fire and cloud,
To Thee we owe the peace that still pre-vails,
Thine is the quick'ning pow'r that gives in-crease.
Praise we the good-ness that has crown'd our day;

Thy love has bless'd the
Thro' seas dry - shod; thro'
Still - ing the rude wills
From Thee have flowed, as
Pray we, that Thou wilt
wide world's won - drous sto - ry,
wea - 'ry wastes be - wil - d'ring
of men's wild be - hav - iour,
from a pleas - ant riv - er,
hear us, still im - plor - ing
With light and life since E - den's dawn-ing day.
To Thee, in rev - 'rent love, our hearts are bowed.
And calm-ing pas - sion's fierce and storm - y gales.
Our plen - ty, wealth, pros-per - i - ty and peace.
Thy love and fa - vor, kept to us al-way.

ALL PRAISE TO THEE, MY GOD, THIS NIGHT

THOMAS KEN | CHARLES F. GOUNOD

Evening Hymn, L.M.D.

PROBABLY one of the most famous English hymns; note that Stanza 4 is familiar as the *Doxology*. Often sung to Tallis' *Canon*, it dates from 1692. It was Thomas Ken, brother-in-law of Izaak Walton the angler, who refused to accommodate Nell Gwyn when she visited Winchester with Charles II. The King so admired his courage that he appointed him Bishop of Bath and Wells.

1. All praise to Thee, my God this night For
3. Oh, may my soul on Thee re - pose, And
all the bless - ings of the light.
may sweet sleep my eye - lids close,
Keep me, oh, keep me, King of kings, Be-
Sleep that shall me more vig-'rous make To
neath Thine own al - might - y wings.
serve my God when I - a - wake!

2. For - give me Lord, for Thy dear Son, The
4. Praise God from whom all bless-ings flow; Praise
ill that I this day have done That
Him all crea-tures here be - low; Praise
with the world, my - self, and Thee I,
Him a - bove, ye heav'n - ly host; Praise
ere I sleep, at peace may be.
Fa - ther, Son, and Ho - ly Ghost.

FAITH OF OUR FATHERS

FREDERICK W. FABER

HENRI F. HEMY
JAMES G. WALTON

St. Catherine, L.M.

FREDERICK FABER was brought up a Calvinist. After he was ordained at Oxford, he came under the influence of John H. Newman and followed him into the Catholic Church. This hymn was written some years later and the original text plainly applied to the Oxford Movement and the Catholic Communion:

Faith of our Fathers! Mary's prayers
Shall win our country back to Thee;
And through the truth that comes from God,
England shall then indeed be free.

1. Faith of our fa - thers, liv - ing
2. Faith of our fa - thers, we will
3. Faith of our fa - thers, we will
still In spite of dun-geon, fire and
strive To win all na-tions un - to
love Both friend and foe in all our
sword, Oh how our hearts beat
thee; And through the truth that
strife, And preach thee, too,— as

high_ with joy When - e'er we
comes from God Man - kind shall
love_ knows how By kind - ly
hear that glo - rious word!
then in - deed be free.
words and vir - tuous life.
REFRAIN
Faith of our fa - thers, ho - ly faith,
We will be true to thee till death. A - men.

DEAR LORD AND FATHER OF MANKIND

JOHN GREENLEAF WHITTIER FREDERICK C. MAKER

Rest (*Elton*), 8.6.8.8.6.

MEDITATION was a favorite theme to the great poet, and in this hymn he pays tribute to the self-knowledge that is found in solitude. The verses are part of a major poem, *The Brewing of Soma,* wherein Whittier compares our communion of the spirit with the Indian use of the intoxicant "soma," mistakenly believed to have produced rapport with God. The tune was first published in London, in *The Church Hymnary,* in 1887. Frederick Maker used commendable restraint in finding a perfect musical form without resorting to a repetition of the last line of each stanza, which would seem the obvious way out of a difficult pattern.

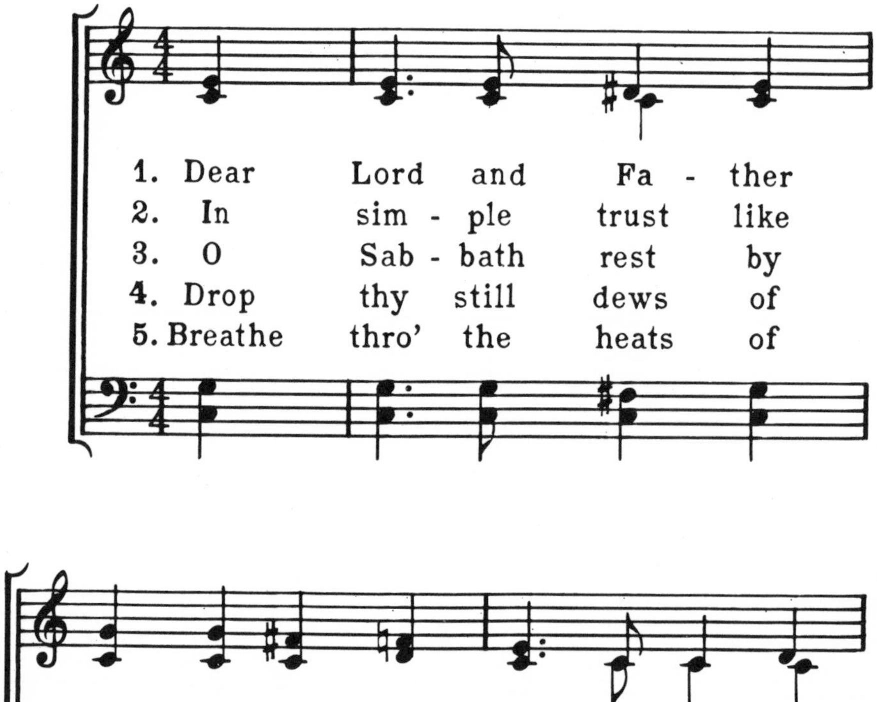
1. Dear Lord and Fa - ther
2. In sim - ple trust like
3. O Sab - bath rest by
4. Drop thy still dews of
5. Breathe thro' the heats of
of man-kind, For - give our fe - v'rish
theirs who heard, Be - side the Syr - ian
Gal - i - lee! O calm of hills a -
qui - et - ness, Till all our striv - ings
our de - sire Thy cool - ness and thy

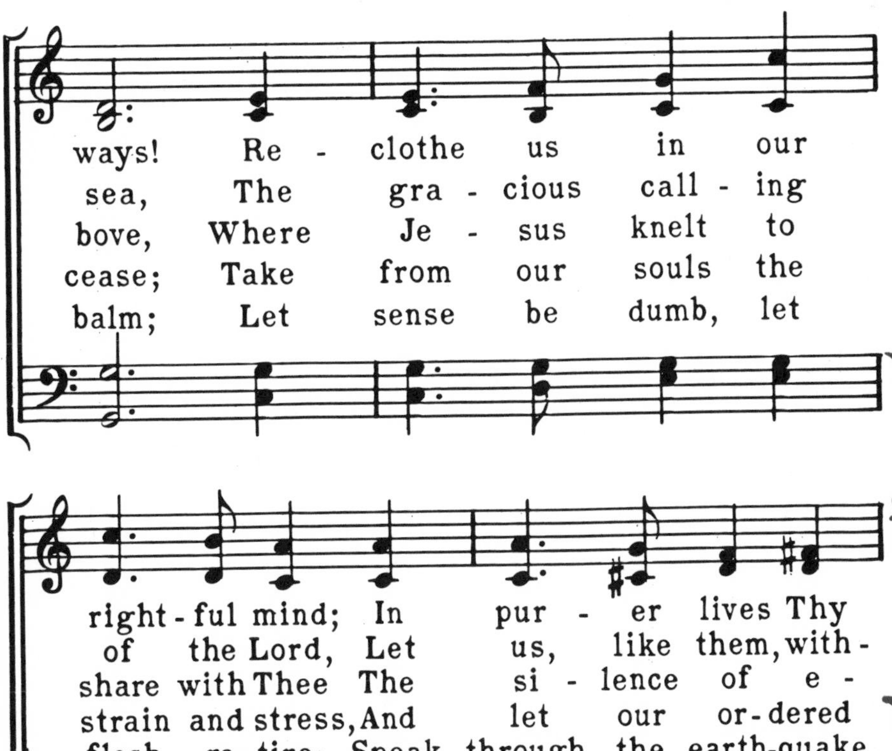
ways! Re - clothe us in our
sea, The gra - cious call - ing
bove, Where Je - sus knelt to
cease; Take from our souls the
balm; Let sense be dumb, let
right - ful mind; In pur - er lives Thy
of the Lord, Let us, like them, with -
share with Thee The si - lence of e -
strain and stress, And let our or - dered
flesh re - tire; Speak through the earth-quake,
serv - ice find, In deep - er rev - 'rence, praise.
out a word, Rise up and fol - low Thee.
ter - ni - ty, In - ter - pret - ed by love!
lives con-fess The beau - ty of Thy peace.
wind, and fire, O still small voice of calm!

NEARER, MY GOD, TO THEE

SARAH (FLOWER) ADAMS — LOWELL MASON

Bethany, 6s, 4s.

MRS. ADAMS was a talented actress, but her health would not permit her to follow that profession. She turned to writing, together with her sister Elizabeth. Tuberculosis struck Elizabeth, and she died in 1846. Sarah, who had contracted the disease while acting as nurse, died two years later. When the great liner *Titanic* went down in 1912, the band played NEARER, MY GOD, TO THEE as the water rose, and 1,500 passengers and crewmen sang the inspiring words as if they too saw the vision of Jacob at Bethel (GENESIS 28:10-22).

1. Near - er, my God, to Thee, near - er, to Thee:
2. Though like the wan - der - er, the sun gone down,
3. There let the way ap - pear steps un - to heav'n;
E'en though it be a cross that_ rais - eth me,
Dark - ness be o - ver me, my__ rest a stone,
All that Thou send - est me in__ mer - cy giv'n;
Still all my song shall be,
Yet in my dreams I'd be
An - gels to beck - on me,
Near - er my God, to Thee,
Near - er, my God, to Thee, near - er to Thee.

GIVE TO OUR GOD IMMORTAL PRAISE

ISAAC WATTS — DUKE STREET L.M. — JOHN HATTON

THIS HYMN RANKED FIFTH in popularity among Lutherans (according to a poll taken by *The Lutheran* magazine) in 1965. It was in Sir Isaac Watts' *Psalms of David* in 1719 and it has been set to other tunes—just as the tune below has been used for other hymns, notably *I Know That My Redeemer Lives.* The composer John Hatton died in 1793 and was not the more prolific John Hatton of Liverpool, born 1809; in fact, no connection between them can be proved. But there must have been one, for the earlier John Hatton lived and died near Liverpool in the village of St. Helens and on Duke Street,

1. Give to our God im - mor - tal praise,
2. Give to the Lord of lords re - nown,
3. He sent His Son with pow - er to save
4. Through this vain world He guides our feet
Mer - cy and truth are all His ways.
The King of kings with glo - ry crown,
From guilt and dark - ness and the grave.
And leads us to His heav'n - ly seat.
Won - ders of grace to God be - long,
His mer - cies ev - er shall en - dure,
Won - ders of grace to God be - long,
His mer - cies ev - er shall en - dure,
Re - peat His mer - cies in your song.
When lords and kings are known no more.
Re - peat His mer - cies in your song.
When this vain world shall be no more.

COME, THOU ALMIGHTY KING

ANONYMOUS FELICE GIARDINI

Trinity, 6s, 4s.

THE WORDS are often ascribed to Charles Wesley because they were first printed in a leaflet published by the Wesleys, but there is no evidence that he wrote them and certainly he never claimed them. Also, the meter is one he never used. Probably the poem was written in imitation of *God Save Our Gracious King*, which had been sung to the same tune a few years earlier. In Britain the tune is known as *Moscow* (where Giardini died). It is also known as *Florence, Fairford*, and *Giardini.*

1. Come, Thou al - might - y
2. Come, Thou in - car - nate
3. Come, ho - ly Com - fort -
4. To the great One_ in
King, Help us Thy
Word, Gird on Thy
er! Thy sa - cred
Three, The high - est
name_ to sing,
might - y sword;
wit - ness bear,
prais - es be,

Help us to praise:
Our pray'r at - tend:
In this glad hour:
Hence ev - er - more!
Fa - ther! all glo - ri - ous,
Come and Thy peo - ple bless
Thou, who al - might - y art,
His sov - 'reign ma - jes - ty
O'er all vic - to - ri - ous, Come and reign
And give Thy word suc-cess: Spir - it of
Now rule in ev - 'ry heart And ne'er from
May we in Glo - ry see, And to e -
o - ver us, An - cient of Days!
ho - li-ness! On us de - scend.
us de-part, Spir - it of pow'r!
ter - ni - ty Love and a - dore.

GUIDE ME, O THOU GREAT JEHOVAH

William Williams — Thomas Hastings

Zion, 8s, 7s, 4s, 7s.

William Wilialms was born in 1717 on a farm in Pantycelyn, Wales. And, says Albert E. Bailey, the Williams family still lives there. Of the hundreds of hymns that he wrote, only this one is important in today's hymnals. He wrote it originally in Welsh. The first stanza was translated by Peter Williams (not related to W.W.) in 1771. Stanzas 2 and 3 were also translated by him, but John Williams, son of William, retranslated them in 1772. (Some sources say the senior Williams retranslated them himself.) The hymn has been translated into 75 languages.

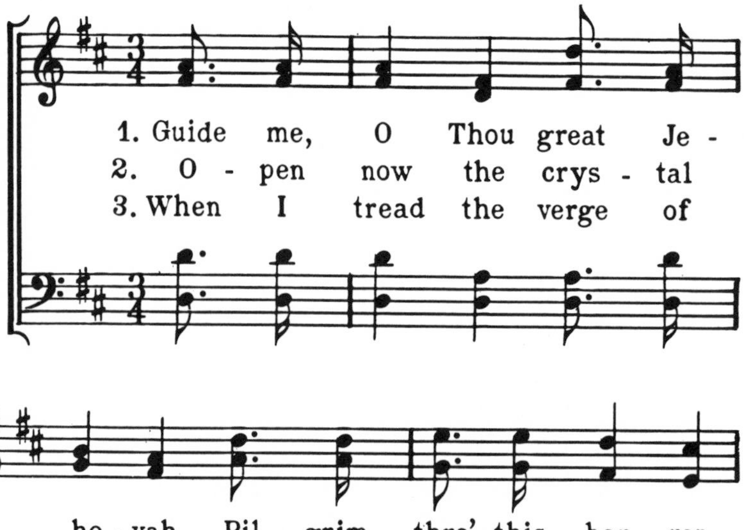
1. Guide me, O Thou great Je - hovah, Pil - grim thro' this bar - ren land: I am weak, but Thou art
2. O - pen now the crys - tal foun-tain, Whence the heal - ing wa - ters flow; Let the fier - y, cloud - y
3. When I tread the verge of Jor - dan, Bid my anx - ious fears sub- side; Bear me through the swel - ling

might - y, Hold me with Thy pow'r - ful
pil - lar Lead me all my jour - ney
cur - rent, Land me safe on Ca - naan's
hand: Bread of heav - en, Feed me
thro': Strong De - liv - 'rer, Be Thou
side: Songs of prais - es I will
till I want no more, Bread of
still my strength and shield, Strong De -
ev - er give to Thee, Songs of
heav - en, Feed me till I want no more.
liv - 'rer, Be Thou still my strength and shield.
prais - es I will ev - er give to Thee.

COME, THOU FOUNT OF EVERY BLESSING

ROBERT ROBINSON JOHN WYETH

Nettleton, 8.7.8.7.D.

REPENTANT after a youth misspent in carousing, Robinson became a minister. He was essentially a nonconformist, although at various times he functioned as a member of many denominations. This was the favorite hymn of Mrs. Francis E. Clark, who with her husband founded the Christian Endeavor Society. At her suggestion, an ebenezer, or collective stone monument (1 SAMUEL 7:13), was raised in its honor.

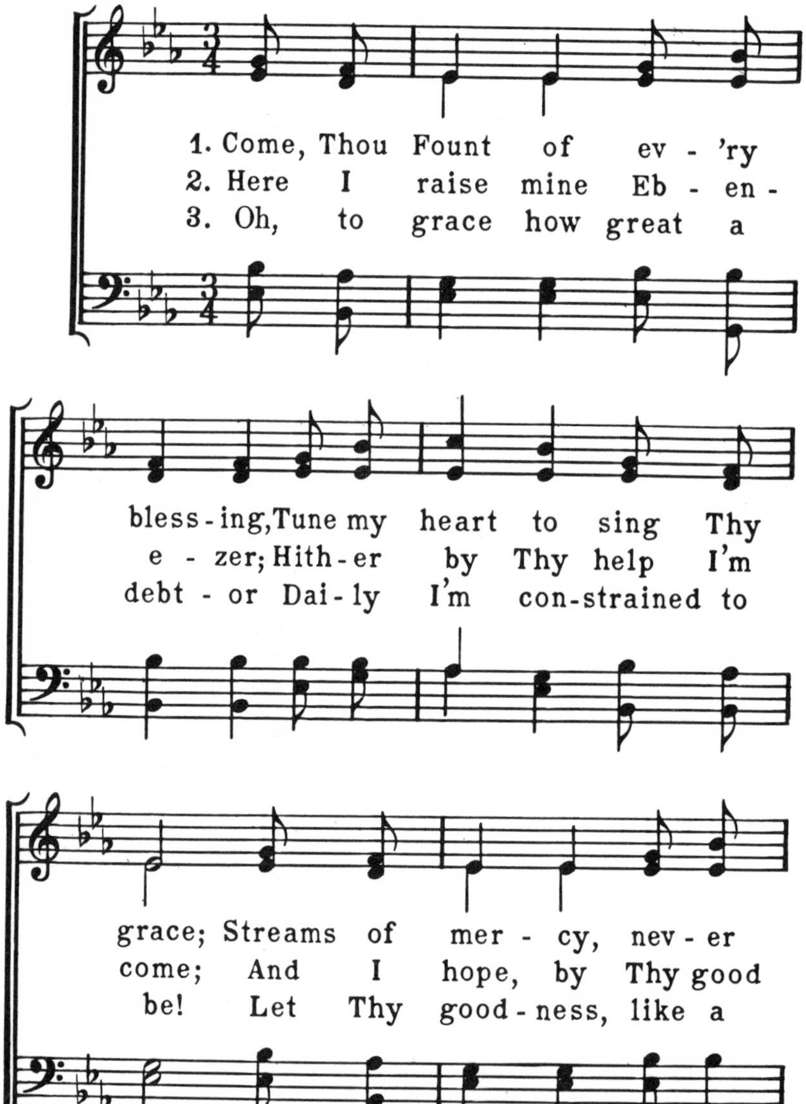
1. Come, Thou Fount of ev - 'ry
2. Here I raise mine Eb - en -
3. Oh, to grace how great a
bless - ing, Tune my heart to sing Thy
e - zer; Hith - er by Thy help I'm
debt - or Dai - ly I'm con-strained to
grace; Streams of mer - cy, nev - er
come; And I hope, by Thy good
be! Let Thy good - ness, like a

ceas-ing, Call for songs of loud-est praise.
pleas-ure, Safe-ly to ar-rive at home.
fet-ter, Bind my wan-d'ring heart to Thee:
Teach me some me-lo-dious son-net, Sung by
Je-sus sought me when a stran-ger, Wan-der-ing
Prone to wan-der, Lord, I feel it, Prone to
flam-ing tongues a-bove; Praise the
from the fold of God; He, to
leave the God I love; Here's my
mount I'm fixed up-on it Mount of Thy re-deem-ing love.
res-cue me from dan-ger, In-ter-posed His pre-cious blood.
heart, Oh, take and seal it; Seal it for Thy courts a-bove.

ROCK OF AGES

AUGUSTUS M. TOPLADY | THOMAS HASTINGS

Toplady, seven 6s

THE WORD *rock* appears metaphorically throughout the Old and New Testaments. In 1 CORINTHIANS 10:4, Paul says, "They drank of that spiritual Rock . . . and that Rock was Christ." Toplady was a militant opponent of Wesley, at whom he hurled constant insult and invective. His hymn contains his creed, but today the old feud is forgotten, and this is one of the most popular hymns in English. In the original version "wounded side" read "riven side"; and the last line of the first stanza appears as "Cleanse me from its guilt and power."

1. Rock of A - ges, cleft for
2. Not the la - bor of my
3. While I draw this fleet - ing
me, Let me hide my - self in
hands Can ful - fil Thy law's de -
breath, While mine eyes shall close in
Thee; Let the wa - ter and the
mands; Could my zeal no res - pite
death, When I soar to worlds un -

blood, From Thy wound - ed side which
know, Could my tears for - ev - er
known, See Thee on Thy judg - ment
flowed, Be of sin the dou - ble
flow, All for sin could not a -
throne, Rock of A - ges cleft for
cure, Save from guilt and make me pure.
tone, Thou must save, and Thou a - lone.
me, Let me hide my-self in Thee.

LEAD, KINDLY LIGHT

JOHN H. NEWMAN — JOHN BACCHUS DYKES

Lux Benigna, Irregular

CARDINAL NEWMAN credited Dykes' superb tune with the success of his hymn. It became prominent here through having been sung at the funeral of President McKinley, but its use at funerals is probably misinterpretation. Newman had been torn by indecision for many years whether to become a Catholic, which he subsequently did. The words are most probably a prayer for guidance, wherein "light" means a "pillar of fire" such as led the Israelites through the wilderness (EXODUS 13:22), and "kindly" has the Elizabethan sense of "inner" or "innate."

1. Lead, kind-ly Light, a-mid th'en-cir-cling
2. I was not ev - er thus, nor prayed that
3. So long Thy pow'r hath blest me, sure it
gloom, Lead Thou me on! The night is
Thou Shouldst lead me on; I loved to
still Will lead me on O'er moor and
dark, and I am far from home;
choose and see my path; but now
fen, o'er crag and tor-rent, till

Lead Thou me on! Keep Thou my feet; I
Lead Thou me on! I loved the gar - ish
The night is gone, And with the morn those
do not ask to see___ The dis - tant
day, and spite of fears,___ Pride ruled my
an-gel fa - ces smile,___ Which I have
scene; one step e - nough for me.___
will. Re-mem-ber not___ past years!
loved long since, and lost___ a - while!

SWEET HOUR OF PRAYER

WILLIAM W. WALFORD WILLIAM B. BRADBURY

Prayer, L.M.D.

THE REVEREND THOMAS SALMON, of Coleshill, England, sailed for New York on a visit, taking with him some verses he had taken in dictation from his blind friend, the Reverend William Walford. He had the verses published in the New York *Observer*. This was in 1845. Fourteen years later the poem came to the attention of the organist and composer William Bradbury, and the hymn was published among his *Cottage Melodies.* When we remember that Walford's life was filled with "seasons of distress and grief" it is good to know that his hymn has brought comfort to so many in like adversity.

1. Sweet hour of pray'r! Sweet hour of
2. Sweet hour of pray'r! Sweet hour of
3. Sweet hour of pray'r! Sweet hour of
pray'r! That calls me from a world of care, And
pray'r! Thy wings shall my pe - ti - tion bear, To
pray'r! May I thy con-so - la - tion share; Till
bids me, at my Fa-ther's throne, Make
Him whose truth and faith-ful - ness En -
from Mount Pis-gah's loft - y height, I

all my wants and wish - es known.
gage the wait - ing soul to bless.
view my home, and take my flight.
In sea - sons of dis-tress and grief, My soul has
And since He bids me seek His face, Be-lieve His
This robe of flesh I'll drop, and rise To seize the
oft - en found re - lief, And oft es - caped the
word and trust His grace, I'll cast on Him my
ev - er - last-ing prize; And shout, while pass - ing
tempt-er's snare, By thy re-turn sweet hour of pray'r.
ev - 'ry care, And wait for thee, sweet hour of pray'r.
thro' the air, Fare-well, fare-well, sweet hour of pray'r.

WHAT SHALL I PRAY FOR TODAY?

Albert *and* James Morehead
Tilly Foster, P.M.

Here is a question with which one may search himself in a materialistic world. Shall we pray, as St. Augustine admits that he did, "God make me pure . . . but not yet"; or, as the Reverend Frank H. Ferris suggests, shall we "run the calculated risks of prayer: of seeing ourselves as we are; of having our prayers answered"? The message here is that one should pray for strength and faith but not for the fulfilment of desire selfishly felt.

1. What shall I pray for to - day?
2. How shall I pray when I pray,
3. What shall I say when I pray,
Pray for a heart that is true;
Sunk - en in sin and in shame?
Say to our Fath - er a - bove?
True to Him Who is free from
Mark His word that your pray'r is
"Lord Di - vine, let the praise be

sin, Who will share your pray'r with you;
heard, if you ask in Je - sus' name;
Thine, Who art truth, and hope, and love;
Pray to be strong in your faith; His is the
Fall on your knees when you pray, Bow to His
Thine be the glo - ri - ous Name, Name re -
grace to for - give, Know that He is your
Heav - en - ly might, Find sal - va - tion in
vered and a - dored, Hear this pray'r, our
Sav - iour, Who died that you might live.
Je - sus, The Way, the Life, the Light.
Fath - er, Thru Je - sus Christ, our Lord."

WHAT A FRIEND WE HAVE IN JESUS

JOSEPH SCRIVEN | CHARLES C. CONVERSE

Erie, 8.7.8.7.D

THE DAY before Joseph Scriven was to have been married, his young bride-to-be was tragically drowned. He never recovered from the shock. Migrating to America from his native Ireland, he devoted the rest of his life to the poor, doing odd jobs and accepting only enough money for his simple needs. Ira D. Sankey, in *My Life and Sacred Songs,* says that a neighbor discovered the poem while visiting Scriven during his illness, and was told that "The Lord and I did it between us."

1. What a Friend we have in Je - sus,
2. Have we tri - als and temp - ta - tions?
3. Are we weak and heav - y - la - den,
All our sins and griefs to bear!
Is there trou - ble an - y - where?
Cum-bered with a load of care?
What a priv - i - lege to car - ry
We should nev - er be dis - cour - aged,
Pre - cious Sav - ior, still our ref - uge,

Ev - 'ry - thing to God in prayer!
Take it to the Lord in prayer.
Take it to the Lord in prayer.
Oh what peace we oft - en for - feit,
Can we find a friend so faith - ful
Do thy friends de-spise, for - sake thee?
Oh what need-less pain we bear, All be-cause we do not
Who will all our sor-rows share? Je-sus knows our ev-'ry
Take it to the Lord in prayer; In His arms He'll take and
car - ry Ev - 'ry-thing to God in prayer!
weak-ness, Take it to the Lord in prayer.
shield thee, Thou wilt find a sol-ace there.

ABIDE WITH ME

HENRY F. LYTE — WILLIAM H. MONK

Eventide, four 10s

THERE ARE many conflicting stories as to both words and music of this beautiful hymn, and none can be verified. Lyte died soon after the hymn was written, in 1847, and it was not until 1861 that the music was composed. The hymn is in all hymnbooks. It is a moving and tender poem that compares with anything in the English language. Its metaphorical suggestions can be found in LUKE 24:29, "Abide with us, for it is toward evening."

1. A - bide with me! Fast
2. Swift to its close ebbs
3. I need Thy pre - sence
4. Hold Thou Thy cross be -
falls the e - ven - tide,
out life's lit - tle day,
ev - 'ry pass - ing hour,
fore my clos - ing eyes;
The dark - ness deep - ens,
Earth's joys grow dim, its
What but Thy grace can
Shine thro' the gloom and

Lord, with me a - bide!
glo - ries pass a - way;
foil the tempt - er's pow'r?
point me to the skies;
When oth - er help - ers
Change and de - cay in
Who, like Thy - self, my
Heav'n's morn - ing breaks and
fail, and com - forts flee, Help of the
all a - round I see; O Thou, who
guide and stay can be? Thro' cloud and
earth's vain shad - ows flee! In life, in
help - less, oh! a - bide with me!
chang - est not, a - bide with me!
sun - shine, oh, a - bide with me!
death, O Lord, a - bide with me!

PASS ME NOT, O GENTLE SAVIOUR

Fanny J. Crosby | **William Howard Doane**

***Pass Me Not,* 8s, 5s.**

Fanny Jane Crosby was blind from the sixth week of her life, due to a physician's mistake. As a young woman she taught at the New York School for the Blind, where the secretary was Grover Cleveland. It was he who took down some of her first verses, and they became lifelong friends. The number of hymns written by Miss Crosby is estimated at 8,000. More than 500 are known to have been published, and many were signed Fanny C. Van Alstyne after she married Alexander Van Alstyne, a blind musician, when she was 38. As many as 60 of her hymns have been included in a single hymnal.

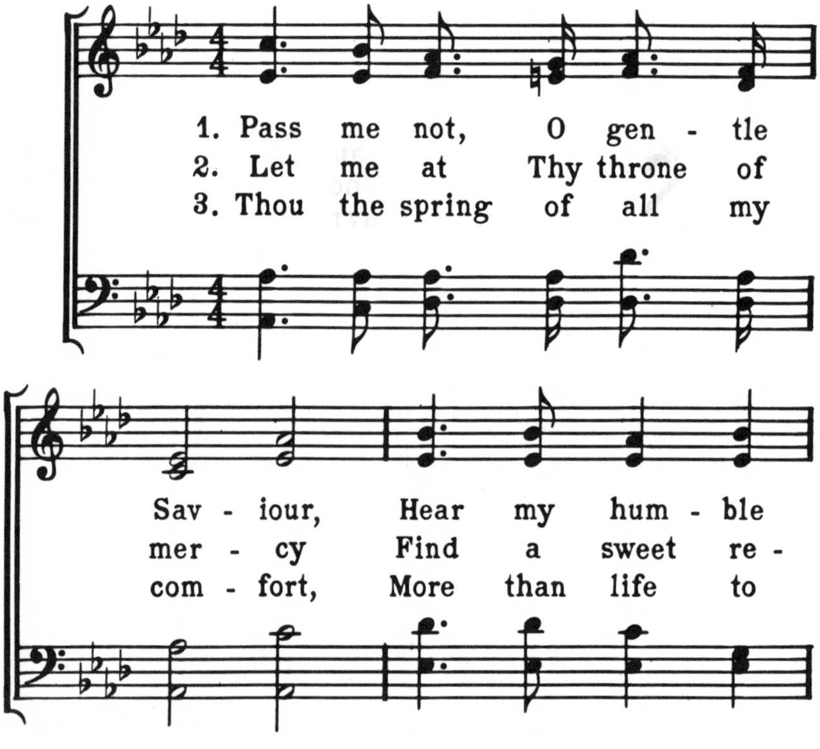

1. Pass me not, O gen - tle
2. Let me at Thy throne of
3. Thou the spring of all my
Sav - iour, Hear my hum - ble
mer - cy Find a sweet re -
com - fort, More than life to
cry; While on oth - ers Thou art
lief; Kneel - ing there in deep con -
me, Whom have I on earth be -

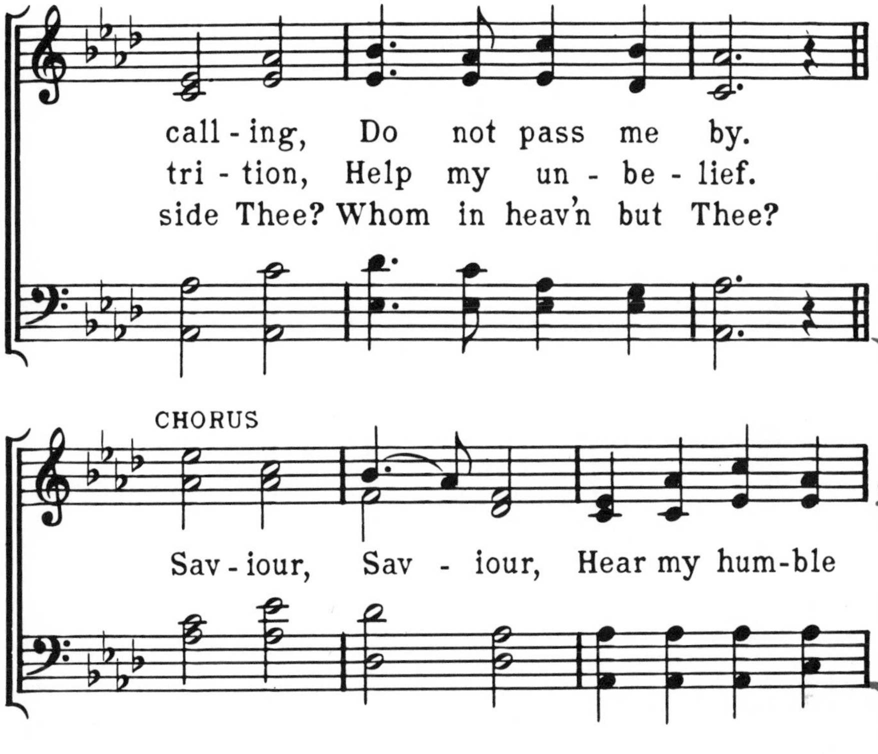
call - ing, Do not pass me by.
tri - tion, Help my un - be - lief.
side Thee? Whom in heav'n but Thee?
CHORUS
Sav - iour, Sav - iour, Hear my hum-ble
cry; While on oth - ers Thou art
call - ing, Do not pass me by.

JUST AS I AM

CHARLOTTE ELLIOT — WILLIAM B. BRADBURY

Woodworth, L.M.

AN INVALID for fifty years, Charlotte Elliot was inspired by the words, "Him that cometh to me I will in no wise cast out" (JOHN 6:37), to write a hymn dedicated to the handicapped and the unwanted. Her brother, a clergyman, was organizing a bazaar for the purpose of establishing a school. She wrote and published a hymn, hoping that the money she made would assist in the project. Needless to say, her offering brought in more money than a hundred bazaars.

1. Just as I am, with - out one plea, But
2. Just as I am, though tossed a-bout With
3. Just as I am, Thou wilt re-ceive, Wilt
that Thy blood was shed for me, And that Thou bidd'st me
many a con-flict, many a doubt, Fight-ings and fears with-
wel-come, par-don, cleanse, re-lieve, Be-cause Thy prom-ise
come to Thee, O Lamb of God, I come! I come!
in, with-out, O Lamb of God, I come! I come!
I be-lieve, O Lamb of God, I come! I come!

JESUS CALLS US

MRS. CECIL F. ALEXANDER — WILLIAM H. JUDE

Galilee, 8.7.8.7.

THIS HYMN is sung on St. Andrew's Day, November 30. It is also the adopted hymn of the St. Andrew Society of the United States and Canada. Strangely, the second stanza, which gave the poem its direct scriptural foundation, is no longer sung; the editors have been unable to ascertain the reason.

1. Je-sus calls us; o'er the tu-mult Of our
2. Je-sus calls us from the wor-ship Of the
3. Je-sus calls us: by Thy mer-cies, Sav-iour,
life's wild, rest-less sea, Day by day His sweet voice
vain world's gold-en store, From each i - dol that would
may we hear Thy call, Give our hearts to Thy o -
sound-eth, Say - ing, "Chris-tian, fol-low Me."
keep us, Say - ing, "Chris-tian, love Me more."
be-dience, Serve and love Thee best of all.

SAVIOUR, LIKE A SHEPHERD LEAD US

Ascribed to
DOROTHY A. THRUPP
From Hymns for the Young, 1836 — WILLIAM B. BRADBURY
Bradbury, 8s, 7s.

THOUGH IT IS probable that Miss Thrupp wrote this hymn, many authorities believe Henry Francis Lyte (of *Abide With Me*) is the author. It has been said that the text shows a preoccupation with the phrases of the Bible, the mark of the Evangelical. This would not aptly apply either to Lyte or Miss Thrupp. Bradbury wrote the tune expressly for his publication *Oriola,* a Sunday-school songbook.

1. Sav-iour, like a shep-herd lead_ us,
2. We are Thine; do Thou be - friend_us,
3. Ear-ly let us seek Thy fa - vor;
Much we need Thy ten-der care;
Be the Guar - dian of our way;
Ear - ly let us do Thy will;
In Thy pleas - ant pas-tures feed_ us,
Keep Thy flock, from sin de - fend_ us,
Bless - ed Lord and on - ly Sav - iour,

For our use Thy folds pre - pare:
Seek us when we go a - stray:
With Thy love our bos - oms fill:
Bless-ed Je-sus, Bless-ed Je-sus, Thou hast
Bless-ed Je-sus, Bless-ed Je-sus, Hear Thy
Bless-ed Je-sus, Bless-ed Je-sus, Thou hast
bought us, Thine we are; Bless-ed Je-sus, Bless-ed
chil-dren when they pray; Bless-ed Je-sus, Bless-ed
loved us, love us still; Bless-ed Je-sus, Bless-ed
Je-sus, Thou hast bought us, Thine we are.
Je-sus, Hear Thy chil - dren when they pray.
Je-sus, Thou hast loved us, love us still.

JESUS, LOVER OF MY SOUL

CHARLES WESLEY SIMEON B. MARSH

Martyn, eight 7s.

HENRY WARD BEECHER said, "I would rather have written that hynm of Wesley's than have the fame of all the kings that ever sat on earth." This, in a prodigious total of 6,500 hymns, is the most famous of all that Wesley wrote. It has been translated into all languages and appears in virtually every hymnbook. The tune, though criticized by musicians for the monotony of its inner voices, is nevertheless unfailing in its appeal, due to the beauty and simplicity of the melody and its easy range of a sixth.

1. Je - sus, Lov - er of my soul,
2. Oth - er ref - uge have I none;
3. Plen-teous grace with Thee is found,
Let me to Thy bo-som fly, While the near-er
Hangs my help - less soul on Thee; Leave, ah! leave me
Grace to cleanse from ev-'ry sin; Let the heal-ing
wa - ters roll, While the tem-pest still is high!
not a-lone, Still sup-port and com-fort me!
streams a-bound, Make and keep me pure with - in.

Hide me, O my Sav - iour, hide,
All my trust on Thee is stayed;
Thou of life the foun - tain art;
Till the storm of life is past;
All my help from Thee I bring;
Free - ly let me take of Thee;
Safe in - to the ha - ven guide,
Cov - er my de - fense - less head
Spring Thou up with - in my heart,
Oh receive my soul at last!
With the shad - ow of Thy wing.
Rise to all e - ter - ni - ty.

ALL HAIL THE POWER OF JESUS' NAME

Edward Perronet **Oliver Holden**

Coronation, C.M.

The Reverend Mr. Perronet disagreed with the Wesley brothers, for whom he had preached and written hymns. John Wesley officially banned Perronet's hymns from the hymnal. But Perronet continued to write anonymously, and one day Oliver Holden, the American carpenter-composer, found these verses in an English magazine. He found that they fitted his new tune perfectly, and the great hymn was born that was to become a universal favorite, especially among the Methodists!

1. All hail the pow'r of
2. Let ev - 'ry kin - dred,
3. Oh, that with yon - der
Je - sus' name! Let an-gels pros - trate
ev - 'ry tribe, On this ter - res - trial
sa-cred throng We at His feet may
fall; Bring forth the roy - al
ball, To Him all maj - es -
fall; We'll join the ev - er -

di - a - dem, And crown Him
ty— as - cribe, And crown Him
last - ing song, And crown Him
Lord of— all; Bring forth the roy - al
Lord of— all; To Him all maj - es -
Lord of— all; We'll join the ev - er -
di - a - dem, And crown Him Lord— of all.
ty as-cribe, And crown Him Lord— of all.
last-ing song, And crown Him Lord— of all.

STAND UP! STAND UP FOR JESUS

George Duffield | George J. Webb

Webb, 7.6.7.6.D.

George Duffield's friend, the Reverend Dudley Tyng, caught an arm in a corn-shelling machine, and it was torn off. A few days later, he lay dying in awful pain. It was during the great revival of 1858, in Philadelphia, and several ministers were at his bedside. When one of them asked Tyng if he wished to send a message to his parishioners, he said, "Tell them, 'Let us all stand up for Jesus'." The next Sunday Mr. Duffield preached from the text of Ephesians 6:14, after which was sung the hymn inspired by Tyng's dying words.

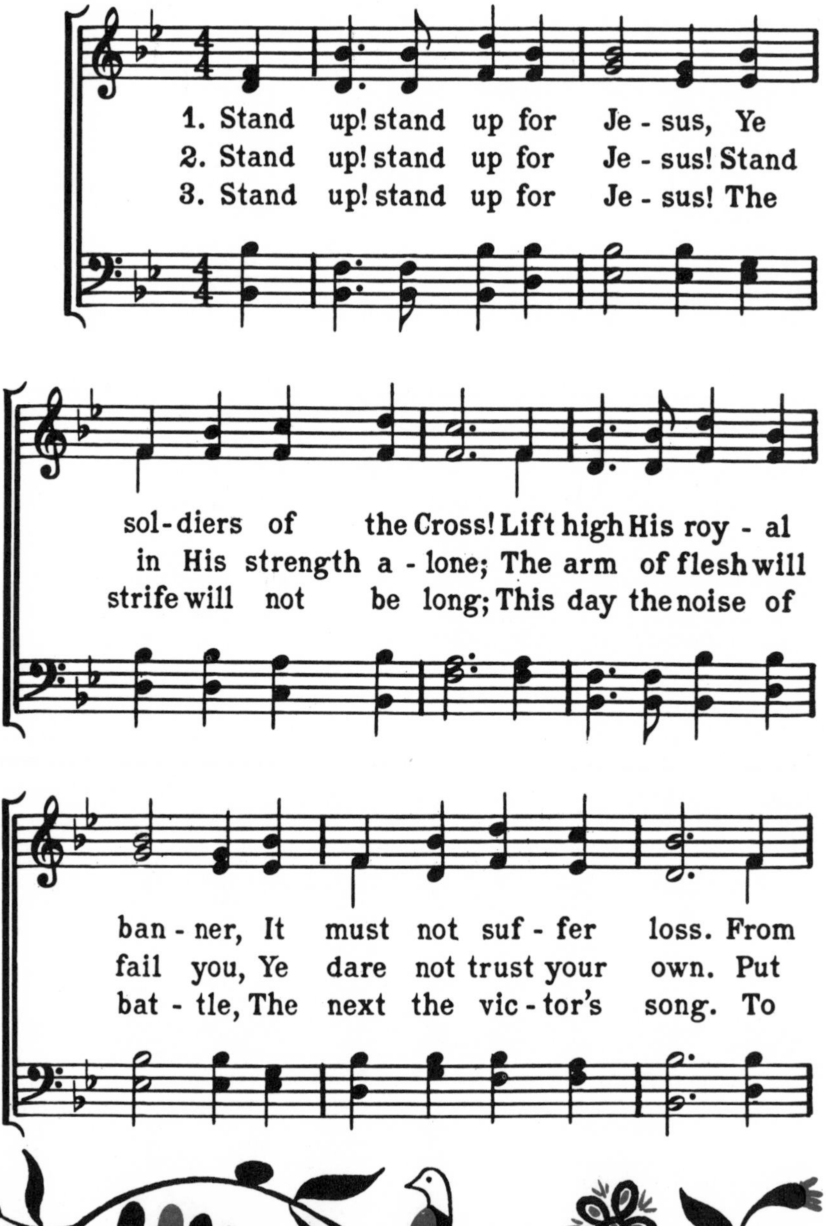

1. Stand up! stand up for Je - sus, Ye
2. Stand up! stand up for Je - sus! Stand
3. Stand up! stand up for Je - sus! The
sol - diers of the Cross! Lift high His roy - al
in His strength a - lone; The arm of flesh will
strife will not be long; This day the noise of
ban - ner, It must not suf - fer loss. From
fail you, Ye dare not trust your own. Put
bat - tle, The next the vic - tor's song. To

vic - t'ry un - to vic - t'ry His
on the Gos - pel ar - mor, Each
him that o - ver - com - eth A
ar - my shall He lead Till ev - 'ry foe is
piece put on with pray'r; Where du - ty calls or
crown of life shall be; He with the King of
van-quished And Christ is Lord in - deed.
dan - ger, Be nev - er want - ing there.
Glo - ry Shall reign e - ter - nal - ly.

FAIREST LORD JESUS

COMPOSER UNKNOWN

ANONYMOUS (c. 1677) *Arranged by* R. S. WILLIS

Crusaders' Hymn

5.6.8.5.5.8

SINCE THIS hymn did not appear until the 17th century, it is hard to say why it is called "the crusaders' hymn." It is most probably of Silesian peasant origin, dealing simply and beautifully with the effects of nature and their symbolism in religion. John Julian states that it was "taken down from oral recitation in the district of Glaz." Glaz is not far from Prague, the home of John Hus. The flight of the Hussites from Bohemia may have provided an association with the Crusades.

1. Fair - est Lord Je - sus, Rul - er of all
2. Fair are the mead - ows, Fair - er still the
3. Fair is the sun - shine, Fair - er still the
na - ture, O Thou of God and
wood - lands, Robed in the bloom - ing
moon - light, And all the twink - ling,
man the Son, Thee will I
garb of spring; Je - sus is
star - ry host; Je - sus shines

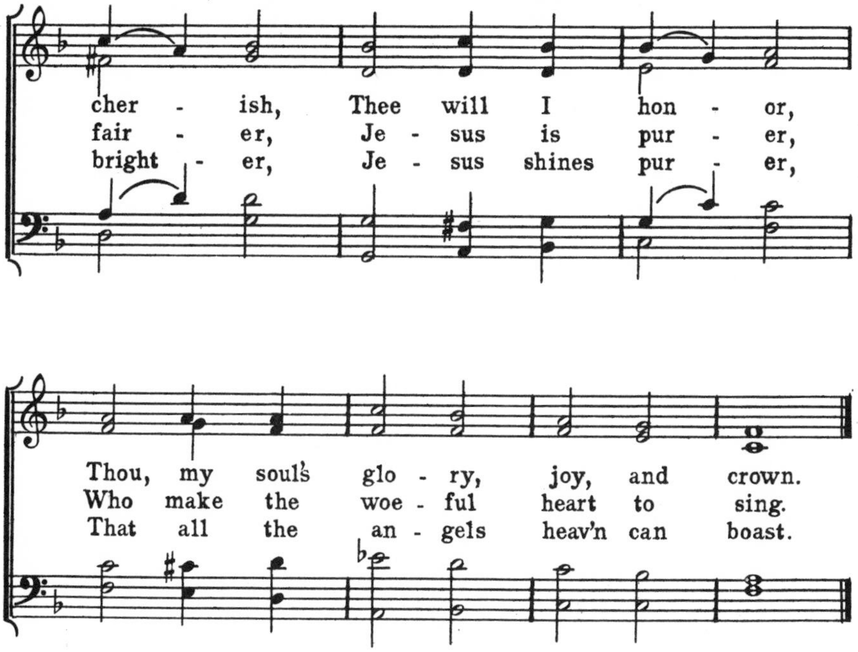
cher - ish, Thee will I hon - or,
fair - er, Je - sus is pur - er,
bright - er, Je - sus shines pur - er,
Thou, my soul's glo - ry, joy, and crown.
Who make the woe - ful heart to sing.
That all the an - gels heav'n can boast.

Beautiful Saviour

THIS TRANSLATION by J. A. Seiss of the same German original *(schönster Herr Jesu)* as FAIREST LORD JESUS was voted the second-favorite hymn of Lutherans in 1965 (behind *Holy, holy, holy!*). The Lutheran Hymnal traces the tune to a Silesian folk song. The Seiss translation is:

1. Beautiful Saviour,
King of Creation,
Son of God and Son of Man!
Truly I'd love Thee,
Truly I'd serve Thee,
Light of my soul, my joy,
my crown.

2. Fair are the meadows,
Fair are the woodlands,
Robed in the flow'rs of blooming
spring;
Jesus is fairer,
Jesus is purer,
He makes our sorrowing spirit
sing.

3. Fair is the sunshine,
Fair is the moonlight,
Bright the sparkling stars on
high;
Jesus shines brighter,
Jesus shines purer
Than all the angels in the sky.

4. Beautiful Saviour,
Lord of the nations,
Son of God and Son of Man!
Glory and honour,
Praise, adoration,
Now and for evermore be Thine!

LOVE DIVINE

CHARLES WESLEY JOHN ZUNDEL

Beecher, 8.7.8.7.D.

HERE is the personalized God, pervading all human affairs: "He that loveth not knoweth not God; for God is Love" (1 JOHN 4:8). Wesley wrote his hymn during days when England was suffering a moral and religious recession. John Zundel was organist at Plymouth Church, Brooklyn, during the pastorate of Henry Ward Beecher. His musical standard was so high that it was not uncommon to hear: "We are going to hear Beecher and Zundel."

1. Love Di-vine, all love ex-cell-ing,
2. Breathe, O breathe Thy lov-ing Spir-it
3. Fin-ish, then, Thy new cre-a-tion;
Joy of heav'n, to earth come down; Fix in us Thy
In-to ev-'ry troub-led breast; Let us all in
Pure and spot-less let us be: Let us see Thy
hum-ble dwell-ing, All Thy faith-ful mer-cies crown:
Thee in-her-it, Let us find the prom-ised rest;
great sal-va-tion Per-fect-ly re-stored in Thee;

Je - sus, Thou art all com - pas-sion,
Take a - way the love of sin-ning;
Chang'd from glo - ry in - to glo - ry
Pure, un-bound-ed love Thou art; Vis-it us with
Al-pha and O - me - ga be; End of faith, as
Till in heav'n we take our place, Till we cast our
Thy sal-va-tion, En-ter ev - 'ry trem-bling heart.
its be-gin-ing, Set our hearts at lib - er - ty.
crowns be-fore Thee, Lost in won - der, love, and praise.

MY FAITH LOOKS UP TO THEE

RAY PALMER LOWELL MASON

Olivet, 6.6.4.6.6.6.4.

THE STORY is best told in the author's own words: "A year or two after the hymn was written . . . Dr. Mason met the author in the street in Boston, and asked him to furnish some hymns for a Hymn and Tune Book, which . . . he was about to publish . . . A copy was made and given to him, which, without much notice, he put into his pocket . . . Two or three days later we met again in the street, when, scarcely waiting to salute the writer, he earnestly exclaimed: 'Mr. Palmer, you may live many years and do many things, but I think you will be best known to posterity as the author of MY FAITH LOOKS UP TO THEE'."

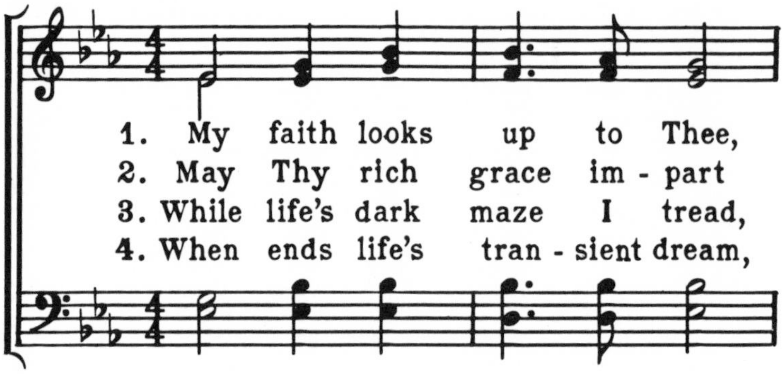
1. My faith looks up to Thee,
2. May Thy rich grace im - part
3. While life's dark maze I tread,
4. When ends life's tran - sient dream,

Thou Lamb of Cal - va - ry,
Strength to my faint - ing heart,
And griefs a - round me spread,
When death's cold, sul - len stream

Sav - iour di - vine! Now hear me
My zeal in - spire; As Thou hast
Be Thou my guide; Bid dark-ness
Shall o'er me roll; Blest Sav - iour,

while I pray, Take all my
died for me, Oh may my
turn to day, Wipe sor - row's
then, in love, Fear and dis -
guilt a - way, Oh let me
love to Thee Pure, warm and
tears a - way, Nor let me
trust re - move; Oh bear me
from this day Be whol - ly Thine!
change-less be, A liv - ing fire!
ev - er stray From Thee a - side.
safe a - bove, A ran - somed soul!

O LOVE THAT WILT NOT LET ME GO

GEORGE MATHESON | ALBERT L. PEACE

St. Margaret, 8.8.8.8.6.

THIS HYMN, of Scottish origin, combines the elements of praise with the language of lyric poetry. The author wrote: "This came like a dayspring from on high. I have never been able to gain once more the same fervor in verse." Matheson was at the time going blind, of which he was well aware. The second stanza points out this distressing fact. The music by the organist Albert Peace is a perfect complement to the poem. Originally written as a gospel song, this hymn has found favor among the strictest purists, and is included in almost all church hymnals.

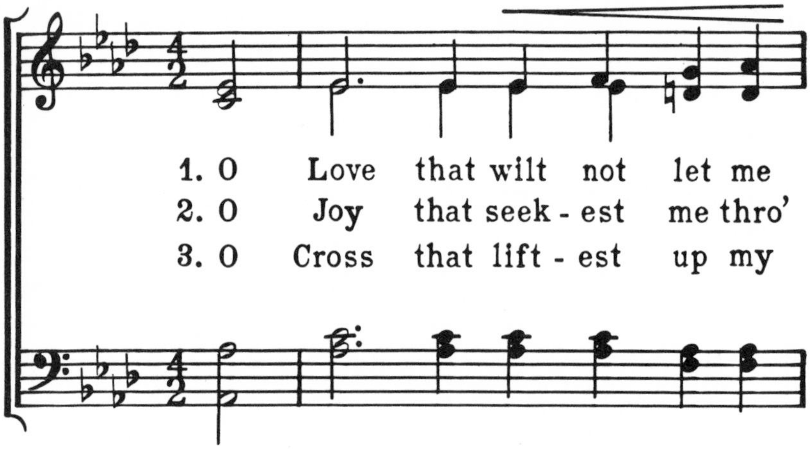
1. O Love that wilt not let me
2. O Joy that seek - est me thro'
3. O Cross that lift - est up my

go,— I rest my wea - ry soul in
pain,- I can - not close my heart to
head, I dare not ask to fly from

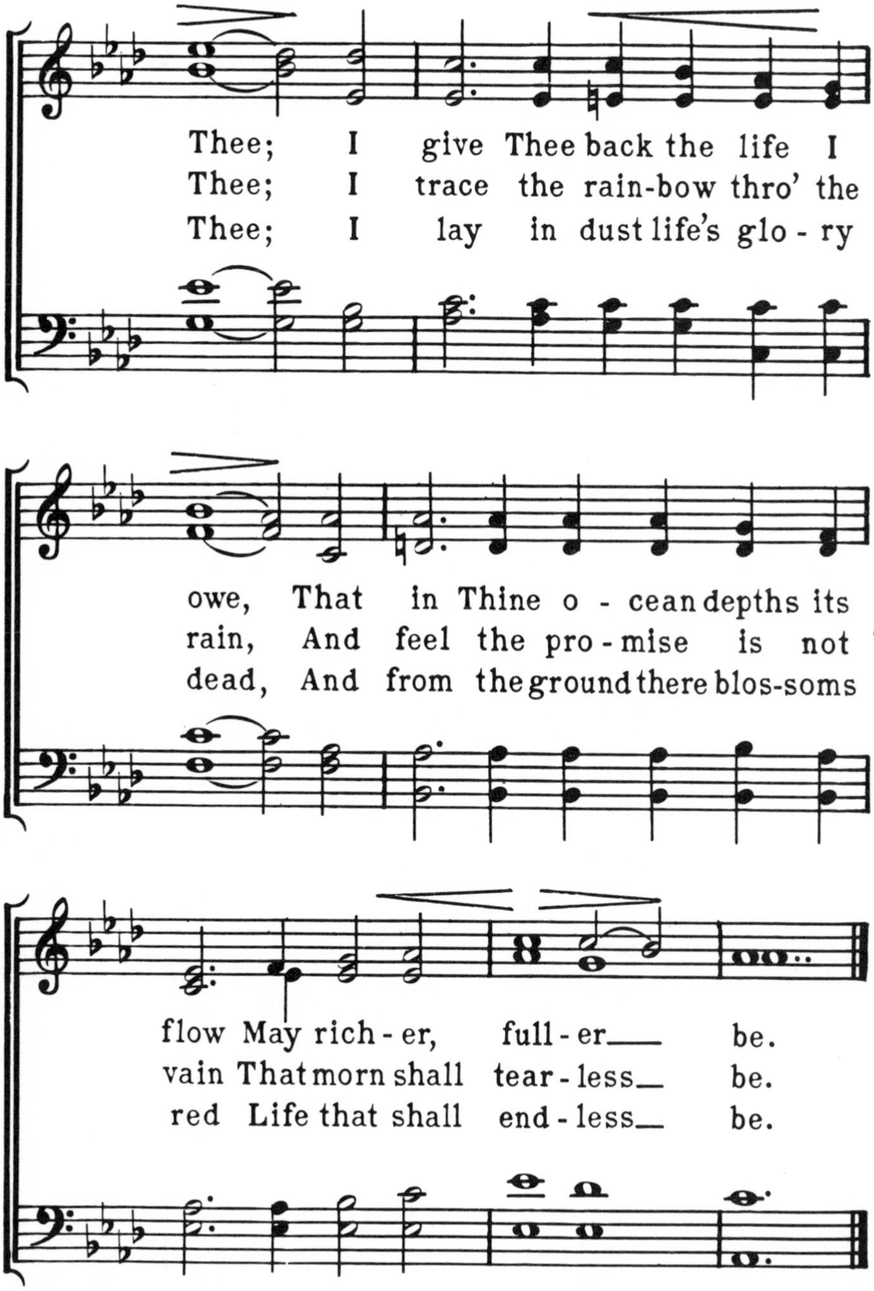
Thee; I give Thee back the life I
Thee; I trace the rain-bow thro' the
Thee; I lay in dust life's glo - ry
owe, That in Thine o - cean depths its
rain, And feel the pro - mise is not
dead, And from the ground there blos-soms
flow May rich - er, full - er___ be.
vain That morn shall tear - less___ be.
red Life that shall end - less___ be.

WHEN I SURVEY THE WONDROUS CROSS

Isaac Watts

Arranged by Lowell Mason
from the 1st Gregorian Tone

Hamburg, L.M.

Matthew Arnold considered this hymn the greatest in the English language. It was sung in church during the service he attended on the last Sunday of his life. On his deathbed he was heard to repeat the lines of the third stanza. George Eliot, evidently drawing upon an actual event, incorporates it in the deathbed scene of old Dinah Morris, in which she recites the hymn.

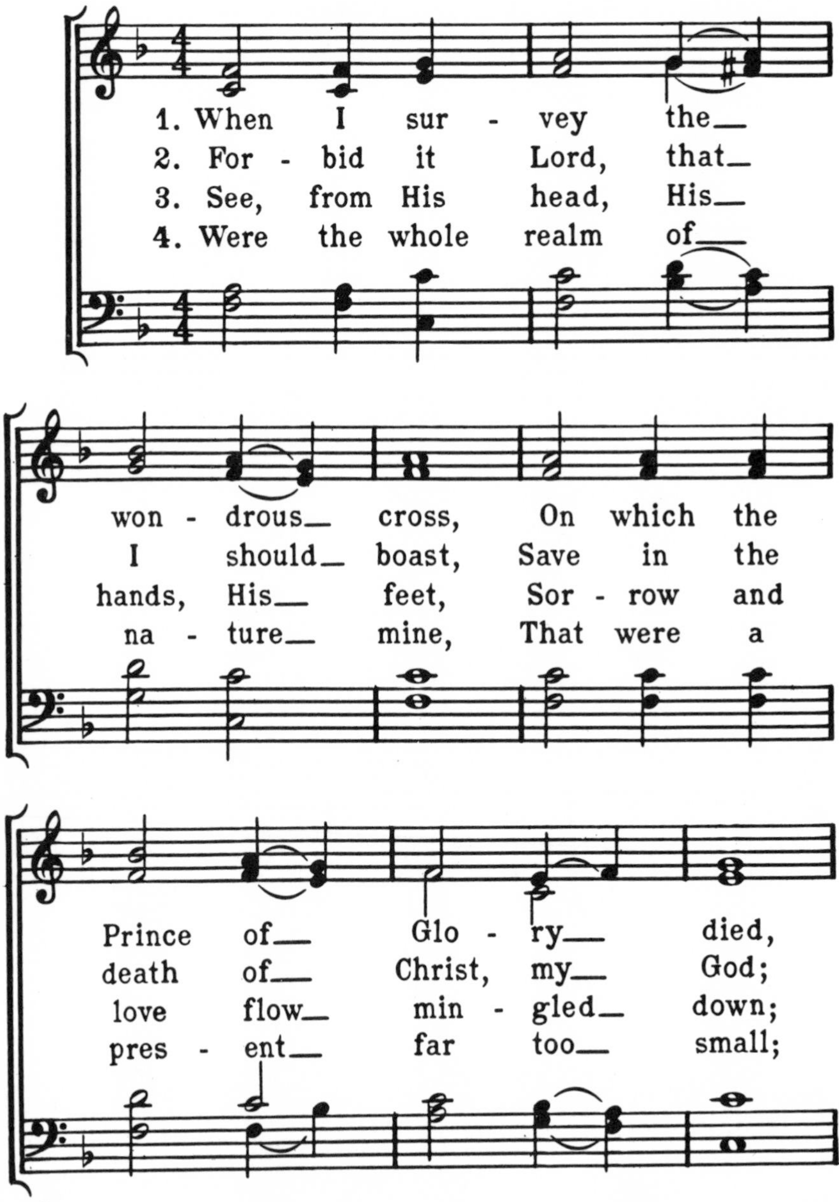
1. When I sur - vey the won - drous cross, On which the Prince of Glo - ry died,
2. For - bid it Lord, that I should boast, Save in the death of Christ, my God;
3. See, from His head, His hands, His feet, Sor - row and love flow min - gled down;
4. Were the whole realm of na - ture mine, That were a pres - ent far too small;

My rich - est gain I
All the vain things that
Did e'er such love and
Love so a - maz - ing,
count but loss, And pour con -
charm me most, I sac - ri -
sor - row meet, Or thorns com -
so di - vine, De - mands my
tempt on all my pride.
fice them to His blood.
pose so rich a crown?
soul, my life, my all.

WHERE CROSS THE CROWDED WAYS OF LIFE

Frank Mason North — **William Gardiner's** *Sacred Melodies*

Germany, L.M.

Doctor North based his hymn on Matthew 22:9, "Go ye therefore into the highways," which is more accurately, as in the Revised Version, ". . . . the parting of the highways." It is a missionary hymn, dedicated to the problem of slum dwellers in large cities, and to the social aspect of religion. In *Time* magazine, Dec. 30, 1946, Marian Anderson said: ". . . Christianity may conceivably become the living faith of a dying civilization for the second time."

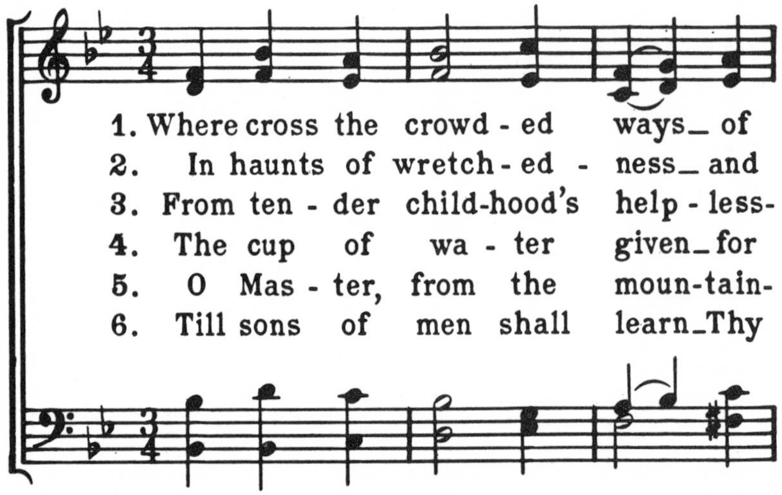
1. Where cross the crowd - ed ways_ of
2. In haunts of wretch - ed - ness_ and
3. From ten - der child-hood's help - less-
4. The cup of wa - ter given_ for
5. O Mas - ter, from the moun-tain-
6. Till sons of men shall learn_Thy

life, Where sound the cries of
need, On shad - owed thresh - olds
ness, From wo - man's grief, man's
Thee Still holds the fresh - ness
side, Make haste to heal these
love, And fol - low where Thy

race and clan, A - bove the
dark with fears, From paths where
bur - dened toil, From fam - ished
of Thy grace; Yet long these
hearts of pain; A - mong these
feet have trod; Till glo - rious
noise of self - ish strife, We
hide the lures of greed, We
souls, from sor - row's stress, Thy
mul - ti - tudes to see The
rest - less throngs a - bide, O
from Thy heaven a - bove, Shall
hear Thy voice, O Son of man.
catch the vi - sion of Thy tears.
heart has nev - er known re - coil.
sweet com - pas - sion of Thy face.
tread the cit - y's streets a - gain.
come the Cit - y of our God.

ONWARD, CHRISTIAN SOLDIERS

SABINE BARING-GOULD | ARTHUR SULLIVAN

St. Gertrude, 6.5.6.5.D.

IT HAS BEEN SAID that Baring-Gould has more titles listed in the British Museum catalog than any of his contemporaries. He wrote a novel a year for more than 50 years. ONWARD, CHRISTIAN SOLDIERS was written in one night, in preparation for a children's parade. The original title was *Hymn for Procession with Cross and Banners*, and the text is figurative (following EPHESIANS 6:12, "we wrestle not against flesh and blood"). The musical setting by Sir Arthur Sullivan, although not the original one, has become universally accepted.

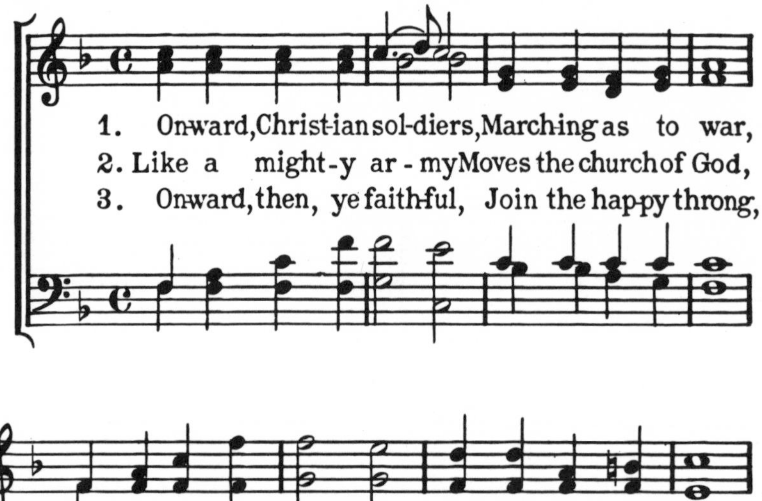
1. Onward, Christ-ian sol-diers, Marching as to war,
2. Like a might-y ar - my Moves the church of God,
3. Onward, then, ye faith-ful, Join the hap-py throng,
With the cross of Je - sus Go - ing on be - fore.
Broth-ers we are tread-ing Where the saints have trod.
Blend with ours your voi - ces in the tri - umph song.
Christ, the roy-al Mas - ter, leads a-gainst the foe.
We are not di - vi - ded All one bod - y we.
Glo - ry, laud, and hon - or Un - to Christ the King.

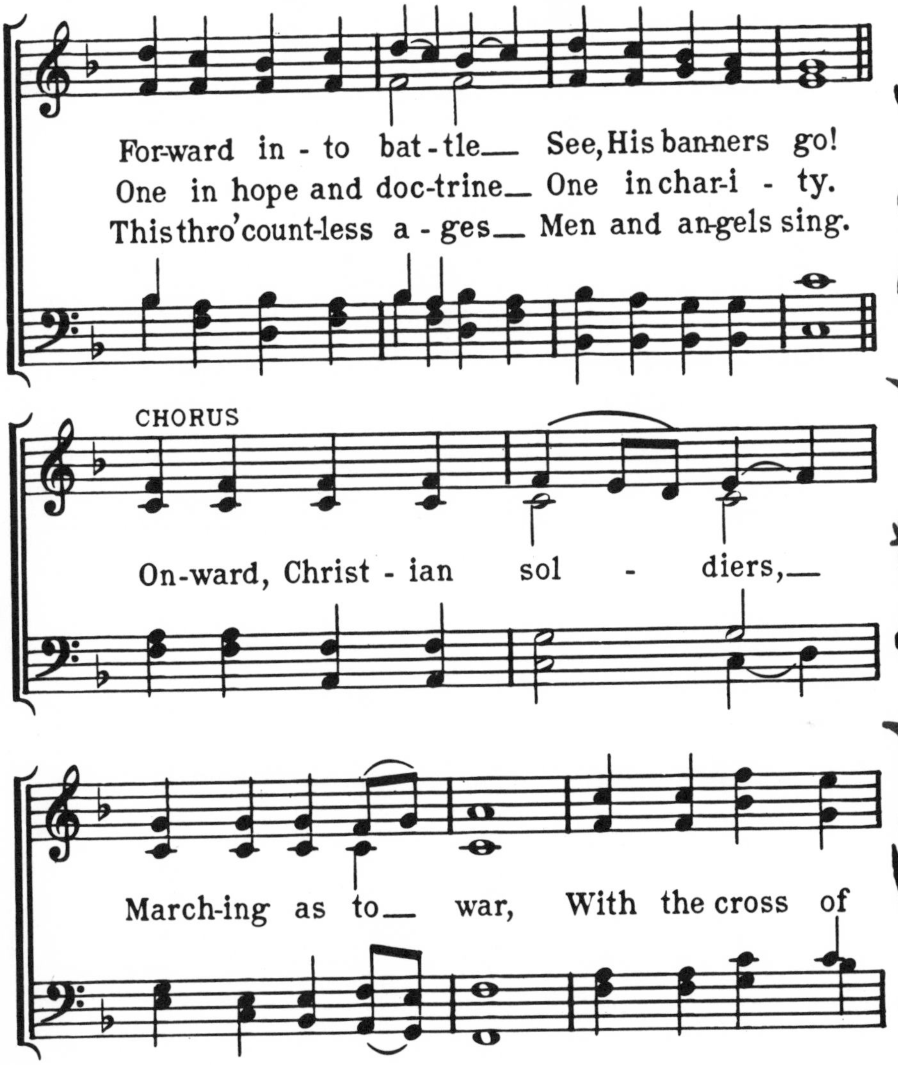
For-ward in - to bat - tle__ See, His ban-ners go!
One in hope and doc-trine__ One in char-i - ty.
This thro' count-less a - ges__ Men and an-gels sing.
CHORUS
On-ward, Christ - ian sol - diers,__
March-ing as to__ war, With the cross of
Je - sus Go - ing on be - fore.

FROM GREENLAND'S ICY MOUNTAINS

SEBASTIAN YRADIER | Missionary Hymn (Heber) | LOWELL MASON

BISHOP HEBER's *Holy, Holy, Holy* and Dr. Mason's *Nearer, My God, To Thee* may have proved more important in the catalogs of their respective authors, but the combination of their talents in this time-honored hymn has made a unique contribution. Protestant missionaries the world over have considered it their "theme song" since the 1820s. The Heber words were written in 1819, the Mason music in 1824, and by 1828 at the latest the combined effort had been internationally adopted. Dr. Mason originally christened his tune *Heber* in honor of the author, whom he never met.

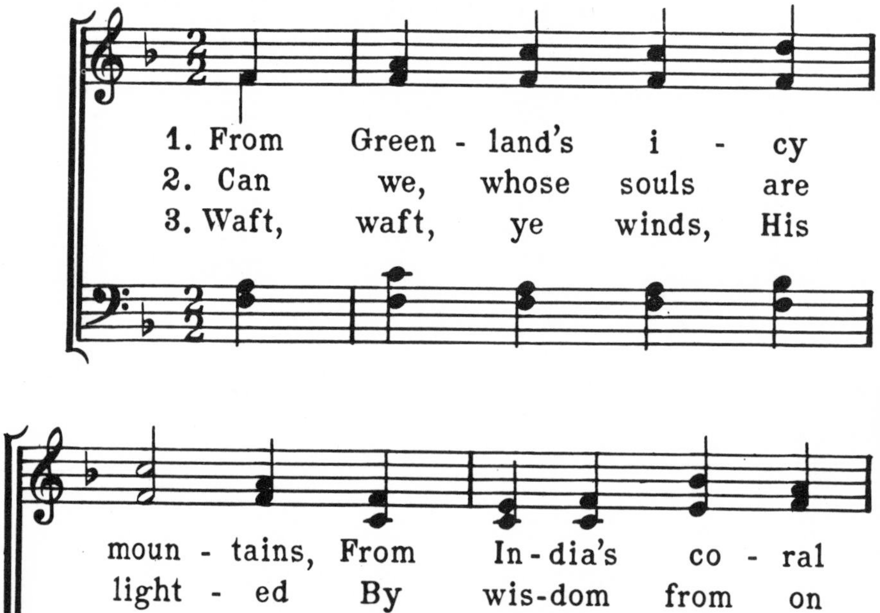
1. From Green - land's i - cy
2. Can we, whose souls are
3. Waft, waft, ye winds, His
moun - tains, From In - dia's co - ral
light - ed By wis - dom from on
sto - ry, And you, ye wa - ters,
strand, Where Af - ric's sun - ny foun - tains Roll
high, Can we to men be - night - ed The
roll, Till, like a sea of glo - ry, It

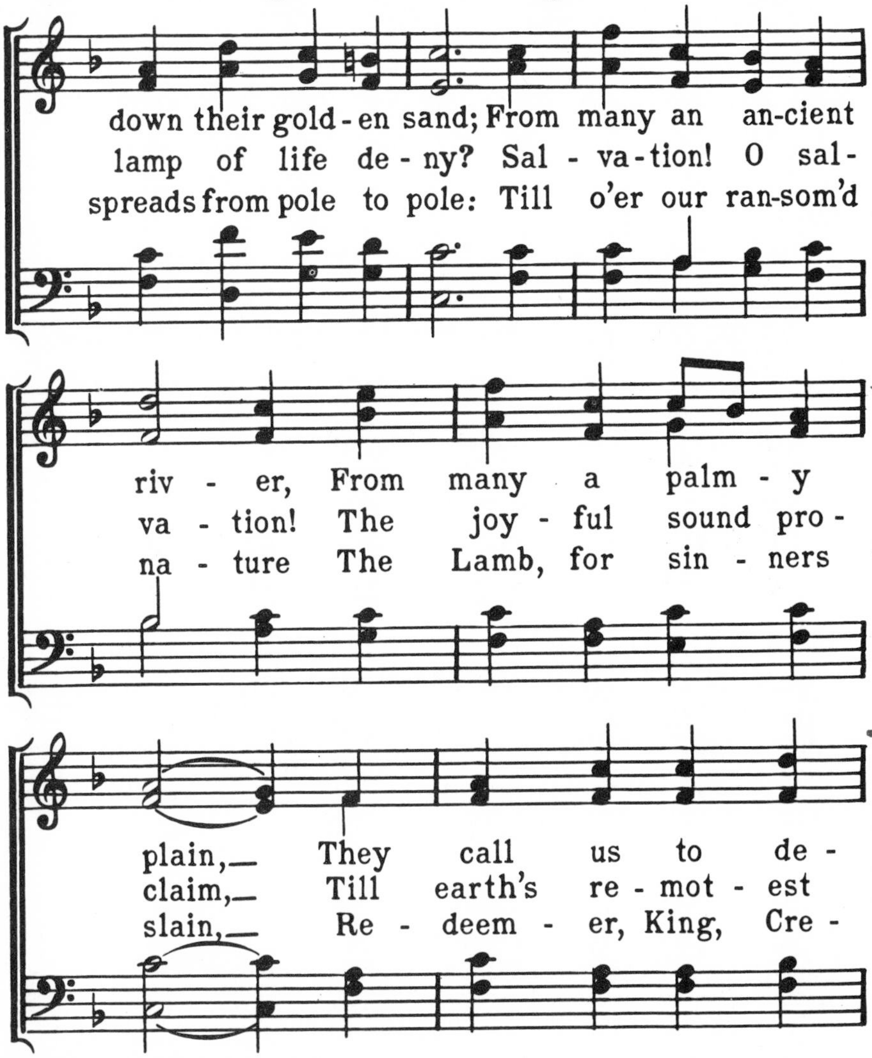
down their gold - en sand; From many an an-cient
lamp of life de - ny? Sal - va-tion! O sal-
spreads from pole to pole: Till o'er our ran-som'd
riv - er, From many a palm - y
va - tion! The joy - ful sound pro -
na - ture The Lamb, for sin - ners
plain,— They call us to de -
claim,— Till earth's re - mot - est
slain,— Re - deem - er, King, Cre -
liv - er Their land from er - ror's chain.
na - tion Has learn'd Mes - si - ah's name.
a - tor, In bliss re - turns to reign.

WONDERFUL WORDS OF LIFE

Philip P. Bliss

Words of Life,
8.6.8.6.6.6. with refrain

Like Abraham Lincoln, Philip Bliss was born in a log cabin. In his boyhood he was always starved for music. As a young man he was employed by the famous musician George F. Root, later joining the staff of D. W. Whittle, the evangelist. All the royalties ($30,000) from his book *Gospel Songs* were donated to that cause. In a railway accident at Ashtabula, Ohio, in 1876, Bliss managed to escape from the wreck but died trying to rescue his wife.

1. Sing them o - ver a - gain to me,
2. Christ, the bless - ed One, gives to all,
3. Sweet - ly ech - o the gos - pel call,
Won - der - ful words of Life;
Won - der - ful words of Life;
Won - der - ful words of Life;
Let me more of their beau - ty see,
Sin - ner, list to the lov - ing call,
Of - fer par - don and peace to all,

Won-der-ful words of Life. Words of life and
Won-der-ful words of Life. All so free-ly
Won-der-ful words of Life. Je - sus, on - ly
beau - ty, Teach me faith and du - ty:
giv - en, Woo - ing us to heav - en:
Sav - iour, Sanc - ti - fy for - ev - er:
CHORUS
Beau - ti - ful words, won-der - ful words,
won-der-ful words of Life; Beau-ti-ful words,
won-der-ful words, won-der-ful words of Life!

I WILL SING THE WONDROUS STORY

FRANCIS H. ROWLEY PETER P. BILHORN

8.7.8.7., with refrain

THIS HYMN was first published in Ira D. Sankey's *Sacred Songs and Solos*, with revisions to which Rowley later objected. The revisions still appear in most hymnals, however. The first and final stanzas here are in their original form; the second is in the altered form. Rowley wrote the hymn at the suggestion of Peter Bilhorn, a young Swiss, during his pastorate in North Adams, Mass. Later he raised money to build the Angell Memorial Hospital for animals in Boston, and became its superintendent.

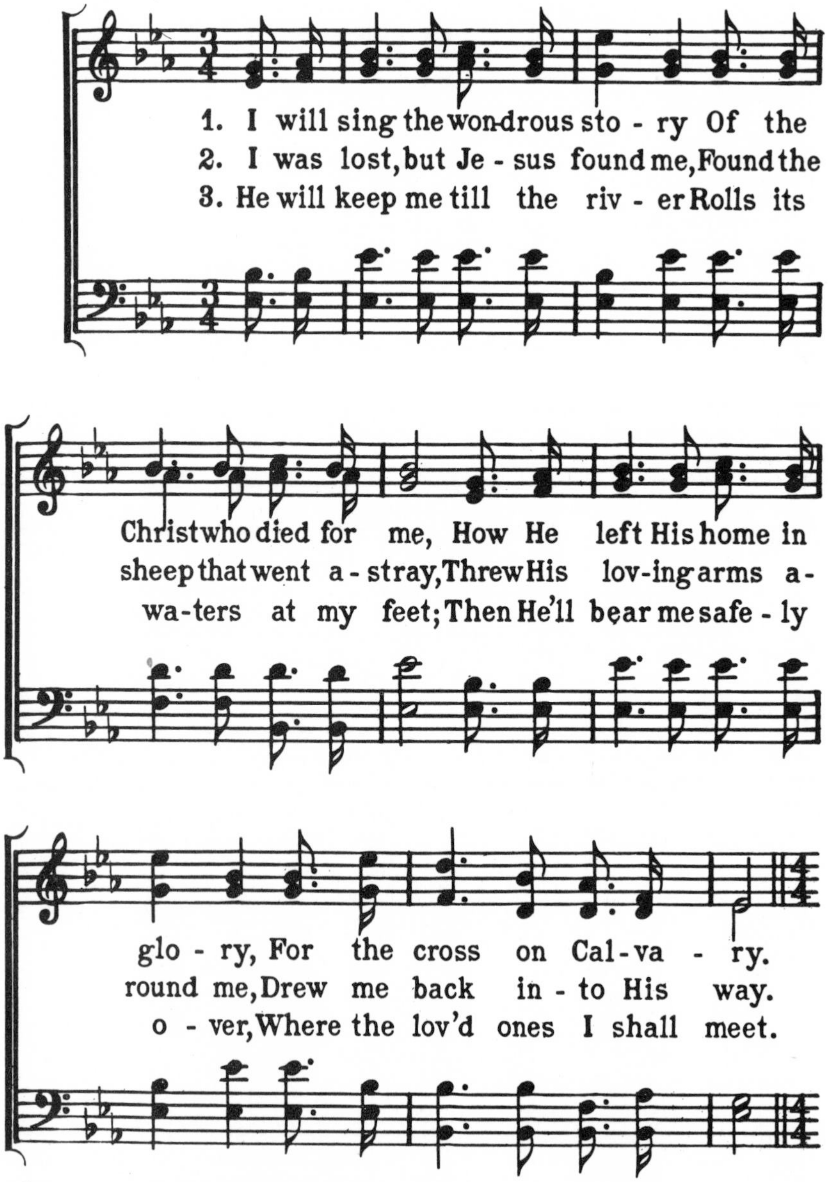
1. I will sing the wondrous sto - ry Of the
2. I was lost, but Je - sus found me, Found the
3. He will keep me till the riv - er Rolls its
Christ who died for me, How He left His home in
sheep that went a - stray, Threw His lov-ing arms a-
wa-ters at my feet; Then He'll bear me safe - ly
glo - ry, For the cross on Cal - va - ry.
round me, Drew me back in - to His way.
o - ver, Where the lov'd ones I shall meet.

CHORUS
Yes, I'll sing the won-drous
Yes, I'll sing
sto - ry Of the Christ who died for
the won-drous sto-ry Of the Christ
me, Sing it
who died for me,
with the Saints in glo - ry, Gath-er'd
Sing it with the Saints in glo-ry
by the crys-tal sea.
Gath-er'd by the crys-tal sea, the crys-tal sea.

I LOVE TO TELL THE STORY

KATHERINE HANKEY — WILLIAM G. FISCHER

Brocton,
7s, 6s, with refrain

THIS HYMN was part of a long poem about the life of Jesus. Miss Hankey was a successful writer on religious subjects and a member of the Clapham sect, an evangelistic order. The tune, written by William Fischer, became a favorite of the Moody and Sankey revival meetings, and the composer once led a thousand-voice choir during a meeting in Philadelphia. He was a prolific composer of gospel hymns.

1. I love to tell the sto - ry Of
2. I love to tell the sto - ry, More
3. I love to tell the sto - ry, For
un-seen things a - bove, Of Je - sus and His
won-der-ful_ it seems, Than all the gold-en
those who know it best. Seem hun-ger-ing and
Glo - ry, Of_ Je - sus and His love! I
fan - cies, Of_ all our gold-en dreams, I
thirst-ing To_ hear it like the rest; And

love to tell the sto-ry, Be-cause I know it's true: It
love to tell the sto-ry, It did so much for me And
when in scenes of glo-ry, I sing the new, new song 'Twill
sat-is-fies my long-ings, As noth-ing else would do.
that is just the rea-son, I tell it now to thee.
be the old, old sto-ry that I have loved so long.
CHORUS
I love to tell the sto-ry! 'Twill be my theme in glo-ry, To
tell the old, old sto-ry of Je-sus and His love.

COME YE SINNERS, POOR AND NEEDY

Joseph Hart — **Jean J. Rousseau**

Greenville, 8s, 7s.

According to his own admission, Joseph Hart's early life was a "curious mixture of loose conduct . . . and endeavors after amendment of life." Certainly some of the spiritual conflict in his early life may have caused him to turn to the passage in Matthew 11:28, "Come unto me, all ye that labour and are heavy laden, and I will give you rest."

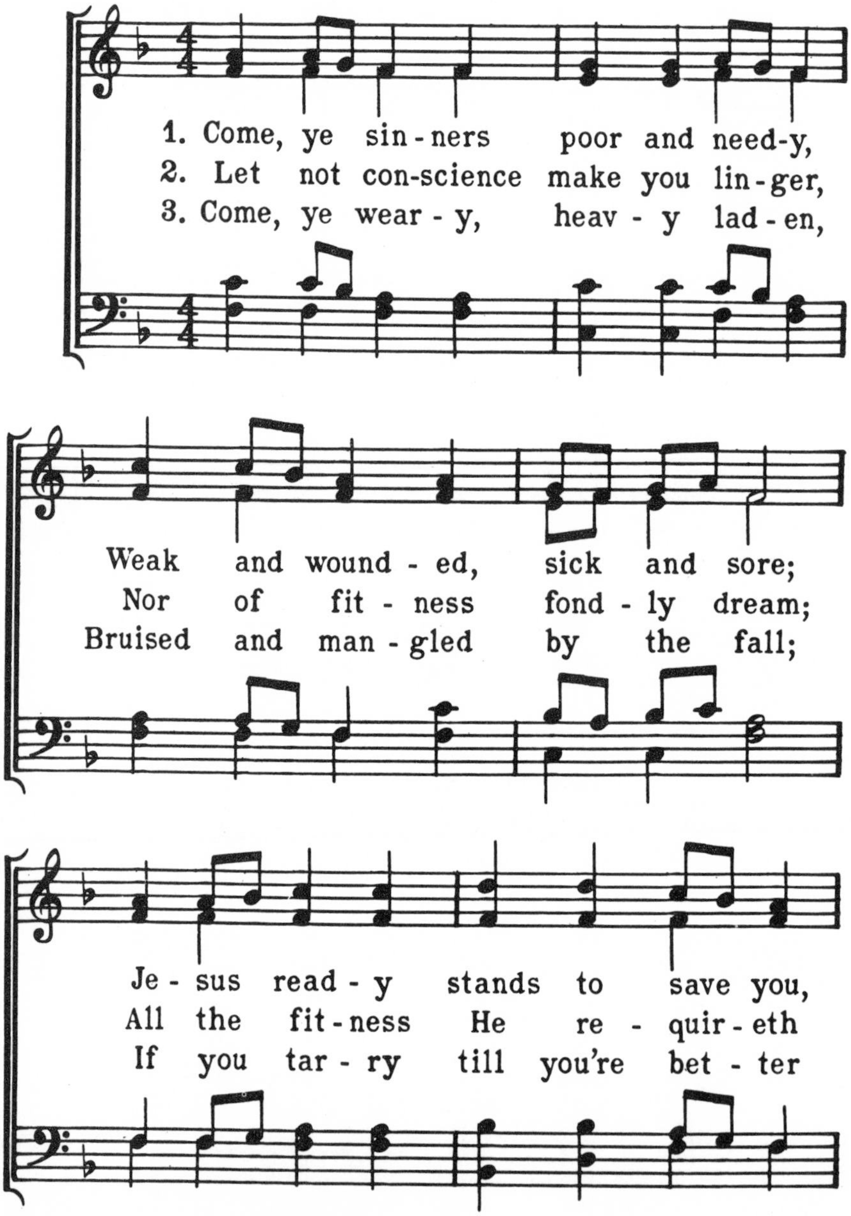
1. Come, ye sin-ners poor and need-y,
2. Let not con-science make you lin-ger,
3. Come, ye wear-y, heav-y lad-en,
Weak and wound-ed, sick and sore;
Nor of fit-ness fond-ly dream;
Bruised and man-gled by the fall;
Je-sus read-y stands to save you,
All the fit-ness He re-quir-eth
If you tar-ry till you're bet-ter

Full of pit - y, love and power:
Is to feel your need of Him:
You will nev - er come at all;
He is a - ble, He is a - ble,
This He gives you, This He gives you,
Not the right - eous, Not the right-eous,
He is will - ing, doubt no more.
'Tis the Spir - it's glim - m'ring beam.
Sin - ners Je - sus came to call.

THE LITTLE BROWN CHURCH IN THE VALE

WILLIAM S. PITTS

IS IT A HYMN or a sectarian song? It certainly has a religious motif, and it appears in many nonsectarian hymnals. It is said that William S. Pitts encountered, in Iowa, the precise setting as pictured in the song; and in 1865 he wrote words and music.

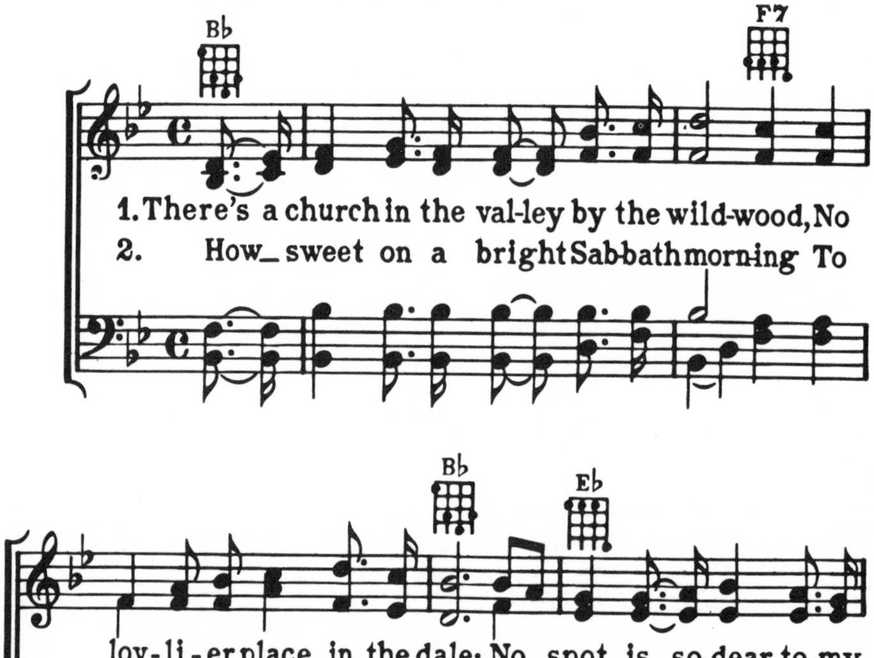
Bb
F7
1. There's a church in the val-ley by the wild-wood, No
2. How_ sweet on a bright Sab-bath morn-ing To
Bb
Eb
lov-li-er place in the dale; No spot is so dear to my
list to the clear ring-ing bell; Its tones so_ sweet-ly are
Bb
F7
Bb
child-hood As the lit-tle brown church in the vale._
call-ing, O_ come to the church in the vale._

F7
B♭
O come Come to the church in the
O come, come, come, come, come, come, come, come,
F7
wild - wood, O come to the church in the
come, come, come, come, come, come, come, come,
B♭
E♭
dale; No
come, come, come, No
spot is so dear to my
B♭
F7
B♭
child-hood As the lit - tle brown church in the vale._

BLESSED ASSURANCE

FANNY J. CROSBY | MRS. JOSEPH F. KNAPP

Blessed Assurance,
9.10.9.9., with refrain

FANNY J. CROSBY, the blind hymn-writer and teacher, had marvelous facility. When she first heard Mrs. Knapp play the tune of this hymn, in 1890, she sat down and within two hours completed the verses. She wrote, altogether, about 8,000 hymns and pious songs, using more than a hundred names. BLESSED ASSURANCE may have been suggested by JOHN 6:47, "He that believeth in Me hath everlasting life."

1. Bless - ed as - sur - ance, Je - sus is
2. Per - fect sub - mis - sion, all is at
mine! Oh, what a fore-taste of glo-ry di -
rest, I in my Sav-iour am hap-py and
vine! Heir of sal - va-tion, pur-chase of
blest, Watch-ing and wait-ing, look-ing a-

God, Born of His Spir-it, washed in His blood.
bove, Filled with His good-ness, lost in His love.
CHORUS
This is my sto - ry, this is my
song, Prais - ing my Sav - iour all the day
long; This is my sto - ry, this is my
song, Prais-ing my Sav-iour all the day long.

TAKE THE NAME OF JESUS WITH YOU

LYDIA BAXTER

WILLIAM H. DOANE

8.7.8.7., with refrain

A LIFELONG Baptist, and contributor to collections for Sunday schools and evangelists, Lydia Baxter wrote many hymns. No fewer than five were included in Ira D. Sankey's *Sacred Songs and Solos,* and she herself published *Gems by the Wayside.* This is the only one of her hymns that has survived to any extent. It is included in most hymnals.

1. Take the name of Je - sus with you,
2. Take the name of Je - sus ev - er,
3. At the name of Je - sus bow - ing,
Child of sor - row and of woe;
As a shield from ev - 'ry snare;
Fall - ing pros - trate at His feet,
It will joy and com - fort give you,
If temp - ta - tions round you gath - er,
King of kings in heav'n we'll crown Him,

Take it, then, wher - e'er you go.
Breathe that ho - ly name in prayer.
When our jour - ney is com - plete.
CHORUS
Pre - cious name, O how
Pre-cious name,
sweet! Hope of earth and joy of heav'n;
O how sweet!
Pre - cious name, O how
Pre - cious name, O how
sweet! Hope of earth and joy of heav'n.
sweet, how sweet!

THAT OLD-TIME RELIGION

ANONYMOUS

Irregular, with refrain

No one knows the origin of this famous old revival hymn. It was sung by the Jubilee Singers of Fisk University during the decade after the Civil War, and there is reason to believe that it was originally a spiritual. There are literally hundreds of versions, the one given here being the most commonly heard in the southern and southwestern United States. The editors attended a camp meeting in the Tennessee mountains during which That Old-Time Religion was sung continuously for three hours, accompanied by hand-clapping and stamping of the feet.

Give me that old-time re - li-gion, Give me that
old-time re - li-gion, Give me that old-time re-
li - gion, It's good e - nough for me!
Fine

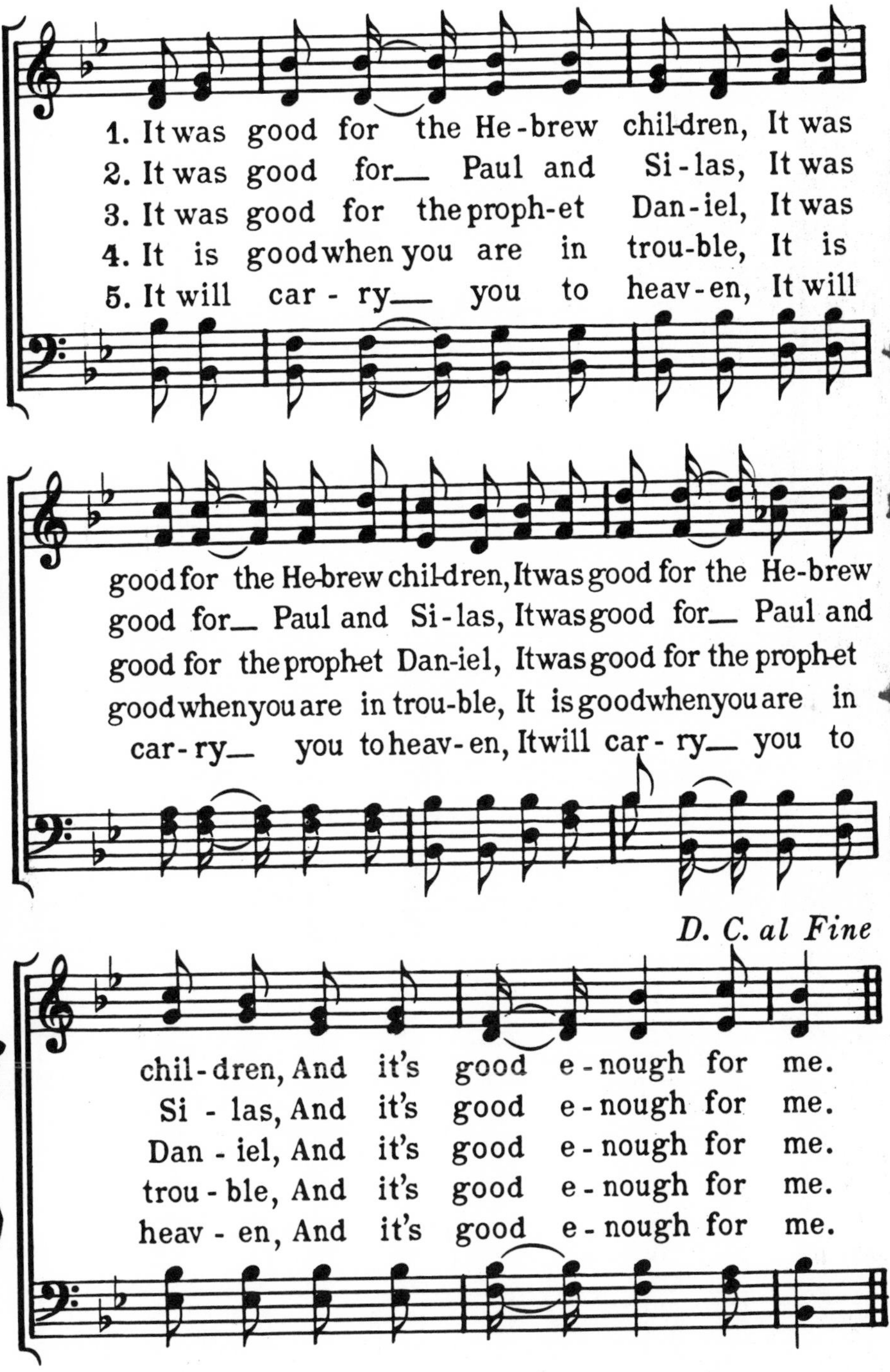
1. It was good for the He-brew chil-dren, It was
2. It was good for__ Paul and Si-las, It was
3. It was good for the proph-et Dan-iel, It was
4. It is good when you are in trou-ble, It is
5. It will car-ry__ you to heav-en, It will
good for the He-brew chil-dren, It was good for the He-brew
good for__ Paul and Si-las, It was good for__ Paul and
good for the proph-et Dan-iel, It was good for the proph-et
good when you are in trou-ble, It is good when you are in
car-ry__ you to heav-en, It will car-ry__ you to
D. C. al Fine
chil-dren, And it's good e-nough for me.
Si-las, And it's good e-nough for me.
Dan-iel, And it's good e-nough for me.
trou-ble, And it's good e-nough for me.
heav-en, And it's good e-nough for me.

WE'RE MARCHING TO ZION

ISAAC WATTS

ROBERT LOWRY

6.6.8.8.6.6., with refrain.

SIR ISAAC WATTS may have intended a stately and restrained mood, but the addition of a refrain by Lowry turned this hymn into a popular revival type, immediately accepted by the public. With his seemingly infallible instinct for pleasing the taste of the public, the Reverend Mr. Lowry could have been one of the most successful writers of popular songs in any period.

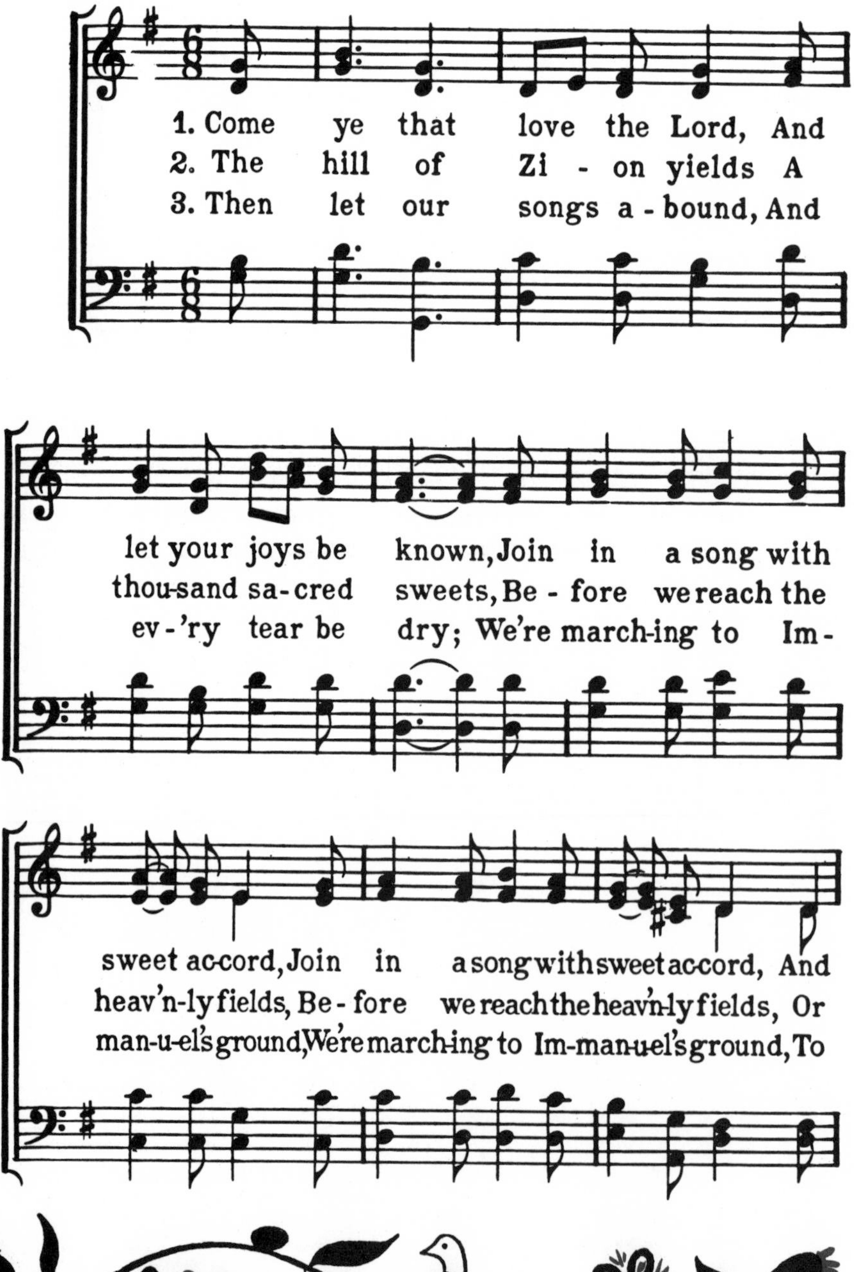
1. Come ye that love the Lord, And
2. The hill of Zi - on yields A
3. Then let our songs a - bound, And
let your joys be known, Join in a song with
thou-sand sa-cred sweets, Be - fore we reach the
ev-'ry tear be dry; We're march-ing to Im-
sweet ac-cord, Join in a song with sweet ac-cord, And
heav'n-ly fields, Be - fore we reach the heav'n-ly fields, Or
man-u-el's ground, We're march-ing to Im-man-u-el's ground, To

thus sur-round the throne, And thus sur-round the throne.
walk the gold - en streets, Or walk the gold - en streets.
fair - er worlds on high, To fair - er worlds on high.
CHORUS
We're march-ing to Zi - on, Beau-ti-ful, beau-ti-ful
Zi - on; We're march-ing up - ward to
Zi - on, The beau - ti - ful cit - y of God.

SHALL WE GATHER AT THE RIVER?

Robert Lowry

8.7.8.7, with refrain

A Baptist minister, the Reverend Robert Lowry is a prominent writer of Sunday-school hymns, though he did not start to write until he was past 40. *Where Is My Wandering Boy Tonight?* was a tremendous "hit" of its time, and his collection *Bright Jewels* sold over a million copies; but Lowry seemed unaffected by success. He said that his greatest pleasure in life was "to preach a sermon to an appreciative congregation." This hymn emphasizes the possibility of mutual recognition in the hereafter.

1. Shall we gath - er at the riv - er,
2. On the mar - gin of the riv - er,
3. Ere we reach the shin - ing riv - er,
Where bright an - gel feet have trod,—
Wash - ing up its sil - ver spray,—
Lay we ev - 'ry bur den down;—
With its crys - tal tide for - ev - er Flow - ing
We will walk and wor - ship ev - er, All the
Grace our spir - its will de - liv - er, And pro -

by the throne of God?
hap - py, gold - en day.
vide a robe and crown.
REFRAIN
Yes, we'll gath - er at the riv - er; The
beau - ti - ful, the beau - ti - ful riv - er;
Gath - er with the saints at the riv - er, That
flows by the throne of God.

TO THE WORK

FANNY J. CROSBY | WILLIAM HOWARD DOANE

Work Song,
12s, with refrain

FOR A BUSY industrialist, William H. Doane managed to do a lot of writing. Before he died he had written over 2,000 compositions, including song books, cantatas, and hymn tunes. It was he who introduced the work of Ira D. Sankey; he contributed many hymns to the famous Moody-Sankey cause, and wrote music for many Fanny Crosby hymns. He became a wealthy philanthropist, endowing the library of Denison University at Granville, Ohio.

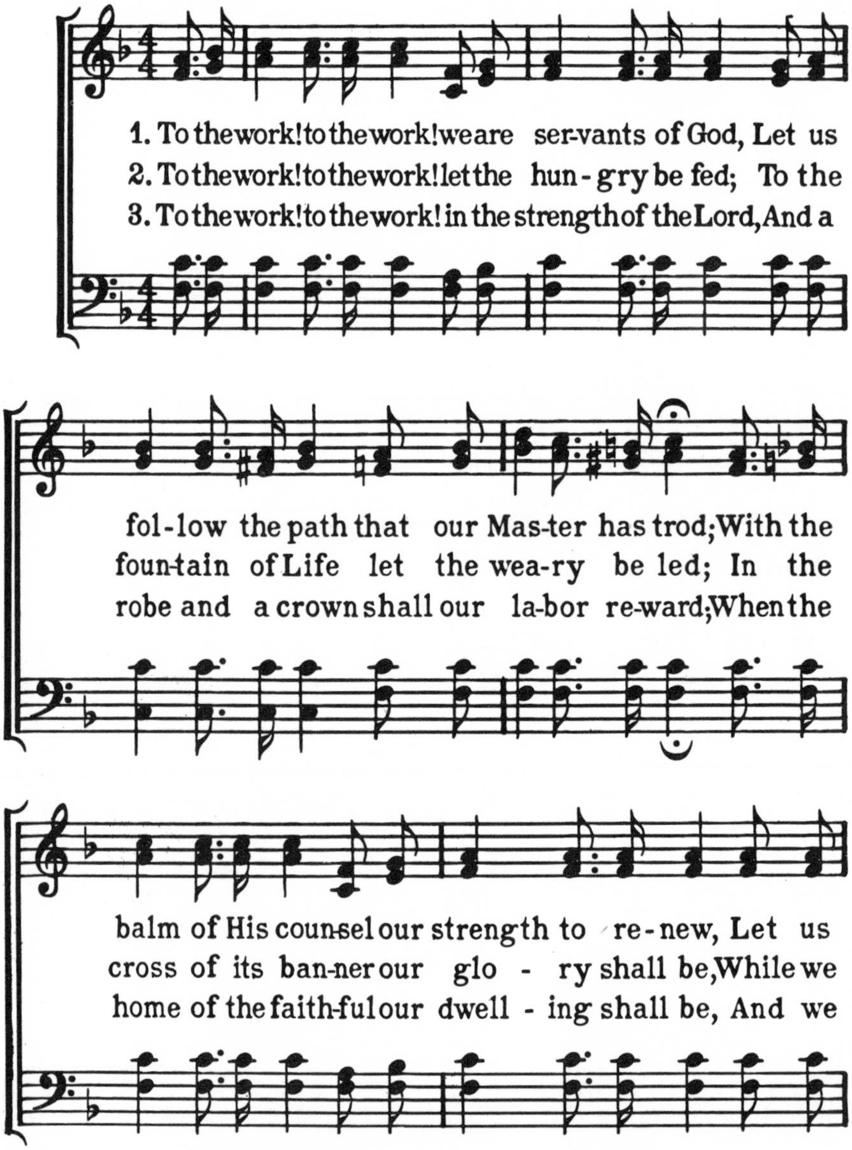

1. To the work! to the work! we are ser-vants of God, Let us
2. To the work! to the work! let the hun - gry be fed; To the
3. To the work! to the work! in the strength of the Lord, And a
fol-low the path that our Mas-ter has trod; With the
foun-tain of Life let the wea-ry be led; In the
robe and a crown shall our la-bor re-ward; When the
balm of His coun-sel our strength to re-new, Let us
cross of its ban-ner our glo - ry shall be, While we
home of the faith-ful our dwell - ing shall be, And we

do with our might what our hands find to do.
her-ald the ti-dings, "Sal-va-tion is free!"
shout with the ran-som'd "Sal-va-tion is free!"
CHORUS
Toil-ing on, Toil-ing
Toil-ing on,
on, Toil-ing on, Toil-ing
Toil-ing on, Toil-ing on,
on, Let us hope, Let us
Toil-ing on, and trust,
watch, And la-bor till the Mas-ter comes.
and pray,

SOFTLY AND TENDERLY JESUS IS CALLING

Will L. Thompson

Thompson,

11.7.11.7., with refrain

Will Thompson wrote his first song at 16, and by the time he was 40 he had written several hits. Then he turned to hymn writing and opened a publishing house and a music store. He loaded a piano on a wagon and drove through the countryside singing his own hymns, perhaps anticipating the "song-pluggers" of 60 years later. When Thompson lay dying, the great Dwight L. Moody said to him, "Will, I would rather have written Softly and Tenderly than anything I have been able to do in my whole life."

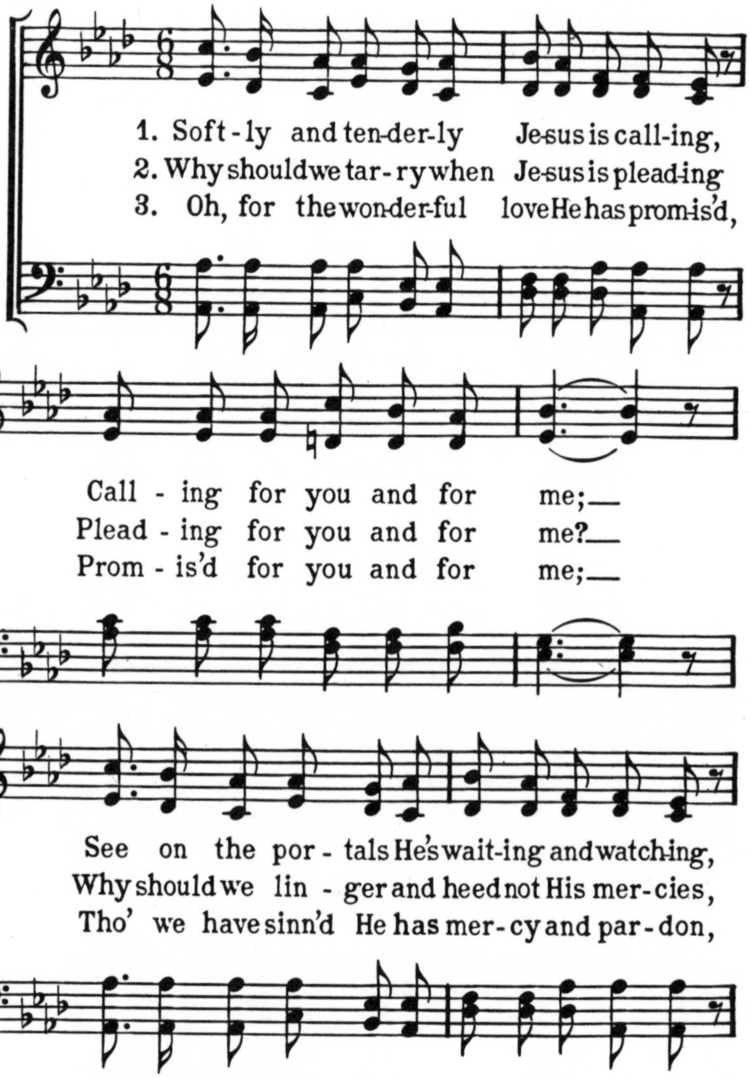

1. Soft-ly and ten-der-ly Je-sus is call-ing,
2. Why should we tar-ry when Je-sus is plead-ing
3. Oh, for the won-der-ful love He has prom-is'd,
Call - ing for you and for me;—
Plead - ing for you and for me?—
Prom - is'd for you and for me;—
See on the por - tals He's wait-ing and watch-ing,
Why should we lin - ger and heed not His mer-cies,
Tho' we have sinn'd He has mer-cy and par-don,

Watch - ing for you and for me.
Mer - cies for you and for me?
Par - don for you and for me.
CHORUS
Come home, Come home,
Come home, Come home,
mf
cresc.
Ye who are wea - ry come home;
a tempo
p
Ear - nest - ly, ten - der - ly Je - sus is call - ing,
rit.
p
Call - ing, O sin - ner, Come home.

TRUST AND OBEY

J. H. SAMMIS — DANIEL B. TOWNER

6.6.9.6.6.8., with refrain

DOCTOR TOWNER was associated with Moody and Sankey, as a singer. In 1893 he was made director of the Moody Bible Institute of Chicago, where he remained until his death. He wrote many hymns, of which TRUST AND OBEY is the best known. The title was suggested to Sammis by Doctor Towner, who had heard a young man say, at a testimony meeting, "I am not sure, but I am going to trust and obey." This story is told in Ira Sankey's *Story of the Gospel Hymns.*

1. When we walk with the Lord In the
2. Not a shad - ow can rise, Not a
3. Not a bur - den we bear, Not a
4. Then in fel - low - ship sweet We will
Light of His Word What a glo - ry He
cloud in the skies, But His smile quick - ly
sor - row we share, But our toil He doth
sit at His feet, Or we'll walk by His
sheds on our way! While we do His good -
drives it a - way; Not a doubt or a
rich - ly re - pay; Not a grief nor a
side in the way; What He says we will

will, He a - bides with us still,
fear, Not a sigh nor a tear,
loss, Not a frown or a cross,
do, Where He sends we will go,
And with all who will trust and o - bey.
Can a - bide while we trust and o - bey.
But is blest if we trust and o - bey.
Nev - er fear, on - ly trust and o - bey.
CHORUS
Trust and o - bey, for there's no oth-er way To be
hap-py in Je-sus, But to trust and o - bey.

YIELD NOT TO TEMPTATION

HORATIO R. PALMER

Fortitude,
11.11.11.12., with refrain

DOCTOR PALMER himself wrote: "This song is an inspiration. I was at work on the dry subject of "Theory" (he wrote *A Theory of Music* in 1868) when the complete idea flashed upon me, and I laid aside the theoretical work and hurriedly penned both words and music as fast as I could write them . . . I am reverently thankful it has been a power for good."

1. Yield not to temp-ta-tion, For yield-ing is sin,
2. Shun e-vil com-pan-ions, Bad lan-guage dis-dain,
3. To him that o'er-com-eth God giv-eth a crown,
Each vic-t'ry will help you Some oth-er to win;
God's name hold in rev'rence, Nor take it in vain;
Thro' faith we shall con-quer, Though oft-en cast down;
Fight man-ful-ly on-ward, Dark pas-sions sub-due,
Be thought-ful and earn-est, Kind-heart-ed and true,
He who is our Sav-iour, Our strength will re-new,

Look ev-er to Je-sus, He'll car-ry you through.
Look ev-er to Je-sus, He'll car-ry you through.
Look ev-er to Je-sus, He'll car-ry you through.
CHORUS
Ask the Sa-viour to help you,
Com-fort, strength-en and keep you; He is will-ing to
aid you, He will car-ry you through.

WORK, FOR THE NIGHT IS COMING

Anna Louise Walker — Lowell Mason

Work Song, P.M.

THIS HYMN was first published as a poem, in 1864. According to Ira D. Sankey, Miss Walker was inspired by Jesus' words: "I must work the works of Him That sent me, while it is day; the night cometh, when no man can work." (JOHN 9:4.) The tune is known in England as *Diligence.*

1. Work for the night is com - ing,
2. Work for the night is com - ing,
Work thro' the morn - ing hours:
Un - der the sun - set skies
Work while the dew is spark - ling
While their bright tints are glow - ing
Work 'mid spring - ing flow'rs;
Work, for day - light flies,

Work when the day grows bright - er
Work till the last beam fad - eth
Work in the glow - ing sun;
Fad - eth to shine no more;
Work, for the night is com - ing
Work while the night is dark'n - ing
When man's work is done.
When man's work is o'er.

BRINGING IN THE SHEAVES

KNOWLES SHAW

GEORGE A. MINOR

12.11.12.11., with refrain

HERE IS a text from MATTHEW 13:30, "The harvest is the end of the world." We are admonished to prepare our lives by thought and deed so that at the end there may be a time of rejoicing, rather than sorrow for the recklessness with which we sometimes ignore the laws of nature and divine help.

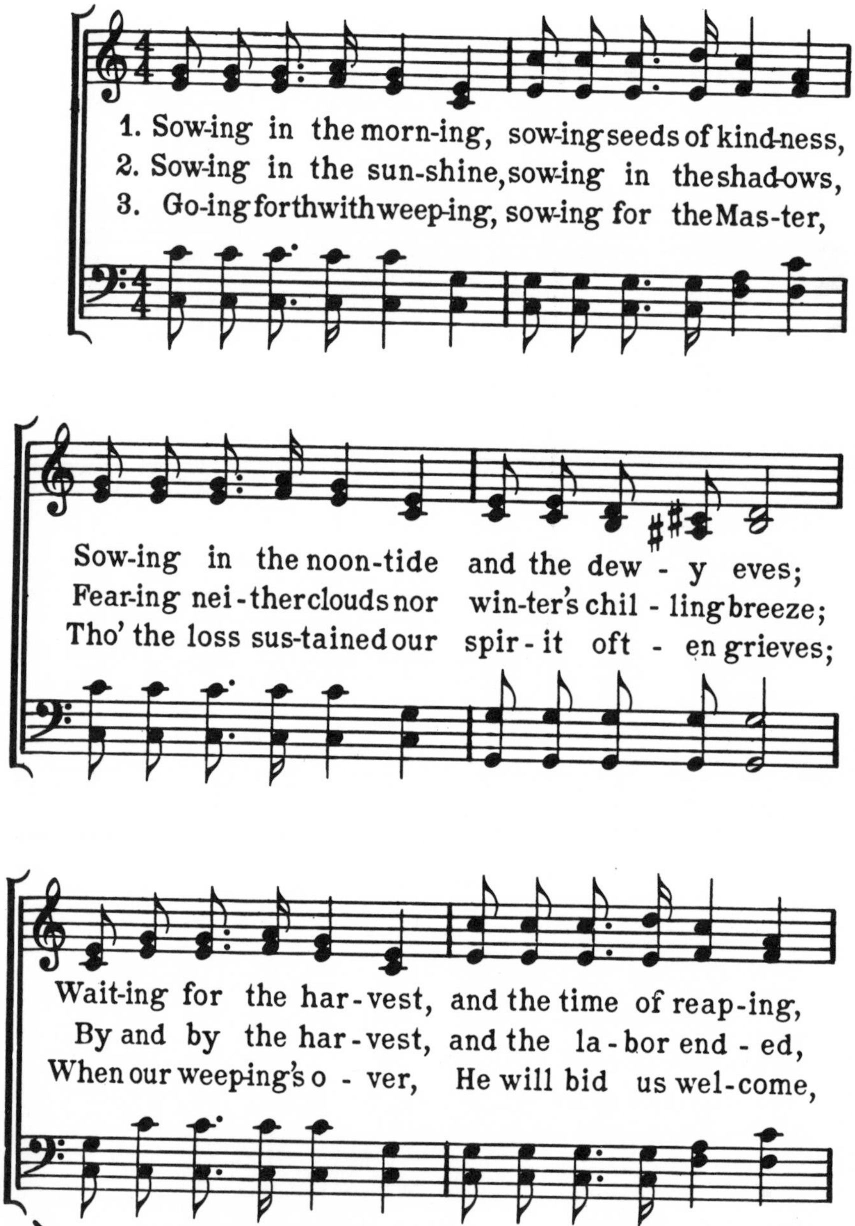
1. Sow-ing in the morn-ing, sow-ing seeds of kind-ness,
2. Sow-ing in the sun-shine, sow-ing in the shad-ows,
3. Go-ing forth with weep-ing, sow-ing for the Mas-ter,
Sow-ing in the noon-tide and the dew - y eves;
Fear-ing nei-ther clouds nor win-ter's chil - ling breeze;
Tho' the loss sus-tained our spir - it oft - en grieves;
Wait-ing for the har-vest, and the time of reap-ing,
By and by the har-vest, and the la - bor end - ed,
When our weep-ing's o - ver, He will bid us wel-come,

We shall come, re-joic - ing, bring-ing in the sheaves.
We shall come, re-joic - ing, bring-ing in the sheaves.
We shall come, re-joic - ing, bring-ing in the sheaves.
CHORUS
Bring-ing in the sheaves, bring - ing in the sheaves,
We shall come, re - joic - ing, Bring - ing in the sheaves;
Bring - ing in the sheaves, bring - ing in the sheaves,
We shall come, re - joic - ing, bring-ing in the sheaves.

THE DAY THOU GAVEST, LORD, IS ENDED

JOHN ELLERTON — CLEMENT C. SCHOLEFIELD

St. Clement, 9.8.9.8

QUEEN VICTORIA chose this hymn for her Diamond Jubilee in 1897. The expanding British Empire must have found symbolic parallels in the sentiment contained in the second verse, but the hymn would be better confined to its original intention—that of a missionary hymn, expressing the movement of the Church to all parts of the world.

1. The day_ Thou gav - est,
2. As o'er_ each con - ti -
3. So be_ it, Lord; Thy
Lord, is end - ed, The dark - ness
nent and is - land The dawn leads
throne shall nev - er, Like earth's proud
falls at Thy_ be - hest; To
on an - oth - er day, The
em - pires, pass_ a - way; Thy

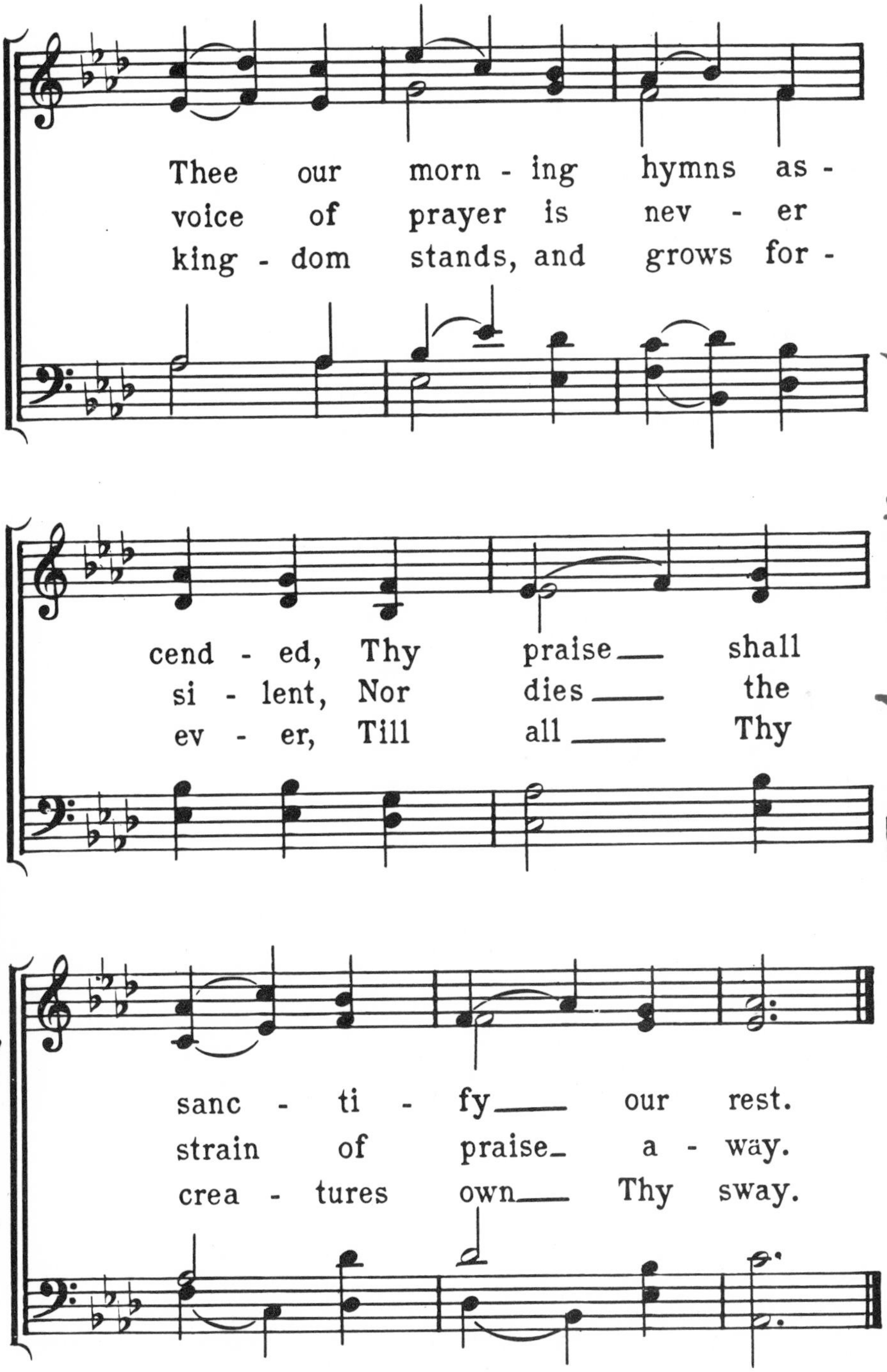
Thee our morn - ing hymns as -
voice of prayer is nev - er
king - dom stands, and grows for -
cend - ed, Thy praise___ shall
si - lent, Nor dies___ the
ev - er, Till all___ Thy
sanc - ti - fy___ our rest.
strain of praise_ a - way.
crea - tures own___ Thy sway.

REVIVE US AGAIN

William Paton Mackay | **John J. Husband**

11s, with refrain

This is one of the most powerful "camp meeting" hymns of all time. The origin of the tune is very hard to trace, but it was almost certainly written by John Husband, a Philadelphia musician of the period after the American Revolution. It has been used also for the folk song *Hallelujah! I'm a Bum!* historically associated with the I.W.W.

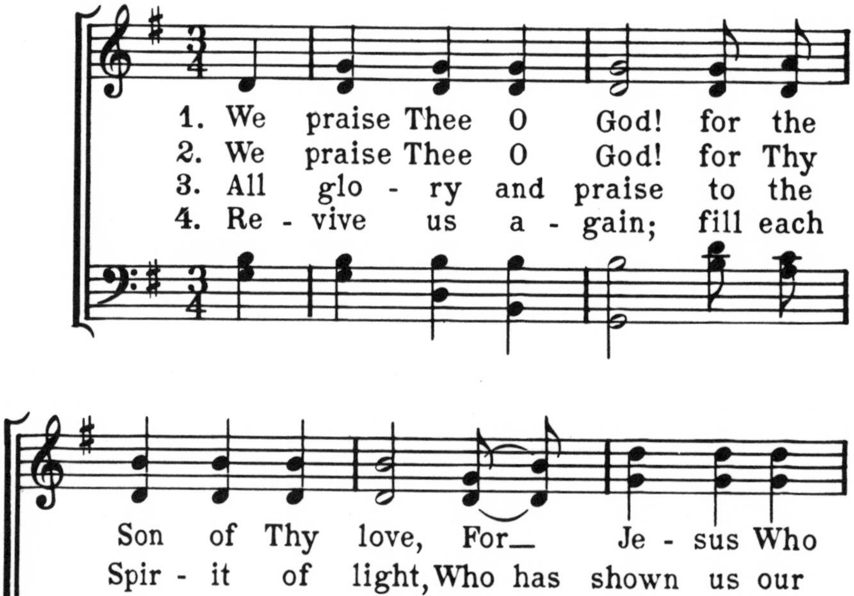
1. We praise Thee O God! for the
2. We praise Thee O God! for Thy
3. All glo - ry and praise to the
4. Re - vive us a - gain; fill each
Son of Thy love, For— Je - sus Who
Spir - it of light, Who has shown us our
Lamb that was slain, Who has borne all our
heart with Thy love; May each soul be re -
died and is now gone a - bove.
Sa - vior, and scat - tered our night.
sins and hath cleansed ev - 'ry stain.
kin - dled with fire from a - bove.

CHORUS
Hal - le - lu - jah! Thine the
glo - ry, Hal - le - lu - jah! A -
men. Hal - le - lu - jah! Thine the
glo - ry, Re - vive us a - gain.

AMAZING GRACE

JOHN NEWTON | SAMUEL STANLEY

Warwick, C.M.

THE EARLY LIFE of John Newton was anything but exemplary. He deserted from the British Navy, and was publicly whipped when caught. Then he became captain of a slave ship, brutal and merciless. His conversion came after a storm almost destroyed him and his human cargo. He educated himself, and after twelve years was ordained a minister. He became a friend of William Cowper, and in 1779 the two men published the *Olney Hymns,* "for the use of plain people."

1. A - maz - ing grace, how sweet the sound, That saved a
2. 'Twas grace that taught my heart to fear, And grace my
3. Thro' man - y dan - gers, toils and snares, I have al -
4. Yes, when this heart and flesh shall fail, And mor - tal

soul like me! I
fears re - lieved; How
read - y come; 'Tis
life shall cease, I
once was lost, but
pre - cious did that
grace that brought me
shall pos - sess with -
now am found: Was
grace ap - pear, The
safe thus far, And
in the vail, A
blind but now I see.
hour I first be - lieved.
grace will lead me home.
life of joy and peace.

INTO THE WOODS MY MASTER WENT

SIDNEY LANIER — PETER C. LUTKIN

Lanier, P. M.

THE ORIGINAL TITLE of Lanier's poem was *A Ballad of Trees and the Master.* It appeared in a volume of his poems that was published posthumously. Lanier lectured at John Hopkins University on "The Interrelation of Music and Poetry," and played first flute with the Peabody Symphony Orchestra of Baltimore, in 1873. He had contracted tuberculosis as a result of imprisonment during the Civil War, and was slowly dying. Here he considers Jesus' last thoughts in the Garden of Gethsemane. INTO THE WOODS MY MASTER WENT was written in 1880, and Lanier died the following year, at the age of 39. His hymn is often sung on Good Friday.

1. In - to the woods my Mas - ter went,
2. Out of the woods my Mas - ter went, And
Clean for-spent, for - spent; In - to the woods my
He was well con - tent; Out of the woods my
Mas - ter came, For - spent with love and
Mas - ter came, Con - tent with death and

shame. But the ol - ives they were not
shame. When death and shame would
blind to Him, The lit-tle gray leaves were
woo Him last, From un-der the trees they
kind to Him, The thorn tree had a
drew Him last, 'Twas on a tree they
mind to Him, When in-to the woods He came.
slew Him last, When out of the woods He came.

THE NINETY AND NINE

ELIZABETH C. CLEPHANE — IRA D. SANKEY

Ninety and Nine, Irregular

A POEM by a little Scottish girl was published in a Glasgow paper in 1876. It attracted the attention of Ira Sankey, the gospel singer, who was on tour with the evangelist Dwight L. Moody. Sankey cut the poem from the paper; a tune was taking form in his mind. When the sermon the next Sunday had as its text "the Good Shepherd," Sankey used it for his solo, although it had not yet been put on paper. The words and music were never changed.

1. There were nine - ty and nine that
2. "Lord,_ Thou hast here Thy nine -
3. But_ all thro' the moun-tains,
safe - ly lay In the shel-ter_ of the
ty and nine; Are they not e-nough for
thun-der-riv'n, And up from the rock - y
fold, But_ one_ was out on the
Thee?" But the Shep-herd made an - swer:
steep, There a - rose a glad cry to the

hills a way, Far off from the gates of
"This of mine Has wan-dered a - way from
gate of heav'n, "Re - joice! I have found my
gold A - way on the moun - tains
me, And, al - though the road _ be
sheep!" And the an - gels ech-oed a -
wild and bare, A-way from the ten - der
rough and steep, I go to the des-ert to
round the throne, "Re-joice! for the Lord brings
Shep-herd's care, A-way from the ten - der Shep-herd's care.
find my sheep, I go to the des-ert to find my sheep.
back His own! Re-joice! for the Lord brings back His own!"

SINCE JESUS CAME INTO MY HEART

R. H. McDaniel — Charles H. Gabriel

12.8.12.8. with refrain

No testament is more powerful than that of a gospel song when the congregation is moved by a communion of spiritual experience. Such an experience brought about the conversion of Policeman Fowler during a Billy Sunday revival in Philadelphia. Scores of other policemen later followed the example of Fowler.

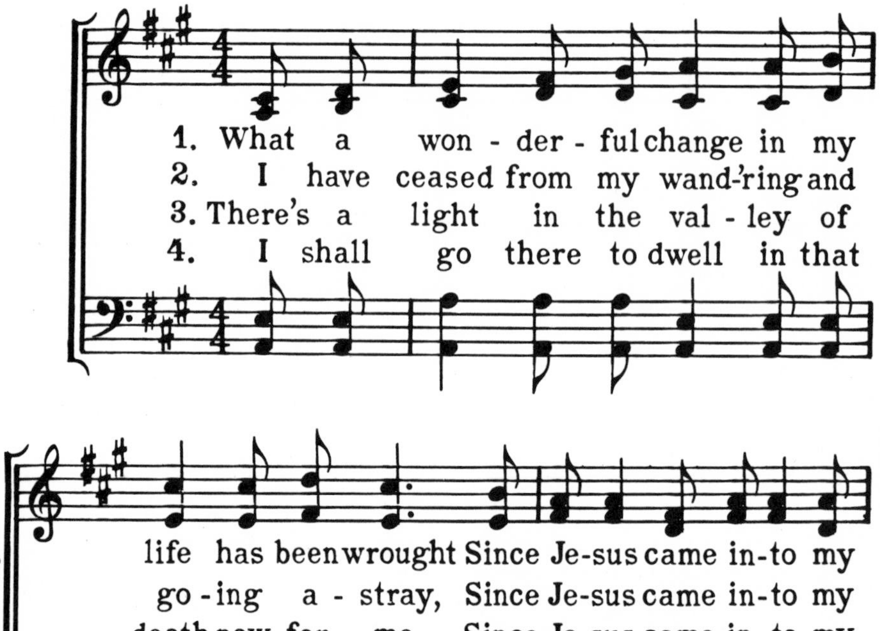
1. What a won - der - ful change in my
2. I have ceased from my wand-'ring and
3. There's a light in the val - ley of
4. I shall go there to dwell in that
life has been wrought Since Je-sus came in-to my
go - ing a - stray, Since Je-sus came in-to my
death now for me, Since Je-sus came in-to my
Cit - y, I know, Since Je-sus came in - to my
heart! I have light in my soul for which long I had sought,
heart! And my sins, which were man-y, are all washed a-way,
heart! And the gates of the Cit - y be - yond I can see,
heart! And I'm hap - py, so hap-py, as on-ward I go

Since Je-sus came in-to my heart!
CHORUS
Since Je-sus came in-to my heart, Since
Since Je-sus came in, came in-to my heart, Since
Je-sus came in-to my heart, Floods of
Je-sus came in, came in-to my heart,
joy o'er my soul like the sea bil-lows roll, Since
Je-sus came in-to my heart.

LOVE LIFTED ME

JAMES ROWE | HOWARD E. SMITH

Irregular, with refrain

THIS GOSPEL SONG was a favorite with the great evangelists of the early part of the 20th century, Billy Sunday and Gipsy Smith. It proved to have such vitality and power that their successor in spirit and effectiveness, Billy Graham, has used it in his revival campaigns nearly fifty years later.

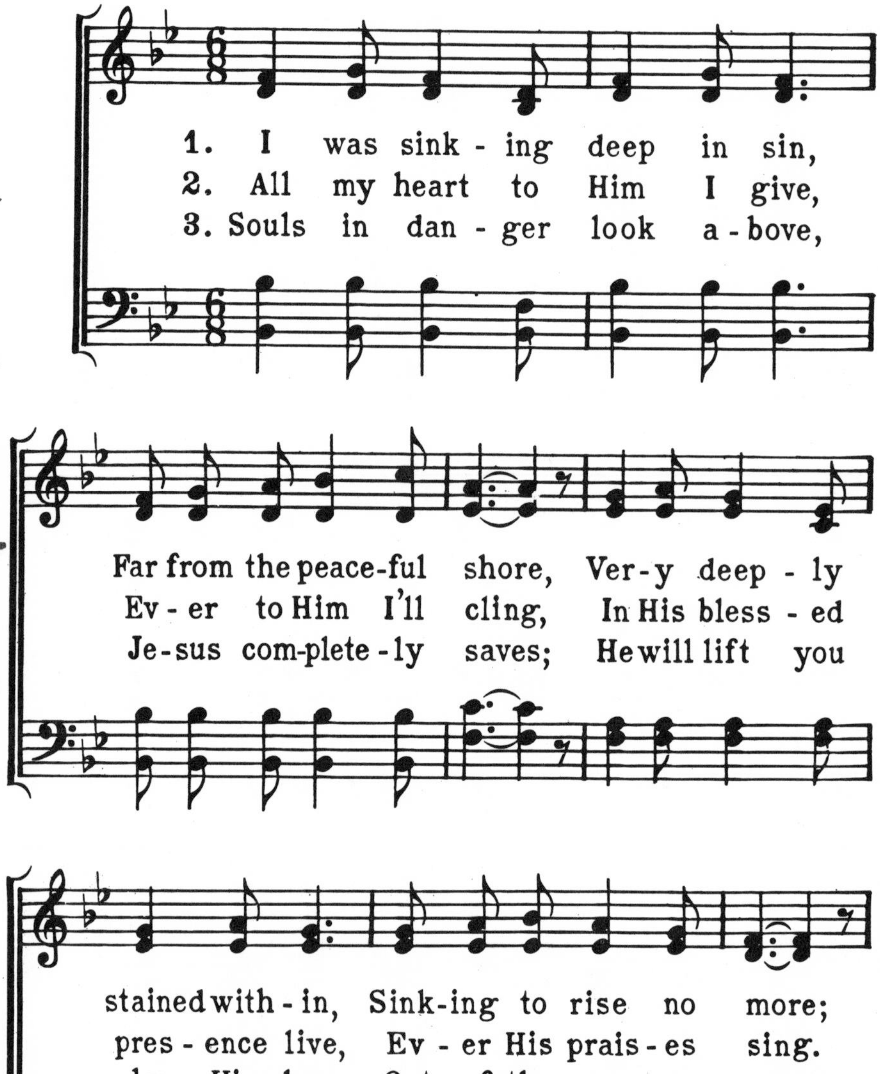
1. I was sink - ing deep in sin,
2. All my heart to Him I give,
3. Souls in dan - ger look a - bove,
Far from the peace-ful shore, Ver-y deep - ly
Ev - er to Him I'll cling, In His bless - ed
Je-sus com-plete - ly saves; He will lift you
stained with - in, Sink-ing to rise no more;
pres - ence live, Ev - er His prais - es sing.
by His love Out of the an - gry waves.

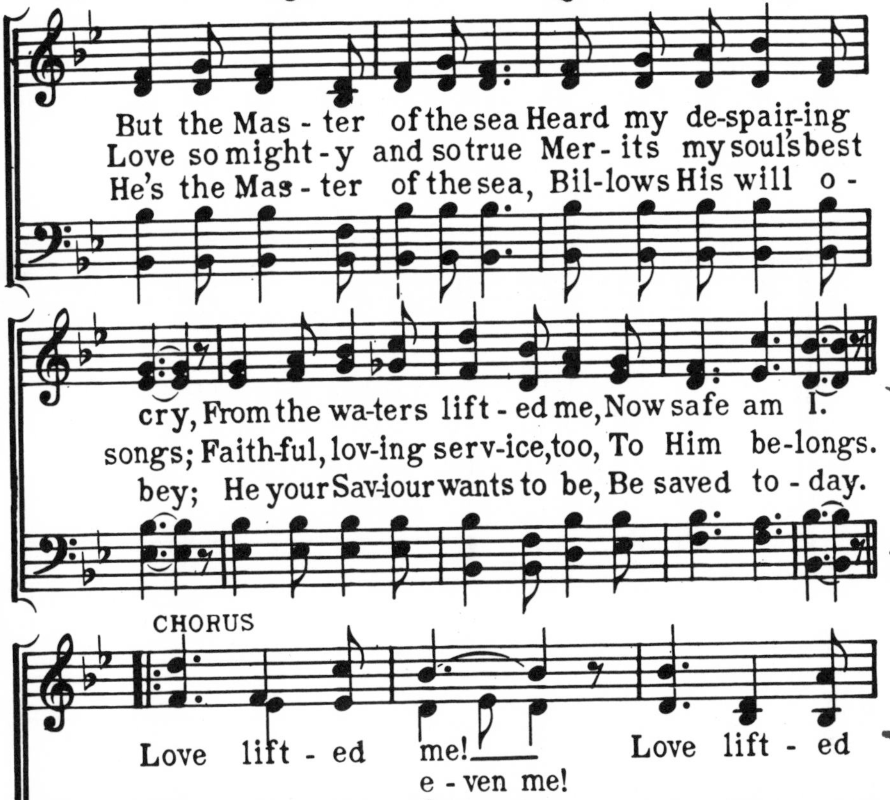
But the Mas - ter of the sea Heard my de-spair-ing
Love so might - y and so true Mer - its my soul's best
He's the Mas - ter of the sea, Bil-lows His will o -
cry, From the wa-ters lift - ed me, Now safe am I.
songs; Faith-ful, lov-ing serv-ice, too, To Him be-longs.
bey; He your Sav-iour wants to be, Be saved to - day.
CHORUS
Love lift - ed me!
e - ven me!
Love lift - ed
me!
e - ven me!
When noth - ing else could help,
1.
Love lift - ed me.
2.
Love lift - ed me.

O HAPPY DAY

PHILIP DODDRIDGE | EDWARD F. RIMBAULT

L. M.

JAMES MONTGOMERY said: "Blessed is the man who can take the words of this hymn and make them his own experience." The Reverend Mr. Doddridge was a prolific writer of hymns, and a friend of the Wesleys. Edward Rimbault was a leading English composer. He was once asked to head the school of music at Harvard University, but did not accept the offer.

1. Oh, hap - py day, that fixed my
2. 'Tis done, the great trans - ac - tion's
3. High heav'n that hears the sol - emn
choice On Thee, my Sav - iour and my
done; I am my Lord's, and He is
vow, That vow re - newed shall dai - ly
God! Well may this glow - ing heart re -
mine; He drew me, and I fol - lowed
hear; Till in life's lat - est hour I

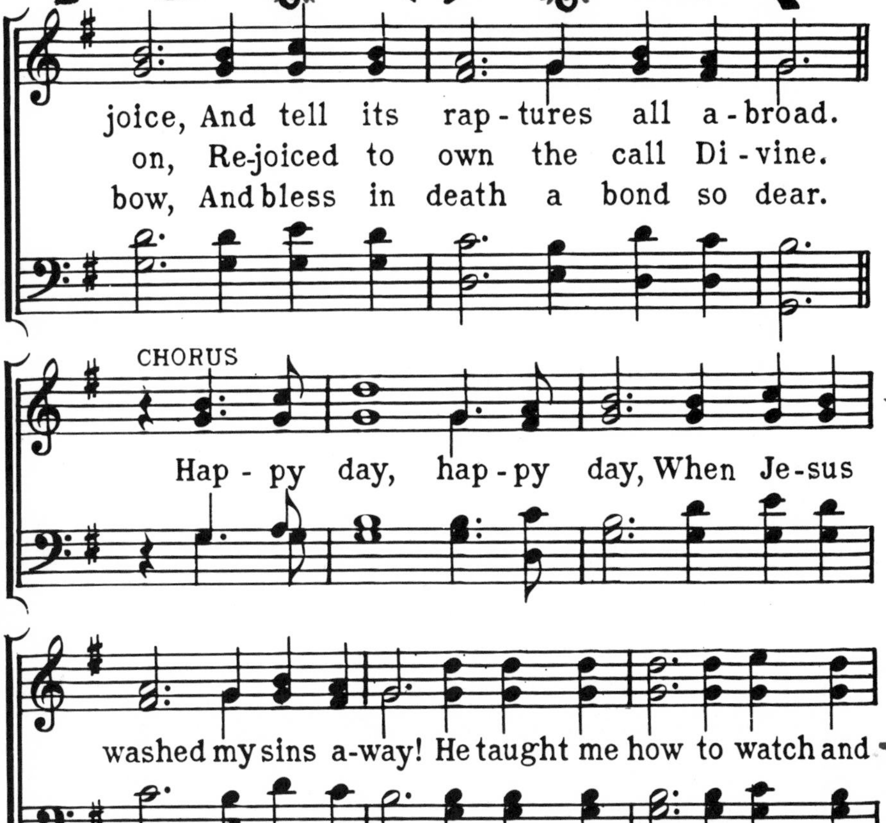
joice, And tell its rap-tures all a-broad.
on, Re-joiced to own the call Di-vine.
bow, And bless in death a bond so dear.
CHORUS
Hap-py day, hap-py day, When Je-sus
washed my sins a-way! He taught me how to watch and
pray, And live re-joic-ing ev-'ry day; Hap-py
day, hap-py day, When Je-sus washed my sins a-way!

BLEST BE THE TIE THAT BINDS

JOHN FAWCETT HANS G. NAEGELI

Dennis, S.M.

AFTER several years of serving the poverty-stricken parish of Wainsgate, England, the Reverend Mr. Fawcett was called to a large church and a large salary; but his parishioners were so heartbroken, and the Fawcetts had become so attached to their friends, that they decided to stay. The following Sunday Fawcett preached from LUKE 12:15, "A man's life consisteth not in the abundance of the things he possesseth," and then all joined in singing his new hymn, BLEST BE THE TIE THAT BINDS.

1. Blest be— the tie— that
2. Be - fore— our Fa - ther's
3. We share— our mu - tual
4. When we— a - sun - der
binds Our hearts— in
throne, We pour— our
woes, Our mu - tual
part, It gives— us
Christ - ian love; The
ar - dent pray'rs; Our
bur - dens bear; And
in - ward pain; But

fel - low - ship of
fears, our hopes, our
oft - en for each
we shall still be
kin - dred minds Is
aims are one, Our
oth - er flows The
joined in heart, And
like to that a - bove.
com - forts and our cares.
sym - pa - thiz - ing tear.
hope to meet a - gain.

THE OLD RUGGED CROSS

GEORGE BENNARD

SAYS George W. Sanville, head of one of the world's most respected publishers of sacred songs, "Around the world, on radio, where it has been the most used gospel song, and in multitudinous religious meetings, this arrow of the gospel, shafted with music, has shot God's truth home to the hearts of men. It is the epitome of the gospel in song; it is in the world of gospel song what JOHN 3:16 is in gospel doctrine . . . the heart of it." Within thirty years of its publication, more than twenty million copies of THE OLD RUGGED CROSS had been sold—more than any other musical composition, of any kind, in all history.

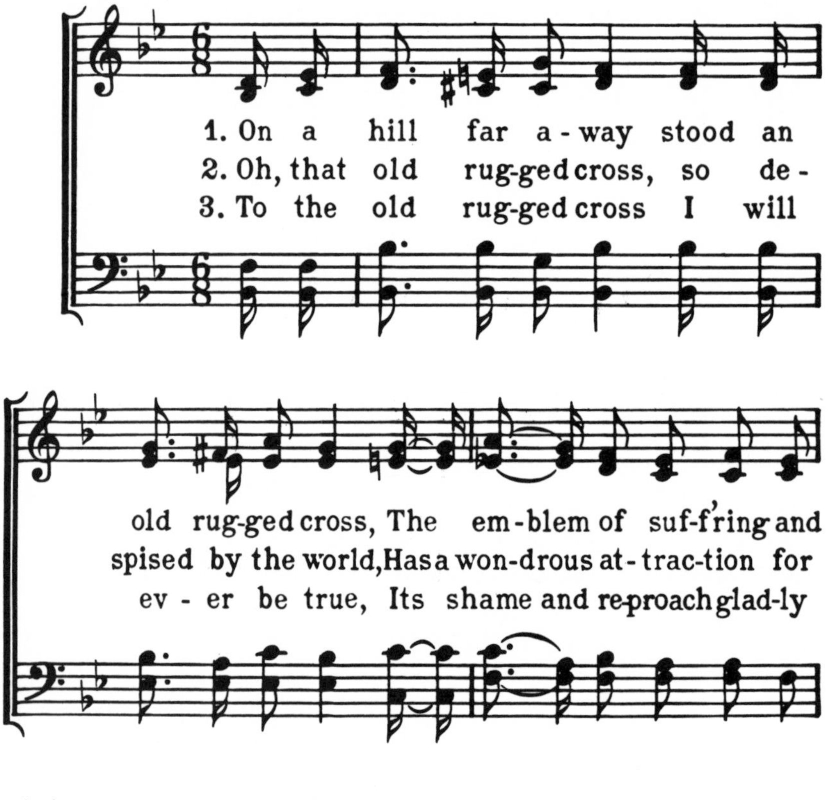
1. On a hill far a-way stood an
2. Oh, that old rug-ged cross, so de-
3. To the old rug-ged cross I will
old rug-ged cross, The em-blem of suf-f'ring and
spised by the world, Has a won-drous at-trac-tion for
ev - er be true, Its shame and re-proach glad-ly
shame; And I love that old cross where the
me; For the dear Lamb of God left His
bear; Then He'll call me some day to my

dear-est and best For a world of lost sin-ners was slain.
glo-ry a-bove, To bear it to dark Cal-va - ry.
home far a-way, Where His glo - ry for - ev - er I'll share.
CHORUS
So I'll cher - ish the old rug - ged
cross, the
cross, Till my tro-phies at last I lay
old rug-ged cross,
down; I will cling to the old rug-ged
cross, the
cross, And ex-change it some day for a crown.
old rug-ged cross,

IN THE GARDEN

C. Austin Miles

In The Garden, irregular.

According to the author, he was working in his dark-room when the Bible fell open at John 20, the scene containing the account of Mary's meeting with Jesus. His senses prepared by the dim light, he saw the entire scene before him, as in a vision. He writes: "Under the inspiration of this vision I wrote as quickly as the words could be formed the poem exactly as it has since appeared. That same evening I wrote the music."

1. I come to the gar - den a -
2. He speaks, and the sound of His
3. I'd stay in the gar - den with
lone,— While the dew is still on the
voice— Is so sweet the birds hush their
Him— Tho' the night a-round me be
ros - es, And the voice I hear Fall - ing
sing - ing, And the mel - o - dy That He
fall - ing, But He bids me go; Thro' the

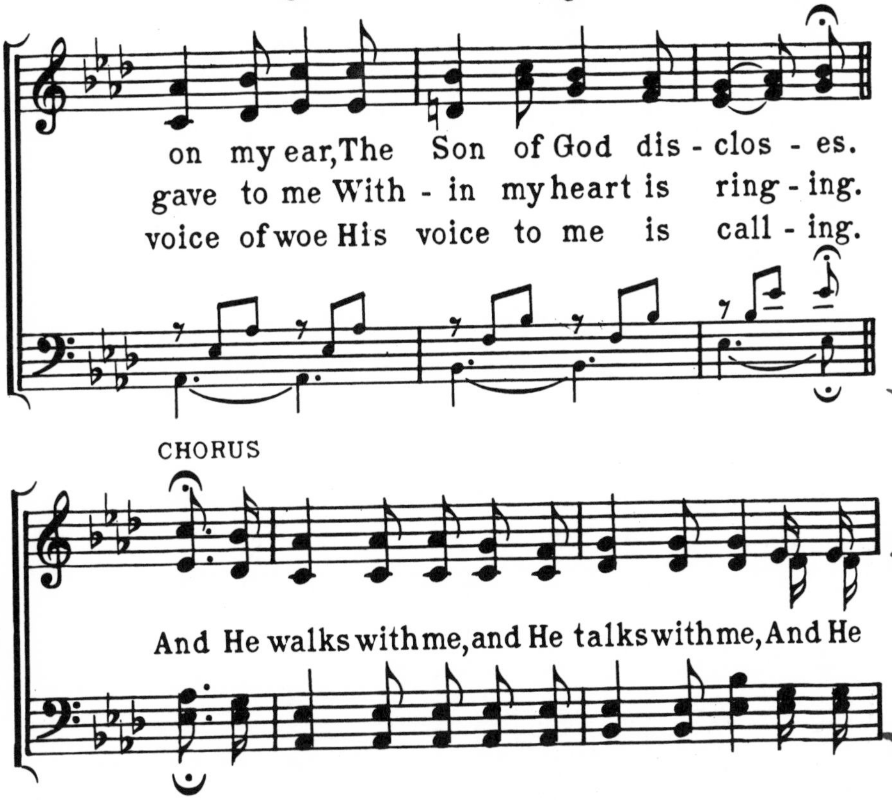
on my ear, The Son of God dis - clos - es.
gave to me With - in my heart is ring - ing.
voice of woe His voice to me is call - ing.
CHORUS
And He walks with me, and He talks with me, And He
tells me I am His own; And the joy we share as we
tar - ry there, None oth - er has ev - er— known.

IN THE SWEET BYE-AND-BYE

S. Fillmore Bennett — Joseph P. Webster

L.M., with refrain

Joseph Philbrick Webster was a musician who settled in Elkhorn, Wis., in 1857. When Dr. Bennett also came to Elkhorn, the two collaborated on popular songs, and wrote several successful ones. One day, so the story goes, Webster was feeling glum. When asked what the trouble was, he replied, "Oh, everything will be all right—bye-and-bye." That gave the doctor an idea, and within an hour they had turned out a hymn. It was to be the only lasting song they wrote, and has even been flattered by the bitter parody of the I.W.W., "There'll be pie in the sky, bye-and-bye."

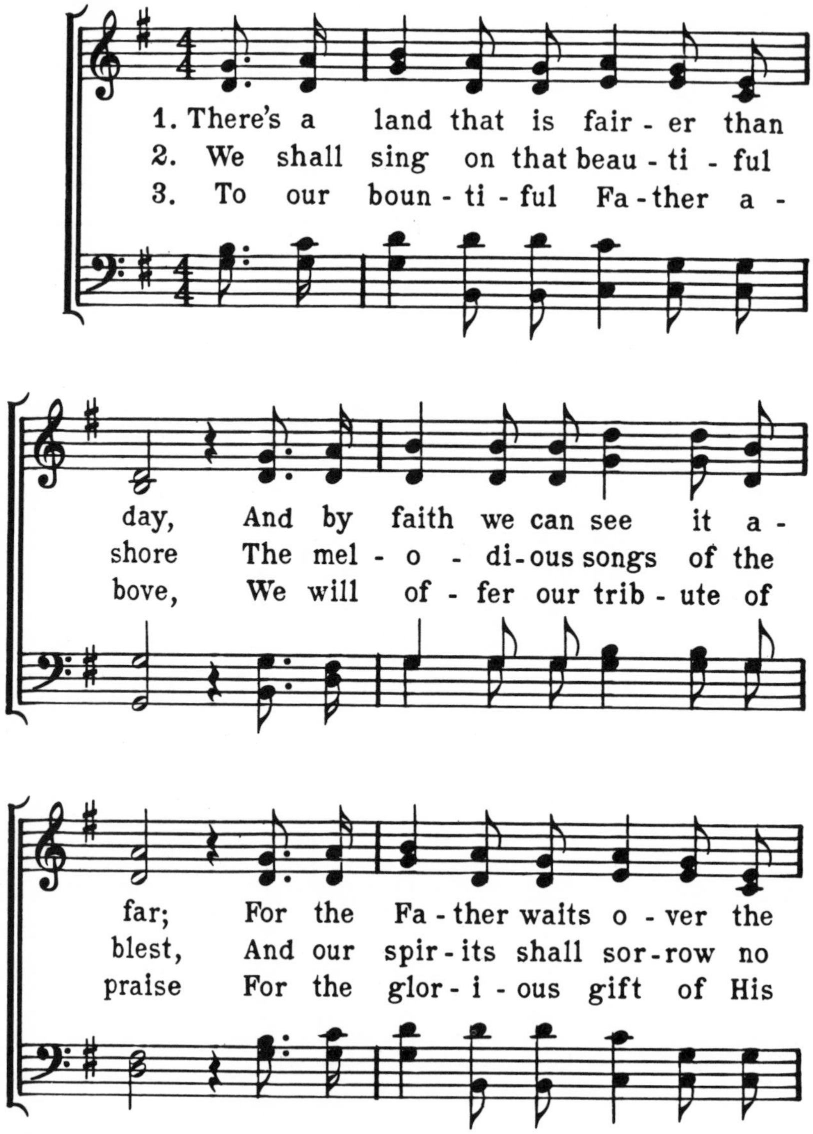

1. There's a land that is fair - er than
2. We shall sing on that beau - ti - ful
3. To our boun - ti - ful Fa - ther a -
day, And by faith we can see it a -
shore The mel - o - di - ous songs of the
bove, We will of - fer our trib - ute of
far; For the Fa - ther waits o - ver the
blest, And our spir - its shall sor - row no
praise For the glor - i - ous gift of His

way To pre-pare us a dwell-ing place there.
more, Not a sigh for the bless-ing of rest.
love, And the bless-ings that hal-low our days.
CHORUS
In the sweet bye-and-bye, we shall
In the sweet bye-and-bye
meet on that beau-ti-ful shore, In the sweet bye-and-
In the sweet bye-and-
bye we shall meet on that beau-ti-ful shore.
bye, bye-and-bye,

WHEN THE ROLL IS CALLED UP YONDER

JAMES M. BLACK

15.11.D., with refrain

JAMES BLACK called the Sunday school roll every week in Williamsport, Pa. But one Sunday he missed the answer of a little girl whom he had befriended. Then he heard that she was ill, and had little chance to live. He remembered the roll-call and wondered if he would be there to answer when the "great roll-call" is made. This hymn is seldom found in church hymnals, but is one of the best known of all gospel songs.

1. When the trum - pet of the Lord shall sound, and time shall be no more, And the
saved of earth shall ga-ther o - ver on the oth - er shore, And the
2. On that bright and cloud-less morn-ing when the dead in Christ shall rise, And the
chos - en ones shall ga-ther to their home be - yond the skies, And the
3. Let me la - bor for the Mas-ter from the dawn till set - ting sun, Let me
all of life is o - ver, and my work on earth is done, And the
1.
morn-ing breaks, e - ter-nal, bright, and fair; When the
glo-ry of His res - ur - rec - tion share; When His
talk of all His won-drous love and care, Then when

2.
roll is called up yon-der, I'll be there.
roll is called up yon-der, I'll be there.
roll is called up yon-der, I'll be there.
CHORUS
When the roll ___ is called up yon - der, When the
When the roll is called up yonder I'll be there,
roll ___ is called up yon der, When the
When the roll is called up yon-der, I'll be there
roll ___ is called up yon-der, When the
When the roll
roll is called up yon-der I'll be there.

BEULAH LAND

EDGAR PAGE | L.M. with refrain | JOHN R. SWENEY

THE BIBLICAL ALLUSION is in Isaiah 62:4, taken from the Hebrew word meaning "married" in the sense of marital bliss; Beulah Land is used in the sense of the Promised Land, this time promised to the Hebrews after their return from the punitive exile in Babylon. John Bunyan used Beulah Land in a similar sense in *Pilgrim's Progress.* Of several hymns that have been written and set to music on the Beulah Land theme, this is the most legitimate; but almost equally popular is a rousing Sunday School song.

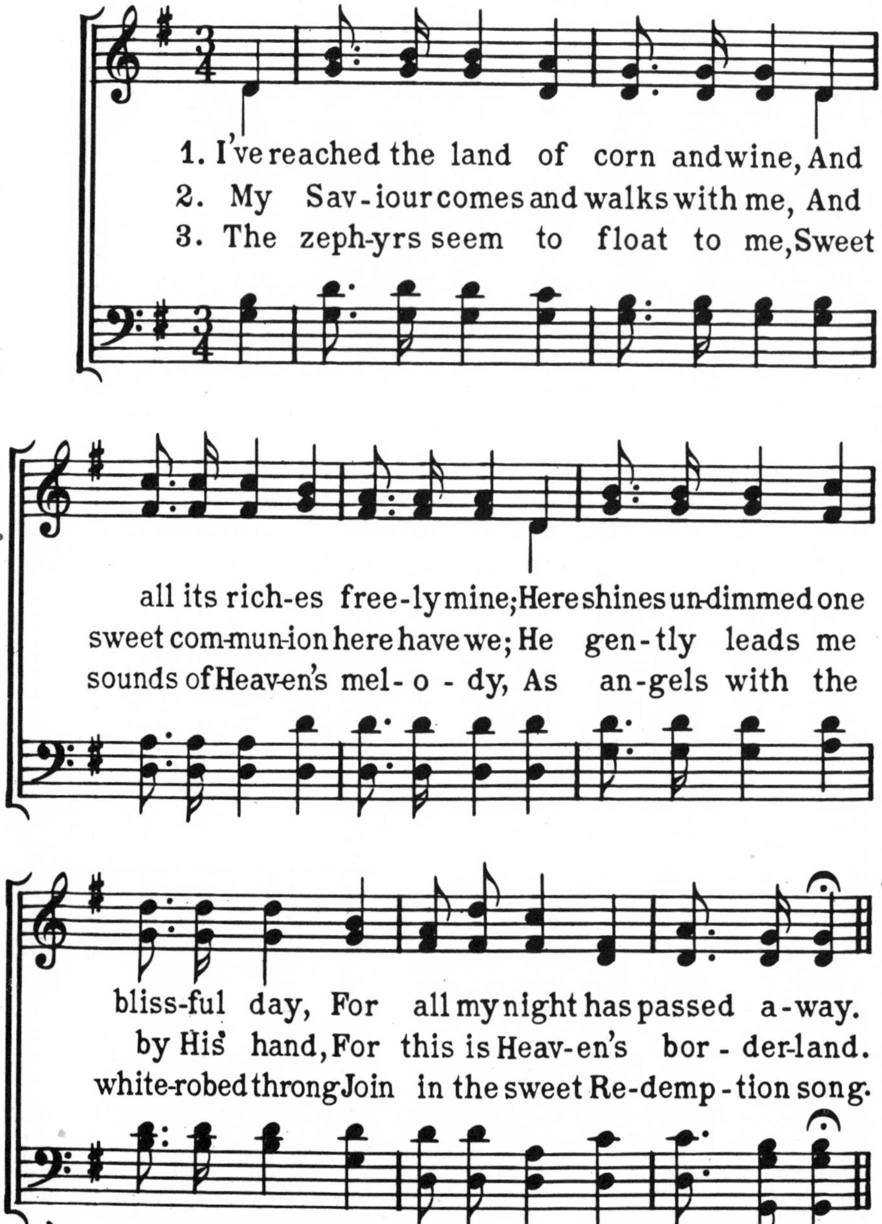
1. I've reached the land of corn and wine, And
2. My Sav-iour comes and walks with me, And
3. The zeph-yrs seem to float to me, Sweet
all its rich-es free-ly mine; Here shines un-dimmed one
sweet com-mun-ion here have we; He gen-tly leads me
sounds of Heav-en's mel-o-dy, As an-gels with the
bliss-ful day, For all my night has passed a-way.
by His hand, For this is Heav-en's bor-der-land.
white-robed throng Join in the sweet Re-demp-tion song.

CHORUS
O Beu - lah Land, sweet Beu - lah Land, As
on thy high - est mount I stand, I
look a - way a - cross the sea, Where
man-sions are pre-pared for me, And view the shin-ing
glo - ry-shore, My Heav'n, my home for - ev - er-more!

WILL THERE BE ANY STARS IN MY CROWN?

12.9.12.9. with refrain

E. E. Hewitt — John R. Sweney

John R. Sweney led an army band during the Civil War. Later he became a professor of music at the Pennsylvania Military Academy, and there he edited about 50 song collections. He often worked with William J. Kirkpatrick, and the team of Sweney and Kirkpatrick became well known. Mr. Hewitt, author of the words, was inspired by the text: "Ye shall receive a crown of glory that fadeth not away." 1 Peter 5:4.

1. I am think - ing to - day of that
2. In the strength of the Lord let me
3. Oh, what joy it will be when His
beau-ti-ful land I shall reach when the sun go-eth
la-bor and pray, Let me watch as a win-ner of
face I be-hold, Liv-ing gems at His feet to lay
down; When through won - der-ful grace by my
souls; That bright stars may be mine in the
down; It would sweet - en my bliss in the

Sav-iour I stand, Will there be an-y stars in my crown?
glo-ri-ous day, When His praise like the sea bil-low rolls.
cit-y of gold, Should there be an-y stars in my crown.
CHORUS
Will there be an-y stars, an-y stars in my crown When at
eve-ning the sun go-eth down? When I
go-eth down?
wake with the blest In the man-sions of rest, Will there
be an-y stars in my crown?
in my crown?

ALMOST PERSUADED

PHILIP P. BLISS

P.M.

ONE SUNDAY, in church, Philip Bliss was listening carefully while the sermon was in progress. The text was from ACTS 26:28, "Then Agrippa said to Paul, almost thou persuadest me to be a Christian." Then the preacher said, "To be almost saved is to be entirely lost!" This theme so impressed Bliss that he wrote ALMOST PERSUADED. For notes on Philip P. Bliss see *Wonderful Words of Life*, page 270.

1. "Al - most per - suad - ed,"
2. "Al - most per - suad - ed,"
3. "Al - most per suad - ed,"
now to be - lieve;
come, come to - day;
har - vest is past!
"Al - most per - suad - ed,"
"Al - most per - suad - ed,"
"Al - most per - suad - ed,"

Christ to re - ceive;
turn not a - way;
doom comes at last!
Seems now some soul to say,
Je - sus in - vites you here,
"Al - most" can - not a - vail;
"Go, Spir - it, go Thy way, Some more con -
An-gels are ling'ring near, Pray'rs rise from
"Al-most" is but to fail! Sad, sad that
ven - ient day On Thee I'll call."
hearts so dear, O wan-d'rer, come.
bit - ter wail, "Al - most," but lost.

HAVE THINE OWN WAY, LORD!

ADELAIDE A. POLLARD GEORGE C. STEBBINS

5s, 4s.

A MODEST and self-effacing little woman, Adelaide Pollard practiced throughout her life the principle of Christian submission to the will of the Almighty. She wrote many hymns, but was too modest to sign her name to them. Constantly traveling from place to place, she devoted her life to the service of others. She died in a railroad station at the age of 72, while on her way to a preaching engagement.

1. Have Thine own way, Lord!
2. Have Thine own way, Lord!
3. Have Thine own way, Lord!
Have Thine own way!
Have Thine own way!
Have Thine own way!
Thou art the Pot - ter;
Wound - ed and wea - ry,
Hold o'er my be - ing

I am the clay.
Help me, I pray!
Ab - so - lute sway!
Mould me and make me
Pow - er, all pow - er,
Fill with Thy Spir - it
Aft - er Thy will, While I am
Sure - ly is Thine! Touch me and
Till all shall see Christ on - ly,
wait - ing, Yield - ed and still.
heal me, Sav - iour Di - vine!
al - ways, Liv - ing in me!

TAKE MY LIFE AND LET IT BE

FRANCES R. HAVERGAL — H. A. CAESAR MALAN

Hendon, 7s.

MISS HAVERGAL herself wrote, according to Percy Dearmer (in *Songs of Praise Discussed*): "I went for a little visit of five days. There were ten persons in the house (Areley House); some unconverted and long-prayed-for, some converted but not rejoicing Christians. He gave me the prayer 'Lord, give me all in this house!' and He just *did.* Before I left the house everyone had got a blessing." ROMANS 12:1 is usually associated with this hymn.

1. Take my life,_ and_ let it be Con - se - cra - ted,_ Lord, to_ Thee; Take my
2. Take my feet,_ and_ let them be Swift and beau - ti - ful for_ Thee; Take my
3. Take my sil - ver_ and my gold, Not a mite_ would_ I with - hold; Take my
4. Take my will,_ and_ make it Thine, It shall be_ no_ lon - ger_ mine; Take my

hands, and let them move
voice, and let me sing,
mo - ments and my days,
heart, it is Thine own;
At the im - pulse of Thy love,
Al - ways, on - ly, for my King,
Let them flow in cease - less praise,
It shall be Thy roy - al throne,
At the im - pulse of Thy love.
Al - ways, on - ly, for my King.
Let them flow in cease - less praise.
It shall be Thy roy - al throne.

GOD WILL TAKE CARE OF YOU

MRS. C. D. MARTIN | W. S. MARTIN

8.6.8.6., with refrain

THE WORDS AND MUSIC of this hymn were written by the Reverend Mr. Martin and his wife. When she was in the hospital, to which she had been rushed for an emergency appendectomy, her only thought was of her husband, and when she saw his distraught expression, she said to him: "Never mind, dear, God will take care of you."

1. Be not dis-mayed what-e'er be-tide,
2. Thro' days of toil when heart doth fail,
3. No mat-ter what may be the test,
God will take care of you; Be-neath His wings of
God will take care of you; When dan-gers fierce your
God will take care of you; Lean, wea-ry one, up-
love a-bide, God will take care of you.
path as-sail, God will take care of you.
on His breast, God will take care of you.

CHORUS
God will take care of you,
Thro' ev - 'ry day, O'er all the way;
He will take care of you,
God will take care of you.—

WHERE HE LEADS ME I WILL FOLLOW

E. W. Blandy | J. S. Norris

Where He Leads Me
8.8.8.7. with refrain

This was the great revival song of Gipsy Smith, the famous evangelist. It is admirably suited to congregational singing, as the harmony parts lie easily for use without accompaniment. It has been impossible to find information concerning the writers. Blandy's name is usually misspelled "Blandly," and nothing is known about J. S. Norris.

1. I can hear my Sav - iour
2. I'll go with Him through the
3. He will give me grace and
call - ing, I can hear my Sav - iour
judg-ment, I'll go with Him through the
glo - ry, He will give me grace and
call - ing, I can hear my Sav - iour
judg-ment, I'll go with Him through the
glo - ry, He will give me grace and

call-ing, "Take thy cross and fol - low, fol-low me."
judg-ment, I'll go with Him, with Him all the way.
glo - ry, And go with me, with me all the way.
CHORUS
Where He leads me I will fol-low, Where He
leads me I will fol-low, Where He leads me I will
fol-low, I'll go with Him, with Him all the way.

HE LEADETH ME

Joseph H. Gilmore | William B. Bradbury

L.M., with refrain

One Evening Joseph Gilmore was inspired to write a hymn. He gave it to his wife and forgot about it. She sent it to *The Watchman and Reflector*. Three years later Dr. Gilmore was in Rochester, N. Y. to preach. On entering the chapel he took up a hymnbook, thinking, "I wonder what they sing!" The book opened at He Leadeth Me.

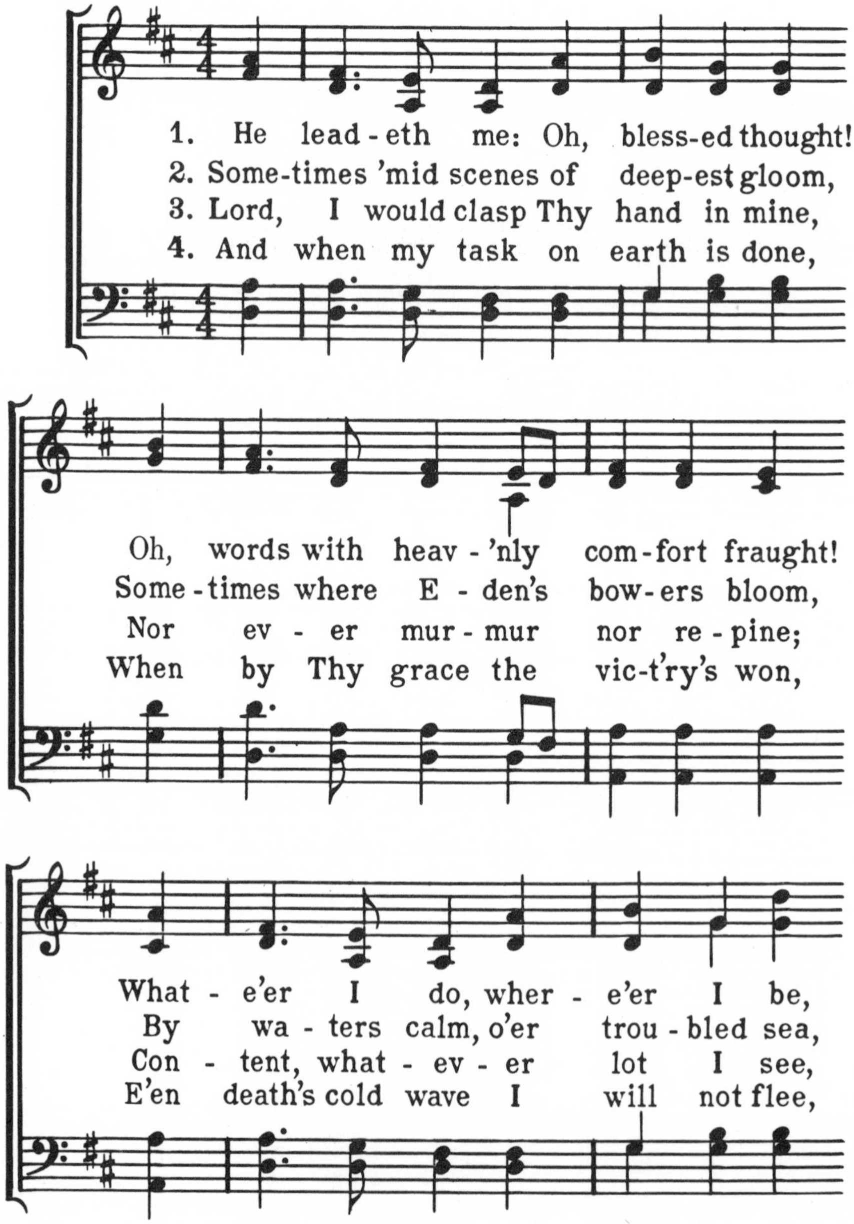
1. He lead-eth me: Oh, bless-ed thought!
2. Some-times 'mid scenes of deep-est gloom,
3. Lord, I would clasp Thy hand in mine,
4. And when my task on earth is done,
Oh, words with heav-'nly com-fort fraught!
Some-times where E-den's bow-ers bloom,
Nor ev-er mur-mur nor re-pine;
When by Thy grace the vic-t'ry's won,
What-e'er I do, wher-e'er I be,
By wa-ters calm, o'er trou-bled sea,
Con-tent, what-ev-er lot I see,
E'en death's cold wave I will not flee,

Still 'tis God's hand that lead - eth me.
Still 'tis His hand that lead - eth me.
Since 'tis my God that lead - eth me.
Since God thro' Jor - dan lead - eth me.
REFRAIN
He lead - eth me, He lead - eth me:
By His own hand He lead-eth me:
His faith - ful fol - low'r I would be,
For by His hand He lead - eth me.

ALL THE WAY MY SAVIOUR LEADS ME

FANNY J. CROSBY — ROBERT LOWRY

8s, 7s.

FANNY CROSBY, the blind hymn-writer, was in desperate financial difficulty. She could think of no way in which to get some money, so she asked the Lord for help. The next day, a man called at her home and handed her the money she needed. In telling the story herself, she said: "I have no way to account for this, except to believe that God, in answer to my prayer, put it into the heart of this good man to bring me the money."

1. All the way my Saviour leads me; What have
2. All the way my Sav-iour leads me; Cheers each
3. All the way my Saviour leads me; Oh, the
I to ask be-side? Can I doubt His ten-der
wind-ing path I tread, Gives me grace for ev-'ry
full-ness of His love! Per-fect rest to me is
mer-cy, Who through life has been my Guide?
tri-al, Feeds me with the liv-ing bread.
prom-ised In my Fa-ther's house a-bove.

Heav'n - ly peace, di - vin - est
Though my wea - ry steps may
When my spir - it, clothed im -
com-fort, Here by faith in Him to dwell!
fal-ter, And my soul a-thirst may be,
mor-tal, Wings its flight to realms of day,
For I know, what-e'er be-fall me, Je-sus
Gush-ing from the Rock be-fore me, Lo! a
This my song thro' end-less a-ges: Je-sus
do - eth all things well; well.
spring of joy I see; see.
led me all the way; way.
1.
2.

LEANING ON THE EVERLASTING ARMS

ELISHA A. HOFFMAN | ANTHONY J. SHOWALTER

Leaning on Jesus,
10.9.10.9., with refrain

THE REVEREND Mr. Hoffman was a Congregational minister. He spent many years at Lebanon, Pa., where he wrote numerous hymns. In writing this hymn, he had been furnished with words and music of the refrain which were written by Showalter, a singing-school teacher of Hartsells, Ala. The sentiment is founded on DEUTERONOMY 33:27, "Underneath are the everlasting arms."

1. What a fel - low-ship, what a joy di - vine,
2. Oh, how sweet to walk in this pil-grim way,
3. What have I to dread, what have I to fear,
Lean - ing on the ev - er - last - ing arms;
Lean - ing on the ev - er - last - ing arms;
Lean - ing on the ev - er - last - ing arms;
What a bless - ed-ness, what a peaee is mine,
Oh, how bright the path grows from day to day,
I have bless - ed peace with my Lord so near,

Lean-ing on the ev-er-last-ing arms.
Lean-ing on the ev-er-last-ing arms.
Lean-ing on the ev-er-last-ing arms.
CHORUS
Lean - ing, lean - ing,
Lean-ing on Je-sus, lean-ing on Je-sus,
Safe and se-cure from all a-larms; Lean - ing,
Leaning on Je-sus,
lean - ing, Lean-ing on the ev-er-last-ing arms.
lean-ing on Je-sus,

GOD BE WITH YOU TILL WE MEET AGAIN

JEREMIAH E. RANKIN — 9.8.8.9 — WILLIAM G. TOMER

DR. RANKIN, A CONGREGATIONAL MINISTER who in 1889 became president of Howard University in Washington, D.C., used this hymn to close his evening services. In his own account of the writing he tells how impressed he was to learn from his dictionary that "goodbye" is a contraction of "God be with ye." The hymn was sung extensively at the revival meetings of Moody, Sankey and others, and was adopted by Christian Endeavor. Purists have found the refrain objectionable, but no one claims literary value for the hymn, only an appeal so great it cannot be questioned.

1. God be with you till we meet a - gain;
2. God be with you till we meet a - gain;
3. God be with you till we meet a - gain;
4. God be with you till we meet a - gain;
By His coun - sels guide, up - hold you,
'Neath His wings pro - tect - ing hide you,
When life's per - ils thick con - found you,
Keep love's ban - ner float - ing o'er you;
With His sheep se - cure - ly fold you;
Dai - ly man - na still pro - vide you;
Put His arms un - fail - ing 'round you;
Smite death's threat - 'ning wave be - fore you;

God be with you till we meet a - gain.
God be with you till we meet a - gain.
God be with you till we meet a - gain.
God be with you till we meet a - gain.
CHORUS
Till we meet, till we meet, Till we
Till we meet, till we meet,
meet at Je - sus' feet; Till we
till we meet;
meet, till we meet, God be
Till we meet, till we meet,
with you till we meet a - gain.

THE LORD BLESS YOU AND KEEP YOU

Numbers 6:24-26 — PETER CHRISTIAN LUTKIN

NO BENEDICTION the Holy Bible contains is more beautifully poetic than this one and no musical setting for it has been so favored as Dr. Lutkin's; ASCAP still lists seventeen special arrangements being sold by different music publishers. Dr. Lutkin was a founder of the American Guild of Organists in 1896 and an editor of early hymnals for both the Methodist and Protestant Episcopal Churches. He studied, performed and composed in many American and European lands. The King James text for this benediction is "The Lord bless *thee* and keep *thee*," using the singular.

The Lord bless you and keep— you, The
Lord lift His coun-te-nance up - on— you; And give you peace,— and give you
peace, The Lord make His face to shine up - on— you, And be
gra-cious un - to you, be gra-cious un - to you. A - men.

RECESSIONAL

Arr. ELISE BRETTON — FOLKINGHAM (1708) — RUDYARD KIPLING

VICTORIA BECAME QUEEN in 1837 and had a golden jubilee in 1887. In 1897, knowing she could not last 75 years, Parliament changed the rules and made a diamond jubilee of the 60th year. Nearly all European royalty and warlords attended ("the captains and the kings"), and at the end Kipling—no favorite of his queen—struck a somber note in commentary, one that might have occurred to Americans as the sun set on V-J Day. Charles Wood and other contemporary composers set RECESSIONAL to music, but most hymnals have preferred the Folkingham tune that it fits so well.

1. God of our fa - thers, known of old, Lord of our far-flung
2. The tu - mult and the shout-ing dies, The cap - tains and the
3. Far called, our na - vies melt a - way; On dune and head-land
4. If drunk with sight of pow'r we loose wild tongues that have not
5. For hea - then heart that puts her trust In reek - ing tube and
bat - tle line, be - neath Whose aw - ful hand we hold do-
kings de - part. Still stands Thine an - cient sac - ri - fice, An
sinks the fire. Lo, all our pomp of yes - ter - day is
Thee in awe, Such boast-ings as the Gen - tiles use or
i - ron shard, All val - iant dust that builds on dust, And,
min - ion o - ver palm and pine, Lord God of
hum - ble and a con trite heart. Lord God of
one with Nin - e - veh and Tyre. Judge of the
less - er breeds with - out the law Lord God of
guard - ing, calls not Thee to guard, For fran-tic
hosts be with us yet, Lest we for-get, Lest we for - get.
hosts be with us yet, Lest we for-get, Lest we for - get.
na - tions, spare us yet, Lest we for-get, Lest we for - get.
hosts be with us yet, Lest we for-get, Lest we for - get.
boast and fool - ish word Thy mer - cy on Thy peo - ple Lord.

I KNOW THAT MY REDEEMER LIVES

Charles Wesley — **F.M.** — **George F. Handel**

From The Messiah, Handel's (and the world's) most celebrated oratorio, the prolific Dr. Wesley abstracted and popularized this as a hymn. The Biblical source is Job 19:25, "For I know that my redeemer liveth, and that he shall stand at the latter day upon the earth"; the words were spoken by Job. This is a favored recessional hymn in some churches.

1. I know that my Re -
2. He lives, tri - um - phant
3. He lives, that I may
4. Let strains of heav'n - ly
deem - er lives, And ev - er prays for
o'er the grave, At God's right hand on
al - so live, And now His grace pro -
mu - sic rise, While all their an - them
me; A to - ken of His love He
high, My ran - somed soul to keep and
claim; He lives, that I may hon - or
sing to Christ, my pre - cious sac - ri -
gives, A pledge of lib - er - ty.
save To bless and glo - ri - fy.
give, To His most ho - ly name.
fice, And ev - er - liv - ing King.

CHRISTMAS CAROLS

O COME, ALL YE FAITHFUL

Translated by
FREDERIC OAKELEY

JOHN FRANCIS WADE'S
Cantus Diversi

Adeste Fideles, P.M., irregular

THIS HYMN, in its Latin form (Adeste Fideles), has been popular since 1700 at least, and was sung in France before reaching England. It may still be considered anonymous, but an early manuscript recently found may point to Wade, a copyist of the early 18th century, as the author. Canon Oakeley's translation is his second version. The first was published in 1852. There is as much disagreement about the words as about the tune.

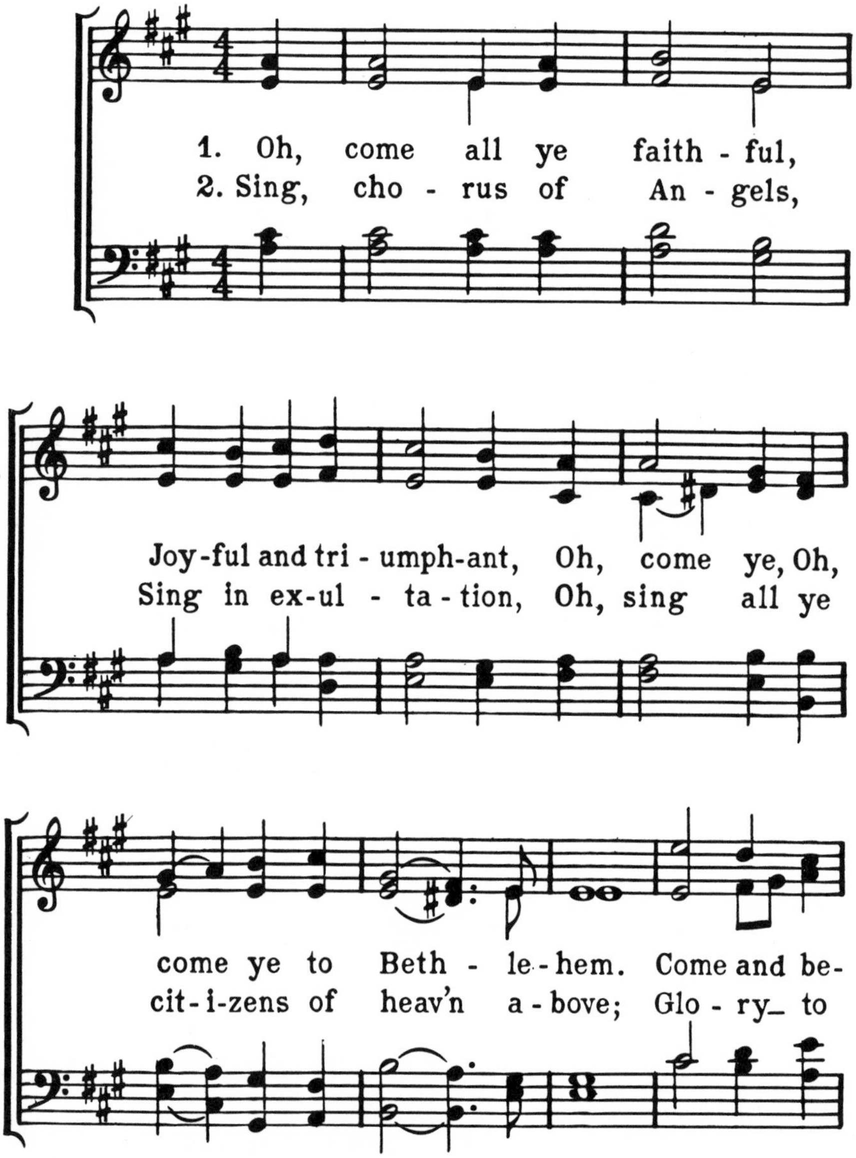
1. Oh, come all ye faith - ful,
2. Sing, cho - rus of An - gels,
Joy-ful and tri - umph-ant, Oh, come ye, Oh,
Sing in ex-ul - ta - tion, Oh, sing all ye
come ye to Beth - le - hem. Come and be-
cit - i - zens of heav'n a - bove; Glo - ry_ to

hold Him, Born the King of An - gels:
God___ In the high-est, glo - ry!
REFRAIN
Oh, come, let us a - dore Him, Oh,
come let us a - dore Him, Oh, come, let us a -
dore Him,_ Christ_ the Lord.

SILENT NIGHT! HOLY NIGHT!

Freely translated from
JOSEPH MOHR | FRANZ GRUBER

Stille Nacht, 6.6.8.8.6.6.

SOME GREAT MASTERPIECES have been the result of patience and long years of work. Others, equally great, seem to spring into existence in a few moments. So it was that on December 24, 1818, with just a few hours before the Christmas service, and the organ out of commission, Father Mohr and the organist Franz Grüber wrote a hymn for two voices and sang it themselves, with Grüber furnishing a guitar accompaniment. No fewer than eleven dramas, in German and English, have been based upon real and imaginary stories of the hymn.

1. Si - lent night! ho - ly night!
2. Si - lent night! ho - ly night!
3. Si - lent night! ho - ly night!
All is calm, all is bright;
Dark - ness flies, all is light;
Won - drous Star, lend thy light!
'Round yon vir - gin moth - er and Child,
Shep-herds hear the an - gels sing:
With the an - gels let us sing

Ho - ly In - fant so ten - der and mild;
Al - le - lu - ia! hail the King!
Al - le - lu - ia to our King!
Sleep in heav - en - ly peace,
Christ the Sav - iour is born,
Christ the Sav - iour is born,
Sleep in heav - en - ly peace.
Christ the Sav - iour is born.
Christ the Sav - iour is born.

AWAY IN A MANGER

ANONYMOUS JAMES R. MURRAY

Mueller, four 11s

THIS HYMN has always been known as *Luther's Cradle Hymn.* Hymnologists, however, and especially biographers of Luther, were disturbed by the fact that it is not to be found in any of his works, nor does it conform to his style. Penetrating research by Richard S. Hill disclosed the true story, published in his article, "Not So Far Away in a Manger: Forty-one Settings of an American Carol," in the December, 1945, issue of *The Music Library Association Notes.* The facts are: The words are anonymous, probably written about 1880, and there is no doubt that the tune was written by James R. Murray, in 1887, and first appeared in a book of songs for children copyrighted by the John Church Company of Cincinnati, in 1887.

1. A - way in a man - ger, No
2. The cat - tle are low - ing, The
crib for a bed, The lit - tle Lord
poor ba - by wakes, But lit - tle Lord
Je - sus laid down His sweet
Je - sus, No cry - ing He

head; The stars in the sky Looked
makes; I love Thee, Lord Je - sus! Look
down where He lay, The lit - tle Lord
down from the sky And stay by my
Je - sus, A - sleep on the hay.
cra - dle To watch lull - a - by.

HARK, THE HERALD ANGELS SING

CHARLES WESLEY FELIX MENDELSSOHN

Mendelssohn
7.7.7.7.D., with refrain

THIS IS ONE of the most important Christmas hymns, written in 1738 and sung every year since. It is considered Wesley's best writing, second only to *Jesus, Lover of My Soul.* The tune was written in 1840 (as part of Mendelssohn's *Festgesang* in celebration of the invention of printing), and was adapted for the hymn by William H. Cummings, in 1856. Mendelssohn himself considered the tune unsuitable for sacred words.

1. Hark! the her - ald an-gels sing,—
2. Christ, by high - est heav'n a - dored;—
3. Hail the heav'n - born Prince of Peace!—
"Glo - ry to the new-born King; Peace on earth, and
Christ,the ev-er - last-ing Lord; Late in time be-
Hail the Sun of Right-eous-ness! Ris'n with heal-ing
mer-cy mild,— God and sin-ners rec-on-ciled!"
hold him come,— Off-spring of the Vir-gin's womb:
in his wings: Light and life to all he brings;

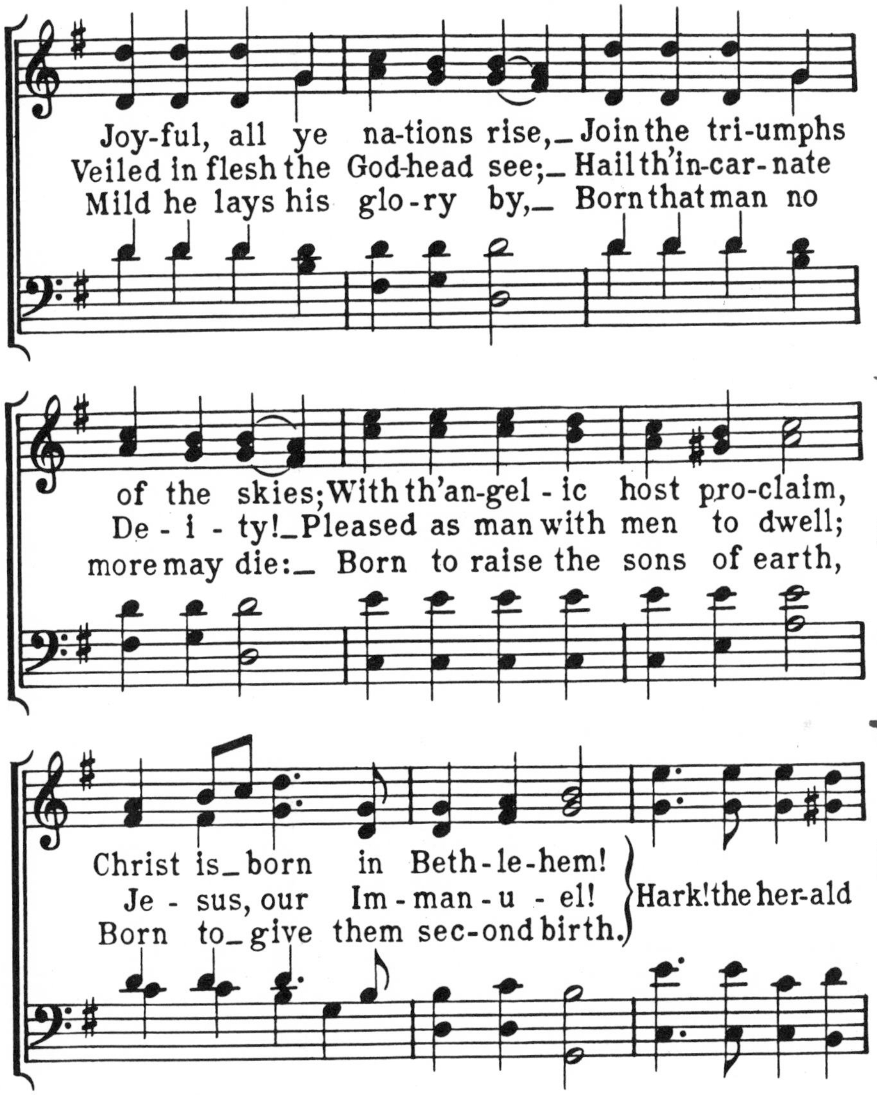
Joy-ful, all ye na-tions rise,_ Join the tri-umphs
Veiled in flesh the God-head see;_ Hail th'in-car-nate
Mild he lays his glo-ry by,_ Born that man no
of the skies; With th'an-gel - ic host pro-claim,
De - i - ty!_ Pleased as man with men to dwell;
more may die:_ Born to raise the sons of earth,
Christ is_ born in Beth-le-hem!
Je - sus, our Im - man - u - el!
Born to_ give them sec-ond birth.
Hark! the her-ald
an-gels sing, "Glo - ry_ to the new-born King!"

IT CAME UPON A MIDNIGHT CLEAR

EDMUND H. SEARS

RICHARD STORRS WILLIS

Carol, C.M.D.

THIS IS an American hymn, written in Boston in 1849. It is based on the Unitarian convictions of the writers, a radical position in that day. Perhaps because of this factor, it was not published in many hymnals for a long time, until public demand prevailed. We include, as being applicable to modern times, the original third stanza (the second stanza given here). The tune *Carol* is from Willis' *Study No. 23.*

1. It came up-on the mid-night clear, That
2. Be-neath the an - gels' strain have rolled Two
3. For lo, the days are has-t'ning on, By
glo - rious song of old, From
thou - sand years of wrong; Yet
proph - et bards fore - told, When
an-gels bend - ing near the earth To
with the woes of sin and strife The
with the ev - er - cir-cling years Comes

touch their harps_ of gold:_ "Peace
world has suf - fered long:_ And
round the age_ of gold;_ When
on the earth,_good will to men, From
man, at war_ with man, hears not The
peace shall o - ver all the earth Its
heav'n's all - gra-cious King:" The world in sol-emn
love song which they bring; Oh, hush the noise, ye
an - cient splen-dors fling, And the whole world give
still-ness lay To hear the an - gels sing.
men of strife, And hear the an - gels sing!
back the song Which now the an - gels sing.

JOY TO THE WORLD

Isaac Watts

Lowell Mason
from themes by Handel

Antioch, C.M.

Sir Isaac Watts gave a joyful interpretation to the beautiful 98th Psalm. It is a Christmas hymn, celebrating the Nativity, and calling upon all nature to join in solemn exultation. Lowell Mason, in 1830, provided the setting by making a composite of two Handelian themes, *Lift Up Your Heads* and *Comfort Ye,* both from the *Messiah.*

1. Joy to the world! the Lord is
2. Joy to the world! the Sav - iour
3. He rules the world with truth and
come; Let earth re - ceive her King;_
reigns; Let men their songs em - ploy;_
grace, And makes the na - tions prove_
— Let ev - 'ry_ heart_ pre -
— While fields_ and_ floods,_ rocks,
— The glo - ries_ of_ His

pare Him room, and
hills and plains, Re-
right-eous-ness, And
heav'n and na-ture sing, And
peat the sound-ing joy, Re-
won-ders of His love, And
heav'n and na-ture sing, And
peat the sound-ing joy, Re-
won-ders of His love, And
heav'n, And heav'n and na-ture sing.
peat, Re-peat the sound-ing joy.
won-ders, And won-ders of His love.

O LITTLE TOWN OF BETHLEHEM

Phillips Brooks | **Lewis H. Redner**

***St. Louis*, irregular**

Bishop Brooks of Massachusetts made a pilgrimage to Jerusalem and the Holy Land in 1867, when he was still a young man. Late one night, from a hilltop, he looked down upon the sleeping village of Bethlehem, and received inspiration for his greatest hymn. He gave the poem to his organist and Sunday school superintendent, Lewis H. Redner, who waited until the following Christmas Eve before composing the tune. Only after 25 years had passed was this carol generally included in hymnals.

1. O lit-tle town of Beth-le-hem, How still we_ see thee lie! A - bove thy deep and dream-less sleep The si - lent_ stars go
2. How si-lent - ly, how si-lent - ly The won-drous gift is giv'n! So God im-parts to hu - man hearts The bless-ings_ of His
3. O ho - ly Child of Beth-le-hem, De-scend to_ us we pray; Cast out our sin and en - ter in, Be born in_ us to -

by; Yet in thy dark streets shin-eth The
heav'n. No ear may hear His com-ing; But
day. We hear the Christ-mas an-gels The
ev-er-last-ing Light; The hopes and fears of
in this world of sin, Where meek souls will re-
great glad ti-dings tell, O come to us, a-
all the years Are met in thee to-night.
ceive Him still, The dear Christ en-ters in.
bide with us, Our Lord Em-man-u-el!

WHAT CHILD IS THIS?

William C. Dix — Greensleeves — *Arr.* John Stainer

Dix, a businessman who for a hobby was a moderately prolific writer of hymns, wrote the words in 1878 for a carol he called *The Manger Throne*, which was fairly successful set to another tune. The great present popularity of the carol was achieved when the verses were found to fit ideally a time-honored English melody popular during the times of Queen Elizabeth (I) and twice alluded to by Shakespeare. The original words to this melody, *My Lady Greensleeves*, are hardly understandable now. The C in the melody (measures 1, 5, 9, 13) is often sung as C-sharp.

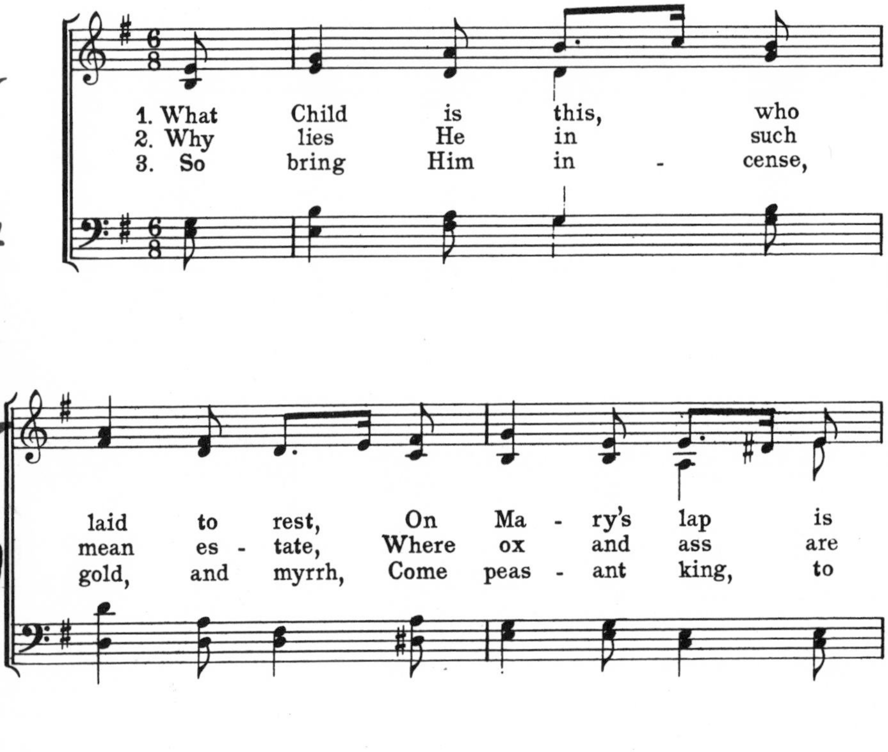
1. What Child is this, who
2. Why lies He in such
3. So bring Him in - cense,
laid to rest, On Ma - ry's lap is
mean es - tate, Where ox and ass are
gold, and myrrh, Come peas - ant king, to
sleep - ing? Whom an - gels greet with
feed - ing? Good Christ - ian fear, for
own Him. The King of kings sal -

an - thems sweet, While shep - herds watch are keep - ing?
sin - ners here, The si - lent word is plead - ing?
va - tion brings, Let lov - ing hearts en - throne Him.
REFRAIN
This, this is Christ the King, Whom
Nails, spear, shall pierce Him through, The
Raise, raise the song on high, The
shep - herds guard and an - gels sing; Haste, haste to
Cross be borne for me, for you: Hail, hail the
Vir - gin sing her lul - la - by: Joy, joy for
bring Him laud,
Word made flesh, The Babe, the Son of Ma - ry.
Christ is born,

DECK THE HALLS

Traditional Welsh

The popularity of this carol, and its applicability to Christmas, are relatively recent. It is a "secular" song, having seasonal rather than religious implications; strictly, it applies less to Christmas than to New Year's festivities. The burning of the Yule (log), the boar's head, and decorations of holly and mistletoe derive from winter celebrations that antedate by hundreds of years the advent of Christianity in Great Britain, and the nonsense tra-la-la refrain is medieval.

1. Deck the halls with boughs of hol - ly,
2. See the blaz - ing yule be - fore us,
3. Fast a - way the old year pass - es,
Fa la la la la, la la la la,
'Tis the sea - son to be jol - ly,
Strike the harp and join the cho - rus,
Hail the new, ye lads and lass - es,

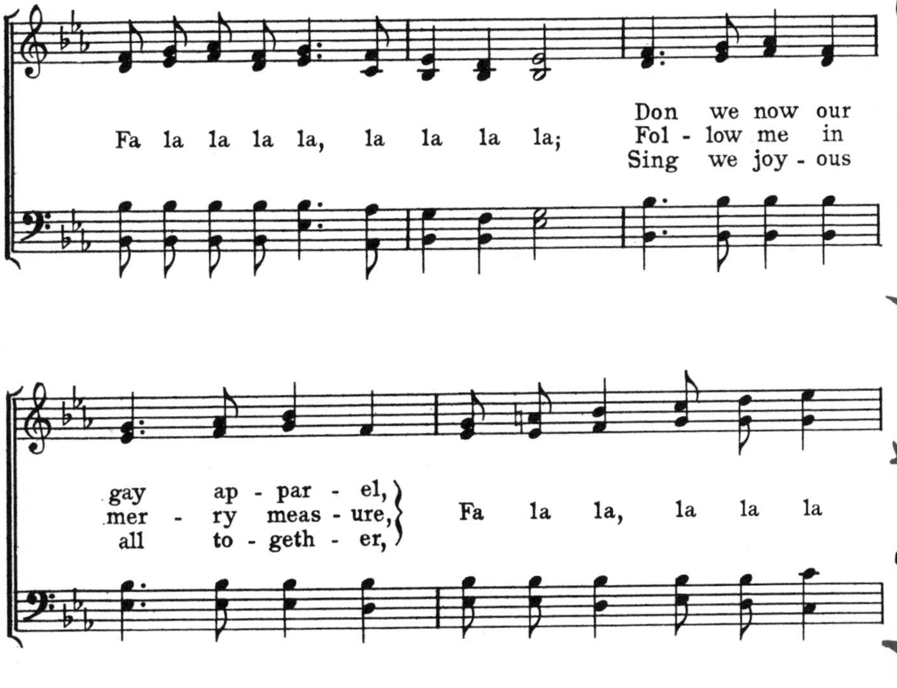
Fa la la la la, la la la la;
Don we now our gay ap - par - el,
Fol - low me in mer - ry meas - ure,
Sing we joy - ous all to - geth - er,
Fa la la, la la la la la la!
Troll the an - cient Christ - mas car - ol,
While I tell of Christ - mas treas - ure,
Heed - less of the wind and weath - er,
Fa la la la la, la la la la!

GOD REST YOU MERRY, GENTLEMEN

Anonymous *Arranged by* **John Stainer**

Observe the placement of the comma, making the first line and title mean "God make you happy, gentlemen." In style and form, this carol seems to be a product of early England, but actually it dates from the sixteenth century. Characteristic of an earlier period, however, is the coupling of a minor melody with joyful words. Sir John Stainer (1840-1901) wrote many cantatas, anthems, and songs, in addition to textbooks on music. His *Treatise on Harmony* was a standard work for thirty years.

1. God rest you mer - ry, gen - tle - men, Let
2. From God our heaven - ly Fa - ther A
3. "Fear not, then," said the an - gel, "Let
4. Now to the Lord sing prais - es, All
noth - ing you dis - may, Re - mem - ber Christ our
bless - ed an - gel came; And un - to cer - tain
noth - ing you af - fright, This day is born a
you with - in this place, And with true love an
Sav - iour Was born on Christ - mas Day; To
shep - herds Brought ti - dings of the same; How
Sav - iour Of a pure Vir - gin bright, To
broth - er - hood Each oth - er now em - brace; This

save us all from Sa - tan's power When
that in Beth - le - hem was born The
free all those who trust in Him From
ho - ly tide of Christ - mas All
REFRAIN
we were gone a stray
Son of God by name.
Sa - tan's power and might."
oth - ers doth de - face
O ti - dings of
com - fort and joy, Com - fort and joy; O
ti - dings of com - fort and joy.

THE FIRST NOWELL

ANONYMOUS

THE FIRST printed copy on record is dated 1823, but the carol was known for some time before. A collection edited by William Sandys, *Christmas Carols, Ancient and Modern* (1833), contained a revised version. Nowell is from the French *Nöel*, or Christmas, and *Noel* is, in turn, from the Latin *natalis*, birthday. Certain features of this carol suggest that it may be a "translation" from very ancient material of Olde Englande.

1. The_ first_ Now - ell the_ an-gel did
2. They_ look - ed_ up and_ saw_ a
3. This_ star_ drew_ nigh to_ the_ north -
4. Then_ en - ter'd_ in there_ Wise - men
say Was to cer - tain poor shep - herds in
star Shin - ing in___ the East___ be -
west, O'er__ Beth - le - hem___ it
three, Full__ rev - 'rent - ly_____ up -
fields as they lay. In__ fields__ where__ they lay__
yond__ them far, And__ to___ the__ earth it__
took___ its rest, And__ there__ it___ did both__
on____ their knee, And__ of - fer'd__ there in__

keep - ing their sheep On a cold win - ter's
gave great light, And so it con -
stop and stay Right o - ver the
His pres - ence, Their gold and
night that was so deep.
tin - ued both day and night.
place where Je - sus lay.
myrrh and frank - in - cense.
REFRAIN
Now - ell, Now - ell, Now - ell, Now ell,
Born is the King of Is - ra - el.

WE THREE KINGS OF ORIENT ARE

Kings of Orient — JOHN HENRY HOPKINS

DR. HOPKINS, AN ANGLICAN RECTOR, wrote both words and music in 1857. They vie with each other in excellence and the music is so imaginative that according to Wallace Brockway (in *A Treasury of Hymns*, 1953) many critics could not credit Dr. Hopkins with the composition and assumed him to be merely the arranger. Strictly the carol applies to Epiphany, January 6, when the gifts of the Magi (Matthew 2:11) were presented. In legend the Magi were named Kaspar, Melchior, and Balthazar; and one was a Negro, emphasizing the absence of racial discrimination in the Christian ethic.

1. We three kings of O - ri - ent are,
2. Born a babe on Beth - le - hem's plain,
3. Frank - in - cense to of - fer have I;
4. Myrrh is mine; its bit - ter per - fume
5. Glo - rious now be - hold Him rise,
Bear - ing gifts we trav - erse far
Gold we bring to crown Him a gain;
In - cense owns a De - i - ty nigh,
Breathes a life of gath - 'ring gloom;
King and God and Sac - ri - fice;
Field and foun - tain, moor and moun - tain,
King for - ev - er, ceas - ing nev - er,
Pray'r and prais - ing all men rais - ing,
Sorr'w - ing, sigh - ing, bleed - ing, dy - ing,
Heav'n sings "Hal - le - lu - jah!" "Hal - le -

Fol - low - ing yon - der Star.
O - ver us all to reign.
Wor - ship God on high.
Sealed in the stone - cold tomb.
lu - jah!" earth re - plies.
REFRAIN
Oh,— star of won-der, star of might, Star with
roy - al beau - ty bright, West - ward lead - ing,
still pro - ceed-ing, Guide us to the per - fect light.

THE TWELVE DAYS OF CHRISTMAS

Traditional

This carol is of old English or Scottish origin. Since the advent of radio and television, it has become well known throughout the United States; before that it was known chiefly in the eastern states, usually in versions adapted to more familiar symbolic materials than, for example, "ten lords a-leaping." The twelve days are those between Christmas and Epiphany (December 25 to January 6). In some Appalachian regions the Julian calendar obtains, with "Old Christmas" on January 6 and "New Christmas" on December 25. This song is of the type called accumulative.

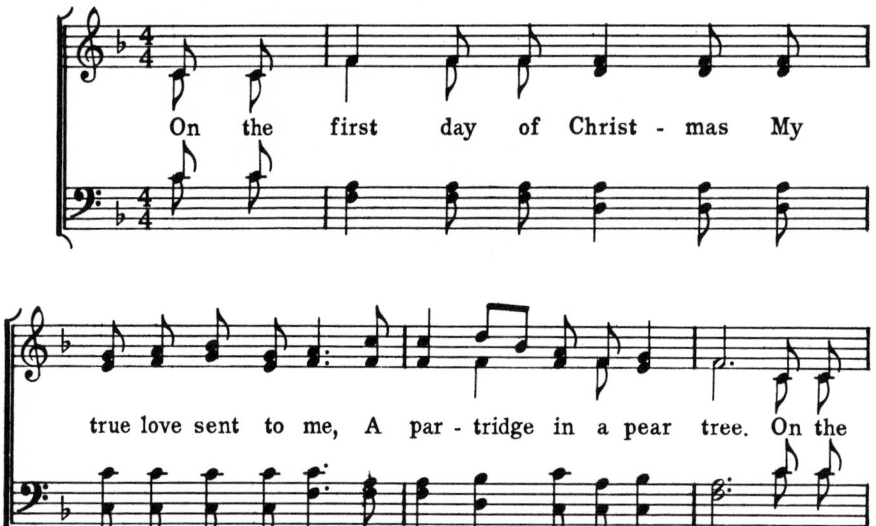
On the first day of Christ - mas My
true love sent to me, A par - tridge in a pear tree. On the
2.
sec - ond day of Christ - mas My true love sent to me,
Two tur - tle doves, and a par - tridge in a pear

3.
tree. On the third day of Christ-mas My true love sent to me,
Three French hens, two tur - tle doves, and a
par - tridge in a pear tree. On the
4.
fourth day of Christ - mas My true love sent to me,
Four call - ing birds, three French hens,

two tur - tle doves, and a par - tridge in a pear
tree. On the
5.
fifth day of Christ - mas My
true love sent to me, Five gold rings,
four call - ing birds, three French hens,
two tur - tle doves, and a par - tridge in a pear tree. On the

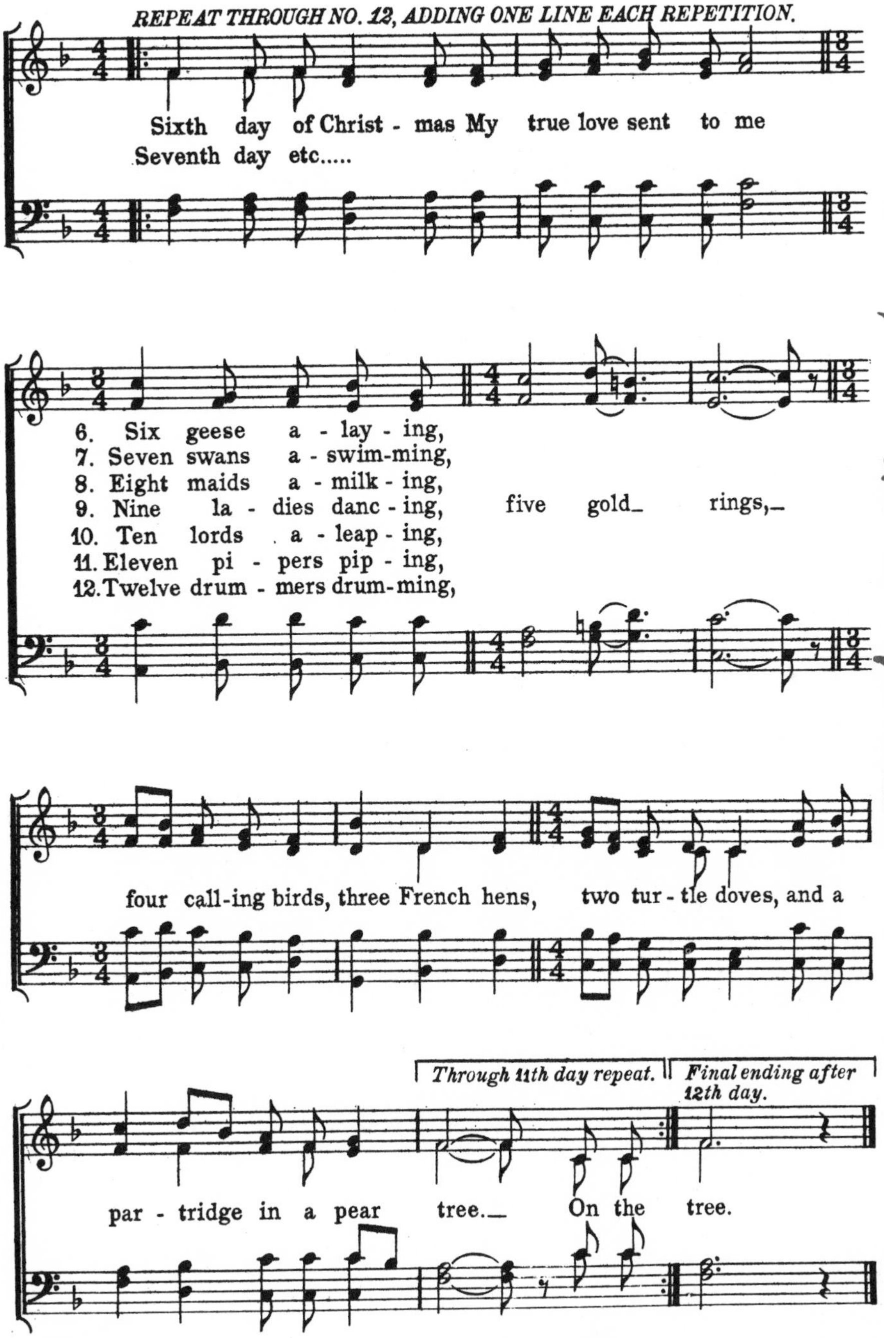
REPEAT THROUGH NO. 12, ADDING ONE LINE EACH REPETITION.
Sixth day of Christ - mas My true love sent to me
Seventh day etc.....
6. Six geese a - lay - ing,
7. Seven swans a - swim-ming,
8. Eight maids a - milk - ing,
9. Nine la - dies danc - ing, five gold_ rings,_
10. Ten lords a - leap - ing,
11. Eleven pi - pers pip - ing,
12. Twelve drum - mers drum-ming,
four call-ing birds, three French hens, two tur - tle doves, and a
Through 11th day repeat.
Final ending after 12th day.
par - tridge in a pear tree._ On the tree.

GOOD KING WENCESLAS

JOHN MASON NEALE *from Piae Cantiones*

WENCESLAUS (as his name is latinized) was reigning Duke of Bohemia, died about 936 A.D., was canonized in the 11th century and is patron saint of Bohemia. This popular carol, for which Dr. Neale wrote the verses in 1853, commemorates one of the deeds of kindness for which Wenceslas was noted—and sainted. The tune, in this version taken from an old Swedish Lutheran hymnal, is used also for the "springtime carol" *Tempus adest floridum* (the time, or season, of flowers is here). The feast day of St. Stephen, the first Christian martyr (Acts 7:59), is December 26.

1. Good King Wen-ces - las looked out, On the feast of Ste - phen,
2. "Hith - er page, and stand by me, If thou knows't it tell - ing,
3. "Bring me flesh and bring me wine, Bring me pine logs hith - er:
4. "Sire, the night is dark - er now, And the wind grows strong - er;
5. In his mas-ter's steps he trod, Where the snow lay dint ed;
When the snow lay round a - bout, Deep and crisp and e - ven.
Yon-der peas - ant, who is he? Where and what his dwell ing?"
Thou and I shall see him dine, When we bear them thith - er."
Fails my heart, I know not how; I can go no long - er."
Heat was in the ver - y sod Which the Saint had print - ed.
Bright - ly shone the moon that night, Though the frost was cru - el,
"Sire, he lives a good league hence, Un - der-neath the moun-tain,
Page and mon-arch, forth they went, Forth they went to - geth - er;
"Mark my foot-steps, my good page, Tread thou in them bold - ly;
There-fore, Christ-ian men be sure, Wealth or rank pos - sess - ing,
When a poor man came in sight, Gath-'ring win-ter fu - el.
Right a-gainst the for - est fence, By Saint Ag - nes' foun - tain."
Through the rude winds wild la - ment, And the bit - ter weath - er.
Thou shalt find the win-ter's rage Freeze thy blood less cold - ly."
Ye who now will bless the poor, Shall your-selves find bless - ing.

SPIRITUALS

STEAL AWAY TO JESUS

Negro Spiritual

In 1872 the famous Jubilee Singers, of the then new Fisk University, visited England. They sang for Queen Victoria, and their first rendition, at the request of the Duke of Argyll, was Steal Away to Jesus. So impressed was the Queen that she extended the full hospitality of London to the party of American singers. As with many other spirituals, this beautiful and tender melody is based on the pentatonic, or five-tone scale.

Steal a - way, steal a - way,
steal a-way to Je - sus! Steal a - way,
Fine
steal a-way home, I ain't got long to stay here.

1. My Lord calls me, He calls me by the
2. Green trees are bend-ing, Poor sin-ner stand a-
3. My Lord calls me, He calls me by the
thun - der;
trem - bling;
light - ning;
The trump - et sounds it
D. C.
in - a my soul: I ain't got long to stay here.

SWING LOW, SWEET CHARIOT

Negro Spiritual

LIKE OTHER FORMS of folk expression, the spirituals of the Negro have a deep basis of originality. Scales and modes are often found that do not conform to the types in general use. SWING LOW, SWEET CHARIOT is founded on a pentatonic, or five-tone, scale, often used in songs of the American Indians. Anton Dvorâk used the melody in his symphony ***From the New World.*** The Fisk Jubilee Singers visited London in 1875, during the tour of Dwight Moody and Ira Sankey. Their rendition of this soft, poignant spiritual brought tears to the eyes of the great revivalists, and Moody asked the singers to take part in the service at the Haymarket Opera House, where they received an enthusiastic welcome.

SOLO
Swing low, sweet char - i - ot,—
CHORUS
Com-ing for to car-ry me home, Swing low, sweet
Fine
char - i - ot,— Com-ing for to car-ry me home.

1. I looked o - ver Jor - dan and what did I see,
2. If you get there be - fore I do,
3. I'm some - times up and some-times down,
Com-ing for to car-ry me home,
A band of an - gels com-ing af-ter me,
Just tell my friends I'm com - ing too,
But still my soul feels heav'n-ly bound,
Com-ing for to car-ry me home.
D. C. al Fine

DEEP RIVER

Negro Spiritual

SAMUEL COLERIDGE TAYLOR was an English composer of African Negro descent. In 1905 he published *Twenty-Four Negro Melodies, Transcribed for the Piano,* and from this source the celebrated American violinist Maud Powell made her concert arrangement of DEEP RIVER. She featured it while on tour with her own concert group, before and during World War I. This departure, and a later transcription by Henry Thacker Burleigh, may have been responsible for the entrance of spirituals into the repertory of serious concert programming.

Deep___ Riv - er, My home is o - ver
Jor - dan,___ Deep___ Riv-er, Lord, I
Fine
want to cross o - ver in - to camp - ground.

(hum)
1. Oh, don't you want to go to that Gos-pel feast, That
2. I'm go-ing in to Heav-en and take my seat,
3. Oh, when I get to Heav-en I'll walk all a-bout, There's
(hum)
prom-is'd land _ Where all is peace?
Cast my crown _ At Je-sus' feet.
no-one there _ To turn me out.
Lord, I
D. C. al Fine
want to cross o-ver in-to camp-ground.

LORD, I'M TROUBLIN'

THIS BEAUTIFUL SPIRITUAL is well known to thousands of persons, especially among Negroes; but for some reason it has not previously appeared in print, so far as the editors can determine. The editors have heard it sung in many parts of the southern United States, in Connecticut, and in Wisconsin. W. C. Handy, in his eightieth year, told the editors that he remembered it from the age of five. The version here presented was sung by a group of field hands on a South Carolina plantation. It is harmonized, so far as it is possible to remember, exactly as they sang it, the intention being to avoid all "copy-book" formalization.

(LEADER)
Lord, I'(h)m_ trou - blin',_ Lord,_ I'(h)m_
Lord, I(h)___ won - der___ where_ my___
Lord, I'(h)m___ trou - blin', Lord, I'm trou - blin', Lord, I'm
(LEADER)
trou - blin', Lord, I'(h)m__ trou - blin' 'bout my
moth - er, Lord I(h)___ won - der where she's
trou - blin', Lord, I'(h)m__ trou - blin' 'bout my
3
(LEADER)
soul,_ Lord!__
gone?_ Lord!__
soul,__ Lord!__
Lord, but_ when I get up in the
(LEADER)
King-dom, Lord, I__ won't be trou-bled no more.

ALL GOD'S CHILDREN GOT SHOES

Negro Spiritual

THIS TRADITIONAL SONG, which was in the repertory of the Fisk Jubilee Singers, has no determinable title. It may be called, after one of its verses, "I've got a robe," or "I've got shoes." Surely it is now widely known by the title, *All God's Chillun Got Wings*, which Eugene O'Neill adopted for one of his most successful plays (on the subject of miscegenation). The editors selected as the title the designation they have most often heard.

1. I got - a shoes, You got - a shoes; All God's chil-dren got-a
2. I got - a robe, You got - a robe; All God's chil-dren got - a
3. I got - a wings, You got - a wings; All God's chil-dren got-a
4. I got - a harp, You got - a harp; All God's chil-dren got-a
shoes; When I get to Heav-en goin' to put on my shoes, goin' to
robe; When I get to Heav-en goin' to put on my robe, goin' to
wings; When I get to Heav-en goin' to put on my wings, goin' to
harp; When I get to Heav-en goin' to take out my harp, goin' to
walk all o-ver God's Heav-en, Heav-en, Heav-en,
shout all o-ver God's Heav-en, Heav-en, Heav-en,
fly all o-ver God's Heav-en, Heav-en, Heav-en,
sing all o-ver God's Heav-en, Heav-en, Heav-en,
Ev'-ry-bod-y talk-in' 'bout Heaven ain't go-in' there, Heav-en.
Ev'-ry-bod-y talk-in' 'bout Heaven ain't go-in' there, Heav-en.
Ev'-ry-bod-y talk-in' 'bout Heaven ain't go-in' there, Heav-en.
Ev'-ry-bod-y talk-in' 'bout Heaven ain't go-in' there, Heav-en.

I AM A POOR WAYFARING STRANGER

White Spiritual

DURING the great revivals and camp meetings that spread from the Kentucky frontier after the Revolutionary War, many white spirituals appeared. They seem to have been influenced by Elizabethan modes and are usually best for solo voice, thereby differing from the Negro musical forms with their more exotic scales and ready harmonizations. The great folk-singer Burl Ives is responsible for the popularization (in the late 1940s) of this spiritual, and is professionally "billed" as "the Wayfaring Stranger."

Dm
I am a poor__ way-far-ing
Gm
stran-ger,__ A-trav-'ling through this world of
Dm
F
woe;__ Yet there's no sick - ness, toil or

B♭ Gm Am
dan-ger_ In that bright world to which I
Dm Gm Am
go._ I'm go-ing home to see my moth-er,_ I'm go-ing
Dm F B♭6
there no more to roam, I'm just a go-ing o-ver
Dm Gm Am7 Dm
Jor-dan,_ I'm just a-go-ing o-ver home.

NOBODY KNOWS THE TROUBLE I'VE SEEN

Negro Spiritual

THIS IS the stirring cry of a people in bondage, and one of the most familiar true spirituals. The Jubilee Singers of Fisk University originally used a minor tune, and a rather different text, which also appears in the W. C. Handy collection. However, the editors of this collection have preferred to use the popular version. An arrangement of this spiritual by Henry Thacker Burleigh, for many years organist at New York's Grace Church, was introduced in 1917.

No-bod-y knows the trou-ble I've seen, No-bod-y knows, but
Je-sus, No-bod-y knows the trou-ble I've seen,
Fine
Glor-y, hal-le-lu-jah! Some-times I'm up, some-
times I'm down, yes, my Lord! Some-times I'm al-most
D.C. al Fine
down to the ground, Yes, my Lord!

I'M GOING DOWN TO THE RIVER OF JORDAN

Traditional

THIS MAY WELL BE one of the spirituals out of the American South that nobody wrote, that "just grew." It may be of white or Negro origin, but the editors have heard it sung most often by Negroes. Anyone who has attended a camp meeting, mass baptism, or revival will comprehend the process: the preacher's impassioned invocation; from here and there a fervent "Amen!" or "Yes, Lord!"; a phrase improvised by a strong singer, a response from the congregation, another phrase, another response, and gradual attainment of musical shape and form. This, one of the oldest and best-loved spirituals, for some reason has seldom appeared in print.

Leader
Hum (optional)
1. I'm ___ go - ing down to the Riv - er of
2. I'm ___ going to put on those Sil - ver
3. I'm ___ going to sing in the Heav - en - ly
4. I'm ___ going to sit down ___ by ___ my
Hum (optional)
Jor - - - dan, Oh, Yes! ___
Slip - - - pers, Oh, Yes! ___
Choir ___ Oh, Yes! ___
Je - - - sus, Oh, Yes! ___
CHORUS
I'm ___ go - ing down to the Riv - er of
I'm ___ going to put on those Sil - ver
I'm ___ going to sing in the Heav - en - ly
I'm ___ going to sit down a - by ___ my

Jor - dan some of these days Hal - le - lu - jah!
Slip - pers some of these days Hal - le - lu - jah!
Choir some of these days Hal - le - lu - jah!
Je - sus some of these days Hal - le - lu - jah!
I'm go - ing down to the Riv - er of
I'm going to put on those Sil - ver
I'm going to sing in the Heav - en - ly
I'm going to sit down a - by my
Jor - dan, I'm go - ing down to the
Slip - pers, I'm going to put on those
Choir I'm going to sing in the
Je - sus, I'm going to sit down a -
Riv - er of Jor - dan some of these days.
Sil - ver Slip - pers some of these days.
Heav - en - ly Choir some of these days.
by my Je - sus some of these days.

INDEX

Titles of songs are in **boldface type;** *first lines* of songs are in *italic type;* NAMES of composers, authors, translators, arrangers and other persons are in SMALL CAPITALS. In this Index all entries are arranged strictly alphabetically. See also the Table of Contents, page vii, for a listing of songs in order of appearance and by classification.

INDEX

INDEX

INDEX

INDEX

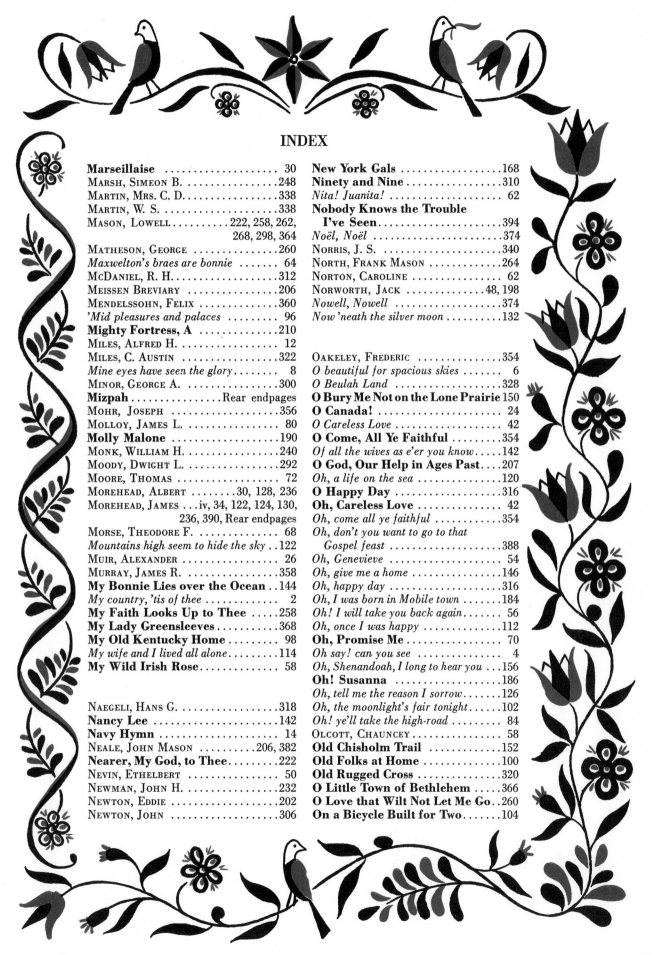

INDEX

INDEX

INDEX

AMENS

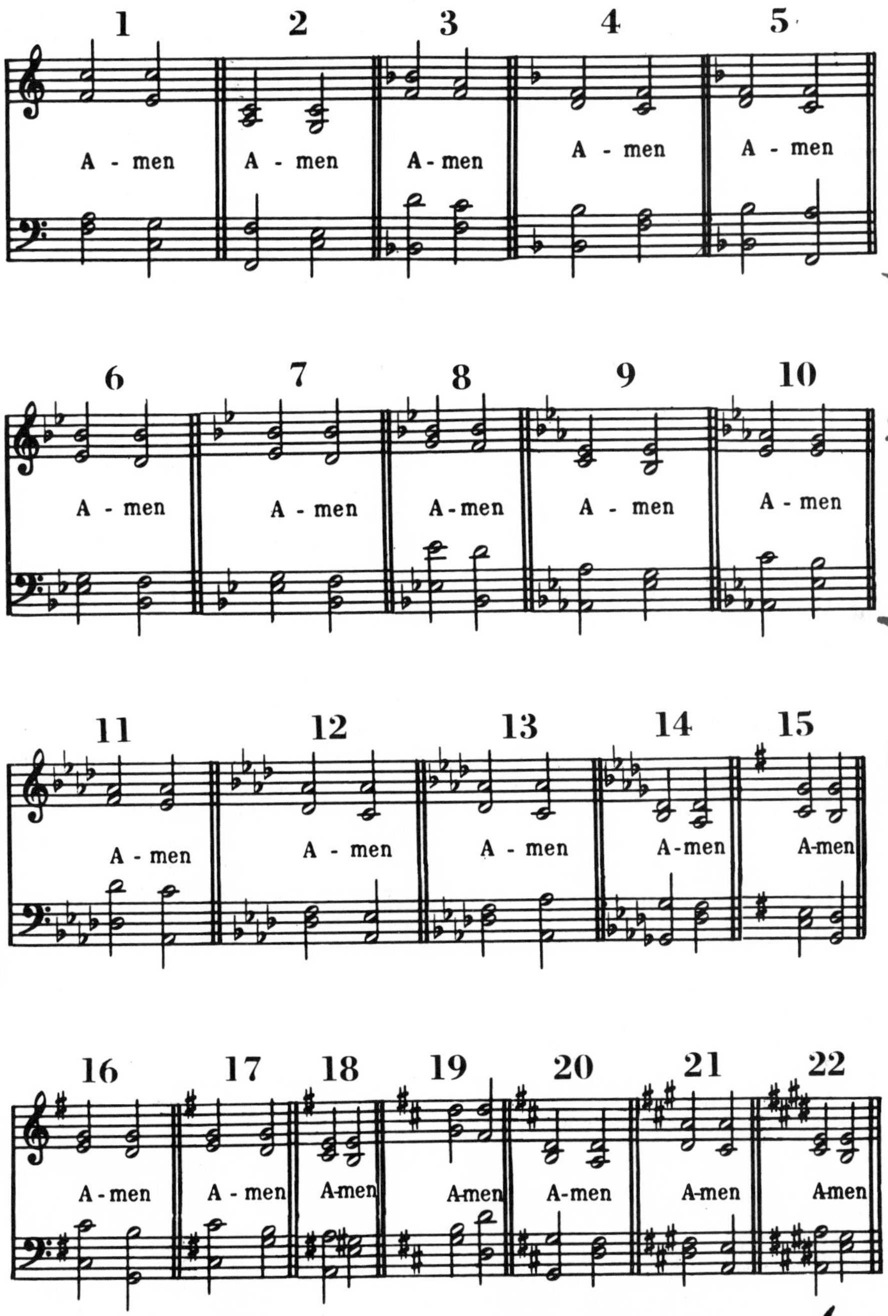
1
A - men
2
A - men
3
A - men
4
A - men
5
A - men
6
A - men
7
A - men
8
A - men
9
A - men
10
A - men
11
A - men
12
A - men
13
A - men
14
A-men
15
A-men
16
A-men
17
A - men
18
A-men
19
A-men
20
A-men
21
A-men
22
A-men

Genesis 31:49
The Lord watch
ab-sent one from
F W